The Essential
Margaret Roberts

The Essential
Margaret Roberts

My 100 favourite herbs

Text by Margaret Roberts

Photographs by Phyllis Green

SPEARHEAD

Published by Spearhead

An imprint of New Africa Books (Pty) Ltd

99 Garfield Road

Claremont, 7700

First edition, second impression 2003

ISBN 0 86486 481 7

Important warning

Never use any plant as a medicine or culinary ingredient unless you are 100 per cent sure of its identification. Many plants are poisonous; in some cases certain parts of a plant may be edible, while other parts may be poisonous. Use only plants that are organically grown, where you can be sure that it has not been sprayed or treated with poisonous chemicals. When in doubt – leave out. The author and publishers take no responsibility for any poisoning, illness or discomfort due to the incorrect identification or use of a plant. You are strongly advised to consult a medical practitioner before treating yourself or your family with home remedies.

Managing editor: Reneé Ferreira

Editor: Frances Perryer

Design and typesetting by Alicia Arntzen, Lebone Publishing Services

Printed and bound by Clyson Printers, 11th Avenue, Maitland

Preface

Since writing *Growing Herbs with Margaret Roberts* in 1985, the world has gone crazy about herbs, and it shows no sign of abating! I have had to continuously set up trials for a huge variety of herbs at the Herbal Centre and the gardens have been visited by thousands of interested gardeners, students and botanists from all over the world, as well as large-scale growers and government officials, and I have watched with delight how the herbal bug bites each one of them.

I have never been so busy nor so excited, and, as I said in those early writings, 'once you start growing herbs you will find yourself becoming more and more fascinated and involved ...' In my case it is an involvement that knows no bounds! I have become even more dedicated to the world of natural healing as the years have gone by, even more convinced of the awesome results herbal medicine has shown even in the face of adversity.

I have treated not only my own family, but the farm staff and friends, as well as birds and animals, all with comforting results and converted many an unbeliever to herbal simplicity! It has been an extraordinary exercise, and a life full of rich and exciting experiences. I am privileged to have met so many fascinating people and animals throughout my busy days and to have worked on so wide a series of projects and products, all with that embracing and satisfying common denominator: the world of herbs.

As I have grown older, I have improved and bettered my abilities, and have had mind-blowing experiences not only growing these precious plants, but also using them in all spheres – food, medicine, cosmetics and the increasingly vital area of natural insecticides. Because of this fascination with herbs I have dedicated my life to sharing that knowledge, and in this new book, based on my original *Growing Herbs*, which has expanded and exploded into new herbs, I share new experiences and new uses of familiar plants and some unfamiliar ones as well.

So it is with a mind buzzing with information and a state of perennial anxiety as I watch the editors prune and tidy up and weed out the bulging voluminous manuscripts to a presentable state, and yet retaining all I want to share with you. I am filled with gratitude that I can once again take you, the reader, down my garden path and once again show you how my garden grows. Let us again share fragrances and tastes, and a way of life that I see as being utterly essential for our own well-being and that of our planet.

I dedicate this book to gardeners everywhere. May it make a difference.

Margaret Roberts

The Herbal Centre
De Wildt
North West Province
South Africa
Spring 2001

Contents

The herbs

Aloe vera	Fennel	Paprika
Amaranth	Fenugreek	Parsley
Anise	Feverfew	Pennywort
Barley	Field poppy	Pyrethrum
Basil	Garlic	Raspberry
Bay	Ginger	Rocket
Bergamot	Ginkgo	Rose
Black seed	Goldenrod	Roselle
Borage	Green tea	Rosemary
Buckwheat	Ground ivy	Rue
Bulbinella	Hawthorn	Sage
Burdock	Honeysuckle	Salad burnet
Calendula	Horseradish	Scented geraniums
Californian poppy	Lavender	Sesame
Caraway	Lemon grass	Silver birch
Carnation	Lemon verbena	Soapwort
Catmint	Linseed	Sorrell
Cayenne pepper	Loofah	Southernwood
Celery	Lovage	Soya bean
Chamomile	Lucerne	St John's wort
Chervil	Maidenhair fern	Stevia
Chives	Melissa	Strawberry
Clover	Milk thistle	Tansy
Comfrey	Mint	Tarragon
Coriander	Moringa	Tea tree
Cornflower	Mullein	Thyme
Costmary	Mustard	Turmeric
Cumin	Myrtle	Vetiver grass
Dandelion	Nasturtium	Violet
Dill	Neem	Watercress &
Echinacea	Nettle	Landcress
Elder	Oats	Winter savory
Eucalyptus	Olive leaf	Wormwood
Evening primrose	Oregano & Marjoram	Yarrow

Acknowledgements

There is always a mountain of work in producing a book, no matter how simply it is put together. I have the greatest team behind me who give me the freedom to write, who work behind the scenes, burning midnight oil in many places and instances. It is these whom I need to thank:

To a publisher who lets me free and who listens to every idea I have and who responds like this, updating a book so long out of print due to public demand, Nicholas Combrinck, thank you for listening so patiently to us all and for giving us extra pages!

To Reneé Ferreira, my managing editor, who takes great loads off me and who never changes – always encouraging, always supportive. Thank you for slowing the frantic pace and getting it in order. It has been a huge amount of work – also in the small hours – and I appreciate it tremendously.

To Frances Perryer whose editor's pen was lenient and kind, thank you for putting together the mass of information and keeping it neatly pruned.

To Alicia Arntzen who laid out the pages and managed to fit everything in!

To Annatjie van Wyk, who takes my thousands of handwritten words and deciphers them and whose farm post box bursts with my comings and goings in the dark dawns after writing in the small hours, and who gets it, and me, into order, my gratitude is huge.

To Phyllis Green, the photographer of each of these beautiful visuals, for her interest in the plants, her quick eye and continuous visits in her spare time to the Herbal Centre to catch the plant at its perfect stage, my heartfelt thanks. How much I enjoy showing you, and having the new growth, the new flowers and the new trials captured on film!

For Kirchoffs Seeds Ball Straathofs, suppliers of 'The Margaret Roberts Herbal Seed Collection', whose distribution countrywide reaches the far and distant corners of our land, and in particular Leonie Coulsen, marketing manager, my most grateful thanks to you all for enthusiastically trialling, testing and putting together so magnificent a collection of herb seeds that gives me the backing to introduce more and more and to write with confidence knowing every nursery and every town has this vital collection of seeds.

No author can operate efficiently without a work and home organisation behind it all. And for all my staff at the Herbal Centre who not only grow, but process the herbs, their part in this book is vital, and for my youngest child, my daughter Sandra, who smoothes the way and lifts the load and who has become my partner at the Herbal Centre and who is an efficient multi-tasker and loyal supporter, words cannot express my gratitude.

It is thanks to this great team that a book like this comes into being, and for the interest and the demands of the public who urged us on impatiently! How grateful I am to be able to put this book in your hands. It is for you, and we all hope everyone who reads it will enjoy it, use it and live that healthy life we all so desperately need, with these precious plants as our little lifesavers. May it be a life-changing experience!

Planning the herb garden

A herb garden can do many things – it may satisfy, inspire, uplift and revitalise. It can help us to overcome the deep stresses and worries we are prone to in our everyday lives. I could even go so far as to say that we dare not live without a herb or two close at hand.

There is so much appeal in the growing of herbs, be it for culinary purposes, a fragrant wealth of flowers, for the medicine chest, or simply as part of a garden's landscape. So many herbs are pleasing to the eye when seen growing in amongst other garden plants, while in containers herbs make aromatic ornaments for a window box, stoep or patio. As they require so little time and effort, herbs make ideal pot plants.

But there are many other reasons for having herbs in the garden. Their scents are actually beneficial to other garden plants. There is less insect damage found in gardens where herbs have been interplanted, and the healing qualities which so many herbs possess are often absorbed by ailing plants nearby. Certain herbs will attract bees and butterflies to your garden, while others act as insect repellents. Herbs can also be used to make your own garden sprays, infinitely preferable to using chemical sprays. Remember that no fertilisers, pesticides or any chemical additives should be used in your herb garden at any time. Herb gardening should be strictly organic.

Once you start growing herbs you will find yourself becoming more and more fascinated and involved and you may even decide to start your own special collection. You could start a collection of fragrant herbs and go on to collect potpourri recipes, perhaps even making and experimenting with your own combinations. Another idea is to put together a kitchen garden of rare food flavourings, such as the giant garlic, or garlic chives or cayenne pepper. Always of interest are the specifically African herbs, particularly to South Africans, and indigenous plants placed in attractive positions will enhance any garden. However you grow your own herbs, there is one thing you can be sure of – the pleasure and interest you will get from them knows no bounds.

A mature herb garden is an enviable possession

My monthly articles on herbs in as many as four magazines a month over the past 20 years has sparked interest in many commercial herb growers, and because I am the farmer still, and always will be, I know the importance of selecting a profitable crop. I have grown every single one of these herbs and have made a good living from them, often concentrating on one particular herb and developing accompanying products. I wrote this book with precisely this thought in mind – is it worth growing commercially? The answer is yes. Start with a row or two and see how it does in an area. Find the market before going into full production, and be happily surprised!

Designing a herb garden

The laying out and style of a herb garden will be dictated by the people who are going to enjoy and use the plants. Formal or informal, a herb garden is a garden both to be used and to give pleasure.

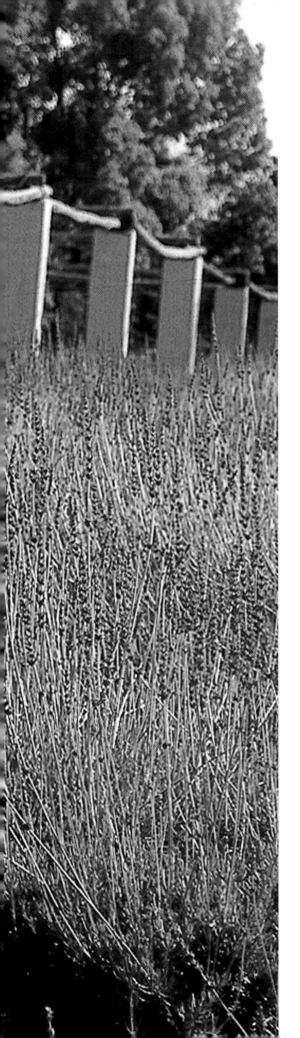

Most herbs are at their best on a site which is relatively protected from searing winds and frost; therefore low walls or fences that can accommodate climbing plants, or pergolas enclosing the area, are beneficial. In South Africa's heat and drought shady areas are a necessity and for this purpose pergolas are an excellent idea, as not only do they provide shade, but they also look beautiful covered with fragrant climbing roses, honeysuckle or jasmine.

It pays to spend time and energy clearing and digging the site for your herb garden and the crop of eager weeds, which will probably appear after the initial work, can easily be eradicated before the new herbs are planted. Ideally the site chosen should be in a sunny position and the soil should be fertile and drainage fairly good. Some form of moisture-retaining material such as a good compost should be dug in at an approximate ratio of 4 spadefuls of compost to 1 square metre of soil. *Never use artificial fertilisers or sprays on herbs as many of these plants are used for medicinal purposes.* Leaf mould or animal bedding straw can also be dug into the soil to provide moisture-retaining humus. For the midsummer South African heat mulching with leaves and grass to retain coolness and moisture is essential.

Whatever size of garden you are planning, level the site and lay the paths before planting. The gardener must be able to get to every part of the garden for easy maintenance. Do not make the paths too narrow; they should be wide enough to accommodate two people walking beside each other, for strolling through a herb garden, sharing it with another person, is one of its greatest pleasures. People need to touch and smell and see the plants close at hand. Paths can be paved; bricked, cemented, grassed or gravelled. Many traditional herb gardens had fine grass paths. This is possibly the cheapest way of making an attractive path, but it does need to be mowed regularly and clipped at the edges. Beds which are edged with stones or bricks will also keep the grass in check. Cost and your personal taste will determine the path material you choose. Paving stones and bricks make beautiful paths and these need a solid, well tramped down foundation. Gravel paths also require a good solid foundation as well as an edging of bricks to contain the gravel.

The simplest herb garden is a square or rectangle divided by crossed paths (traditionally used to scare the devil!), with a sundial in the centre. In a South African herb garden there are primarily four major sections. The ones I choose are a culinary section, an aromatic section, a medicinal section and a natural insecticide section. You can also include an African indigenous section.

The table on the next page gives suggestions of plants to include in each section of the herb garden. All the plants mentioned are discussed in detail in the main part of the book.

LEFT: Pergolas are versatile in the herb garden. Foreground: Lavandula intermedia 'Margaret Roberts'

Plants for the four sections of the herb garden

The **culinary section** could include any of the following:

Amaranth	Dill	Moringa	Sesame
Anise	Fennel	Mustard	Scented geraniums
Basil	Fenugreek	Nasturtium	Sorrel
Bay	Garlic	Oats	Soya bean
Bergamot	Ginger	Oregano	Stevia
Borage	Green tea	Paprika	Strawberry
Caraway	Horseradish	Parsley	Tarragon
Cayenne pepper	Lemon grass	Raspberry	Thyme
Celery	Lovage	Rocket	Turmeric
Chervil	Lucerne	Roselle	Watercress & Landcress
Chives	Marjoram	Rosemary	Winter savory
Comfrey	Melissa	Sage	Yarrow
Coriander	Mint	Salad burnet	

The **aromatic section** could have these herbs:

Bergamot	Honeysuckle	Mint	Scented geraniums
Carnation	Lavender	Myrtle	Southernwood
Catmint	Lemon verbena	Rose	Vetiver grass
Costmary	Melissa	Rosemary	Violet

The **medicinal section** could have these herbs:

Aloe vera	Comfrey	Goldenrod	Oats
Amaranth	Cornflower	Ground ivy	Olive leaf
Barley	Dandelion	Hawthorn	Pennywort
Bergamot	Echinacea	Linseed	Red clover
Black seed	Elder	Loofah	Rue
Buckwheat	Eucalyptus	Maidenhair fern	Soapwort
Burdock	Evening primrose	Milk thistle	Silver birch
Calendula	Feverfew	Mullein	St John's wort
Californian poppy	Field poppy	Myrtle	Tea tree
Catmint	Garlic	Nasturtium	Wormwood
Chamomile	Ginger	Nettle	Yarrow

The **natural insecticide** section would have:

Anise	Costmary	Lemon verbena	Southernwood
Basil	Cumin	Mint & Pennyroyal	Tea tree
Bergamot	Eucalyptus	Myrtle	Wormwood
Caraway	Fenugreek	Neem	
Catmint	Feverfew	Pyrethrum	
Coriander	Garlic	Rue	

An **indigenous African** section of herbs would include:

Aloe	Bulbinella	Pennywort	Scented geraniums

Finally, the following **herb trees** can be planted around the herb garden or elsewhere in the garden:

Elder	Hawthorn	Olive
Eucalyptus	Moringa	Silver birch
Ginkgo	Neem	Tea tree

The designs of course can vary enormously, but because of the ancient lore surrounding these amazing plants I prefer to use the traditional designs that have their roots in ancient civilizations. In these designs knowledge of the past has been mingled with superstition, magic and folklore; it is only by comparing suggestions, however, and by your own trial and error, that yours will be the garden of magic it is intended to be. A mature herb garden is an enviable possession but however small the garden, be it a window box or tub on a sunny patio or balcony, herbs are within the reach of each one of us.

The following are designs for twelve different herb gardens and these can be adapted to any size to fit any piece of ground. They are inspired by the old herb garden designs originating from the cloister gardens, the intricately designed formal knot gardens and the physic gardens. All have the central position for a sundial, a water feature, statue or urn and all can be surrounded by paths for easy access to all points.

Simple herb garden forms from The English Gardener – 1688

But there is no rule that says that herbs must only be grown in formal or patterned gardens. They will look just as beautiful growing freely, interplanted with other perennials in a border. Herbs create interesting patterns and the different textures and fragrances can make your garden a pure delight at all times of the year and throughout any season.

Herbs for culinary use can be planted in hollow concrete blocks set into the soil or in large pots and placed within easy reach of the kitchen door. These are neat, attractive and practical for those everyday flavouring herbs. A wagon wheel, available in concrete, lying in the soil makes an unusual type of planter; the spaces between each spoke of the wheel can be used for a different herb – a good way to grow the rampant mints as it curbs their spread, but do line with plastic deeply inserted into the soil.

Low hedges can be made of lavender, rosemary, southernwood or myrtle and can be an attractive feature in any garden. Leave enough space for the roots so that they do not encroach upon the other herbs. All clippings can be kept for potpourris and herb teas.

Several herbs make interesting groundcovers, including the creeping thymes, pennywort, pennyroyal and violets. Some do well in shade while others, like creeping rosemary, are drought resistant and can cover a bank with greenness and fragrance in the most blazing sun.

Do label your herbs for quick reference and identification. There are numerous ways of doing this and you will choose the method which suits you best. I use a ceramic tile with a hole in it, hooking a thick wire rod through the hole and then pressing it into the ground. On the tiles I carve the herb's common name, its Latin name and its major uses. Markers are available now in many garden centres. You yourself will quickly become familiar with your herbs, but naming is essential if you have others picking your herbs for culinary use!

A well-designed herb garden will bring its owner year-long pleasure

Growing herbs in containers

Growing herbs in containers has many advantages. A few small plants in an attractive container can often be better displayed than in the larger garden beds where they sometimes tend to get lost. Almost every type of herb can be grown in a container if given proper soil, the right amount of sun and water and enough room to grow. For herbs with long tap roots be sure that the container is deep enough.

With so many planters available, ranging from the old-fashioned clay pots, strawberry jars or huge asbestos tubs and barrels, from wooden planters to unusual distinctive ceramic pots and bowls, choosing the right ones is largely a matter of personal taste. Be sure, however, that your planters have good drainage holes so that the roots do not become waterlogged. Do choose a big enough planter if you want to group herbs together. Hanging baskets are suitable for the creeping thymes and creeping rosemary, and even chives look good from aloft. A basket hanging outside the kitchen door can be most useful for the busy cook but it does need lots of water!

Window boxes can serve the needs of the flat-dweller quite adequately: one plant each of thyme, marjoram and parsley, a tiny rosemary bush, with a small group of chives and perhaps a little creeping oregano, will be sufficient for most people's culinary needs. Provided that the box gets a minimum of eight hours of sun a day and the plants get sufficient water this miniature herb garden should give many months of pleasure.

Before putting in your herbs cover the holes at the bottom of your container with small stones or pieces of broken pot. Then use a good potting soil mixture to fill the container. One good mixture is: 7 parts garden soil, 3 parts peat, 1 part sand and 3 parts good compost.

Correct watering is an important aspect of container growing because water evaporates rapidly through the sides of the pot, if it is a clay or wooden pot or even an asbestos container. In very hot weather, therefore, your herbs will need a daily if not twice daily watering. Never allow the pot to dry out completely as this will damage the plant, considerably stunting its growth and causing it to wilt and die back. A good idea is to stand the pot in a bowl of shallow water; this way the water is absorbed through the bottom of the pot. Extra attention must be paid to hanging baskets, as they tend to dry out more quickly. Unless you are growing herbs for their flower heads and seeds, cut off the flowers as they appear so that all the goodness can be stored in the leaves.

Every two weeks or so add a concentrated plant food to your container of herbs; this will ensure lush and beautiful plants that will stand a lot of picking. I would advise using the natural seaweed and organic plant food concentrates to keep the herbs healthy, pure and uncontaminated. Remember that many of the herbs will be used in medicinal preparations so never use artificial or chemical sprays, fertilisers or fumigants.

Planned with thought and care, your herb garden, whether it be a large traditional one or a window box on a balcony, will become a priceless treasure, ever fascinating and ever changing.

Companion planting

An excellent reason for growing herbs in our gardens, apart from their culinary fragrance or medicinal uses, is that the scents of certain herbs actually help protect other plants against insects. For example, a row of cabbages interplanted with a row of marigolds suffers far less insect damage than if planted alone. The fragrance of the marigold, pungent and strong, confuses and repels the egg-laying moths.

Lavender will attract butterflies to the herb garden

Annual herbs such as coriander, anise and mustard, are protective herbs interplanted between rows of vegetables, and seem to aid one another's growth too. Special attention should be paid, therefore, to the layout of a vegetable and herb garden. You will find advice on companion planting under each of the main herb entries.

Plants that have complementary physical demands can be grouped together, for example moisture and shade loving plants can be placed beside taller, non-moisture loving plants, and a pleasing garden can be landscaped bearing such companion planting in mind.

I have grown a most spectacular red and green really unusual garden bed this past summer and I never needed to spray it or give it much attention as it grew so prolifically. The bed is 8 m x 4 m.

- Edging: parsley right round on all sides, planted 20 cm apart.
- Then cayenne peppers, bush grows about 30 cm high, each planted 40 cm apart.
- Next row sweet basil, bush grows 50 cm high, spaced 40 cm apart.
- Next row paprika, bush grows 50 cm high, planted 45 cm apart.
- Next row tomatoes, the tiny cocktail ones trained on green painted metal hoops, they reach 1 m in height, planted 50 cm apart.
- Next row perennial sweet basil, each plant reaches 50 cm height, planted 45 cm apart.
- At the feet of the small-leafed perennial sweet basil I planted Selecta strawberries, 20 cm apart, which in the shade of the basil bore luscious fruits long after Christmas.

This bed was exceptionally productive and I had masses of everything to give away as presents over Christmas and well into autumn, and it looked enchanting. I had dug in copious amounts of compost and with the past summer's rain it literally outgrew itself. But it was so rewarding that I literally worked in it, and picked daily. I would probably say I'm addicted to paprika, and basil, and tomatoes … and the mouth-watering dishes I developed with my crop had everyone ecstatic!

Herbs to attract bees and butterflies

Herbs in the garden that will attract bees:

Amaranth	Comfrey	Field poppy	Rosemary
Borage	Coriander	Melissa*	Sage
Californian poppy	Dill	Raspberry	Stevia
Chamomile	Evening primrose	Red clover	Strawberry
Chives	Fennel	Rose	Winter savory

*Melissa means 'little bee' and if the inside of a hive is rubbed with a handful of melissa leaves after the swarm has come the new swarm will never leave the hive.

Herbs in the garden that will attract butterflies:

Basil	Elder	Honeysuckle	Scented geraniums
Bergamot	Fennel	Lavender	Tarragon
Catmint	Feverfew	Lemon verbena	Violet
Cornflower	Ginger	Mullein	Yarrow
Dill	Goldenrod	Rosemary	

Propagation of plants

The main ways of propagating herbs are: seeds, root division, layering and taking cuttings. The individual herbs have in their descriptions the most appropriate means of propagation but as an easy reference the framework set out below may be useful.

Seed sowing in containers

There are a number of advantages in starting seeds in containers in sheltered positions. Perennial herbs which often take a long time to germinate can be started indoors late in winter and can be moved outside to harden off when the spring comes. Indoors one can control the temperature and soil conditions and can therefore produce superior seedlings, and germination is far more satisfactory.

Commercially made seed boxes are probably the easiest to handle and they already have drainage holes. Any container can be adapted, however – strong cartons and tomato boxes can be lined with plastic and, with a few drainage holes, these can be quite satisfactory. Place a few small stones at the bottom of the container and then fill with your soil mixture to within 15 mm of the top. The soil mixture needs to be loose, well draining and yet one which will hold water. I find equal parts sand, garden loam and a fine, well-matured compost is a good basic mixture. Sieve through a 6 mm mesh screen to remove any clods and sticks and firm down well in the container. Soak in water.

Sprinkle the seeds evenly over the surface and cover with a depth of soil approximately twice the diameter of the seed. Water carefully, using a fine spray so as not to wash the seeds out of the soil or expose them. Another way of watering is to soak the bottom of the seed tray in a pan of water so that the moisture is drawn up into the soil by capillary action. The secret of successful seed sowing is to ensure that the soil never dries out in those first critical weeks of germination.

Label the containers clearly so that you are sure which seeds you have sown and cover them with a pane of glass or hessian to protect them from the drying effect of the wind. The seeds do not need light until they have sprouted but they do need fresh air to prevent fungus formation, so lift off the cover for an hour or two each day, always checking to see that the soil has not dried out. Water with a fine spray daily.

After germination the container can be moved to partial shade where there is good light but not full sun. Turn the container daily so that the seeds can receive equal exposure to light. Always keep moist but be sure not to over-water as at this stage the seedlings are liable to damp off. When two sets of true leaves have formed the seedlings can be transplanted into bigger containers or, if sturdy enough, can be planted into prepared beds in the garden and shaded until stronger. If you want the plants to establish well, plant into the new containers in a richer mixture of soil – 2 parts garden loam, 1 part river sand and 1 part sifted peat moss or compost. Space the seedlings wider apart, at least 5 cm, and water carefully until well established.

Once the plants are strong and big enough, place the seed box in the sun for increasing periods during the few days before planting out in order to strengthen them. Plant out in a prepared bed which should be well dug with compost and have a good amount of leaf mould added to it. As a general guide use 2 spadefuls of compost and 1 spadeful of leaf mould or old manure to 1 square metre of soil.

Planting seeds directly into the garden

Any seeds can be sown into the garden as soon as all danger of frost has passed and the soil has begun to warm up. Some seeds that do well sown directly into their site are: aniseed, barley, black seed, buckwheat, caraway, cornflower, cress, cumin, field poppy, linseed, loofah, nasturtium, mustard, oats, sesame and soya bean.

First choose a place that is suitable for the plant and then turn the soil to a depth of about 30 cm, breaking up the clods. If the soil drains poorly add organic compost, leaf mould, chopped hay or peat moss to lighten it. Fork and level well, then make shallow drills (draw the rake over the soil to indicate the lines) and sow the seeds into these drills, spacing them well. Cover with soil to the depth of about twice the diameter of the seed, firm down well with the back of the rake and water with a fine spray, taking care not to expose the seeds. Label the row so that you are sure of what you have planted as new seedlings all look very similar.

In South Africa's heat and wind it is usually necessary to make a low protective frame of sticks. I use forked sticks driven into the soil at each of the four corners of the bed. Onto these I tie long sticks or reeds to form the frame, as well as a few cross reeds tied at intervals. Arrange a hessian covering over the frame, securing it in place with string. Alternatively a thin layer of thatching grass over the frame will do as well. Secure it by tying sticks over it to weight it down against the wind. I find about 20 cm above the soil is all that is needed for the height of the frame; anything higher will need side flaps to counteract the slanting rays of the hot spring sunshine. Where it is difficult to cover the plants with a shade area I make a small dam around each seed, or a long row of built-up earth, and put dried leaves and grass into it to create a little shade for those newly germinating seeds. Do remember to water at least twice a day to ensure that the seeds remain moist.

The germination period for most annual seeds is 12-14 days and a little longer for perennials – sometimes from 3 weeks up to 1 month. Throughout this period the soil must be kept moist.

Broadcasting is another seed planting method. This is when you want to cover a certain area instead of planting in rows. Prepare the soil as above, water well and scatter the seeds evenly over the area. Cover with sand and water and shade the area as you would rows of seeds.

Propagation by cuttings

Rooting cuttings or slips is perhaps the easiest method of propagating and so much faster than sowing seeds. Many herbs grow well from cuttings, for example lavender, rosemary, sage, the thymes, marjoram, oregano, pineapple sage, lemon balm, bergamot, southernwood, lemon verbena, bay, catmint, St John's wort, mint, rue, tansy and wormwood. Cuttings can be taken at any time during the growing season from healthy, well-established plants. Strong new tip growth makes the best cuttings. Make the cutting just below a leaf bud or node, using a sharp knife or clippers. The length of the cutting should be between 8-15 cm. Keep the cuttings damp by placing them between layers of wet newspaper or cloth and keep them out of the sun until you are ready to plant them. Have seed boxes ready, about 10 cm in depth and filled with river sand.

Mint grows easily from cuttings

If you have just a few cuttings, a pot or a jam tin will suffice as long as it has good drainage (a few stones in the bottom of the container will help). Wet the sand thoroughly and make a row of holes with a stick, about 5-8 cm in depth. Strip the lower leaves from the cuttings and press each one into its prepared hole. You can first dip the cut end into a hormone rooting powder if you like. Press down firmly and complete the rows. Water again and place in a protected, warm place in the shade. If the cuttings are taken before winter, make a miniature greenhouse over them by covering them with plastic, supported on a frame or wire arches, the edges tucked under stones to keep out draughts.

It usually takes from a month to 7 weeks for the cuttings to take and to form strong roots of their own and in all this time they must not be allowed to dry out. Give them a little time in the sun to harden off before transplanting and when you remove them from their seed tray be careful how you take them out – shake the box out gently on its side so as not to pull away the tender new roots.

Transplant into prepared beds which have compost and old manure (2 spades compost and 1 spade manure to 1 square metre) well dug into the area. If you do not have old manure, use extra compost. Make a hole, place the cutting into it, cover the roots with soil, press down firmly and water well. Do not let the cuttings dry out and mulch with coarse compost. Once the plants are established water regularly once or twice weekly.

Layering

Creeping herbs such as the mints, the thymes, catmint, winter savory, southernwood, honeysuckle and elder, when brought into contact with the soil, will take root while they are still attached to the parent plant. Many herbs in any case send down roots naturally from branches that touch the ground, so this is a very quick and easy way to make new plants.

Select a strong, healthy branch growing close to the ground. Dig a shallow hole below it and fill with sand, soil and a little compost. Scratch a small raw place on the underside of the branch and dab on a little hormone powder, then bend the branch down into the hole and anchor it in place with a heavy wire arch. Firm down with soil and water well. Place a stone over the area to keep the soil above the branch undisturbed.

Give the new root-forming branch about 6 weeks and then check on its progress, gently scraping away a little of the soil. When good roots are established sever the stem from the parent plant and leave undisturbed for 3 weeks. Your new sturdy plant is now ready for transplanting to a preferred position. Prepare a hole with well-mixed soil and compost, carefully dig out the plant with a lot of soil around it and place the plant in the hole that is filled with water, covering the roots with soil and pressing down well again. Make a small dam around it and water well. Check twice a week to see that it does not dry out completely.

Root cuttings

Any plant that sends up suckers, for example elder, soapwort, the mints, yarrow, bergamot, catmint, tarragon, ginger, goldenrod and melissa can easily be propagated. Select strong suckers and with a sharp spade chop off, taking as much root as possible. Have ready a deep seed box filled with light garden soil that has a little compost worked into it – 4 spades of soil to one spade of compost.

Place the root cuttings horizontally into the box and cover with soil, firming down and watering well. Put the box in the shade, making sure that it is not in a draught. Remember to keep the cuttings moist. When new growth and leaf buds appear, transplant into individual pots where the cuttings will develop into strong plants. Keep partially shaded, then harden off by placing them in the sun for lengthening periods each day. Once they are established, plant out in the garden into well-prepared beds.

Root division

The best time to divide plants is autumn or early spring when the plants are not forming new growth. Chives, strawberries, tarragon, goldenrod, bergamot, oregano, marjoram, violet, melissa, sorrel, comfrey, tansy and yarrow are amongst those plants that really divide well.

Dig out a clump and, placing 2 forks back to back with their prongs firmly in the clump, pull them apart and split the clump open. Then pull the sections into smaller sections and replant in newly prepared soil. Perennials such as these need fairly rich soil so dig in 3 spadefuls of compost and 2 of old manure to 1 square metre of garden soil. Keep the soil moist until the newly planted pieces have adjusted.

Often the central portion or original mother plant will need to be discarded as it will have become woody and stunted. If you replant into the original position, first dig in some compost and old manure as the soil will have become depleted.

Separate perennials every 2 to 3 years and give a yearly feed of compost and old manure. Perennials form the backbone of the herb garden so they deserve the best care.

The elder can be propagated by layering or by root cuttings

Compost making and mulching

If you are a good compost maker you will be a successful organic gardener and herb grower! Compost is the very heart of the organic method of gardening – using only natural substances to increase the growth and vitality of your plants – and compost is the base for your herb garden. Perhaps a good definition of compost would be to describe this rich black magic as a substance which gives fertility to the soil and thus productivity to the plants grown in that soil. Another advantage that compost has is that it helps maintain the moisture content of the soil and in our drought prone country this is a necessity.

Basically, to make your own compost pile at almost no cost is not difficult. Every potato peeling, grass clipping, raked leaf or pulled up weed, and any manure that you have at hand can be thrown into the compost pile. First build it, then moisten it, turn it a few times and forget it! Some weeks later spade it over and smell the dark richness of converted kitchen waste and weeds and you will never again use any other kind of compost.

Getting started

Firstly, the site you choose should be a small corner about 2 m by 2 m in size where the heap can mature for 2-3 months undisturbed. I find that loosening clay or turf-type soil with a fork before you begin seems to aid the aeration of the heap, but on sandy soil this is not necessary.

A rough bed of coarse garden material can be laid down – or, if available, cabbage and mealie stalks, soft prunings, coarse veld grass and dead flower stalks. The aim is to allow air to get into the heap from the base. Then a mixture of garden residue, kitchen waste, lawn clippings, weeds and crushed eggshells is moistened and mixed with a good sprinkling of manure and packed on top of this base.

Use a soft sprinkling of water all the time while making and packing onto the heap. Tread the heap down now and then while building it up but do not make it too soggy. After packing a layer of your mixture about 15 cm deep spread a thin layer of manure and stable bedding over the layer of this mixture. The manure and stable bedding act as activators and so do the outer leaves of cabbage and cauliflower, as well as free-range chicken manure. (Do not use manure from chicken batteries as it may contain ingredients harmful to humans; do not use it on food crops either.)

Cover the manure layer with a thin layer of soil mixed with some wood ash, dolomitic lime and rock phosphate if you can obtain them. Repeat the 15 cm layers plant refuse, kitchen waste, manure and soil, moistening with a fine spray nozzle on the hose and stamping down until you have a heap 1-1,5 m high. Top it with a 25 mm thick layer of garden soil and then cover the heap with veld grass to maintain the moisture and to keep off the sun. In very wet areas, such as the Cape winter rainfall area, cover with black plastic sheeting to maintain the warmth and to keep the pile from becoming sodden.

Air circulation is an important element in the compost heap. In larger heaps a post or pipe can be driven into the ground at the centre or several posts driven in at various points in the heap. When you have finished building the heap remove the post or pipe to create a ventilation hole. You will be amazed at the degree of heat that builds up in the heap. About three weeks later comes the next important step. This is the turning of the heap. Turn and mix thoroughly and remoisten, as in the initial heating up of the heap there is a marked moisture loss. In South Africa's heat and dryness it is essential to maintain that moisture. The heat build-up reaches 71-77 °C in those first 7-10 days and this is the secret of success. It is a sign of much activity within the heap of the decomposing of material.

Properly made compost has a pleasant odour at all times and does not present a health hazard. Decaying matter which is too wet and without aeration is anaerobic or foul smelling and is a deterrent to compost making.

Comfrey, yarrow leaves, buckwheat, or seaweed, liquid manure or liquid seaweed – provided that none of these is chemically made or preserved – can also be added to the heap and will add essential and beneficial trace elements. In fact, anything that is natural and decomposable is an acceptable addition. I have two kitchen bins at hand, one for plastic, tins, wrappings, etc. and the other for peelings, vegetable pips, outer leaves and fruit skins. Having a separate bin means a quick and effortless daily addition to the pile.

Several compost bins and receptacles are available at garden and hardware shops and it is often useful to have smaller heaps going all the time. Remember that the larger the heap the greater the retention of temperature. A very successful compost can be made in the small bins for the smaller garden. The greatest compost enemies are excessive moisture and excessive dryness. Should your heap become too dry dismantle it and sprinkle with water with a fine hose. Repack the layers, watering each one well, but not so well as to become sodden.

Compost is undoubtedly the best fertiliser there is – it contains no harmful substances and can be easily assimilated by the soil where earthworms and micro-organisms act upon it and convert it into the humus on which plants feed.

Mulching

Mulching and compost making go hand in hand. Many home gardeners are not fully aware of the benefits of mulching but without it weeds grow abundantly and vigorously and the soil rapidly dries out – a very real problem in this country with its periods of water shortages and restrictions. Surface evaporation is prevented when the beds are covered with a 5 cm layer of mulch. At the same time the mulching material is rotting and being incorporated into the soil by worms and other soil inhabitants and the fertility of the soil is thus being maintained. If you are short of compost, mulching is the next best soil saver and in the blazing summer heat it is necessary to conserve coolness as well as moisture.

Mulching materials abound in every garden. They include fallen leaves, roughly chopped stalks and twigs, weeds and grass clippings. (Do not use grass clippings in a green or cut state as they tend to pack and become sour; in ant-infested areas they also provide a wonderful home for a colony.) Mix grass clippings with leaves and twigs and chips of bark and even rough sawdust. I find chopped dried khakibos is a wonderful insect repellent and I add it to the mulching materials to keep everything sweet smelling and ant-free. Exact quantities do not really matter and your own experimenting and experience will give you the best results for your area.

Whatever you use, however, mulching will become a vital part of gardening and in the herb garden it will be of great benefit – so save all those fallen leaves (particularly sage as it is a natural fertiliser) and enjoy a weed-free garden!

The plants in your herb garden will thrive if you regularly add compost to the soil

Harvesting and drying of herbs

The care you have exercised in planting your herbs can easily be to no avail through incorrect harvesting and drying.

Seeds can be collected at the end of the season's growth and should be sorted and stored in clearly marked envelopes or packets when they are quite dry. If roots are to be harvested the plant must reach its full maturity at the end of summer before it is dug up.

To harvest the leaves from a plant the general rule is to pick the leaves once the plant starts flowering. This is the time when the active principles of the plant are of the best quality and it is then that the oils, which give the herb its distinctive fragrance, are the most concentrated.

Choose a sunny, warm morning to do your picking, after the night's dew has dried from the leaves and before the sun gets too hot. The best picking time in South Africa's summer heat is from 8am to 10am. Some annuals flower early in the season and if you cut them back they will grow enough for a second harvest in autumn.

Basil, dill, fennel and celery are amongst those which often give a second picking, but do not cut back too vigorously the first time. After the summer the whole plant can be cut back and dried. Shrubby perennials such as thyme, melissa, marjoram, lavender, rosemary and myrtle can be cut back to encourage bushy, compact growth and of course each twig can be saved and dried.

Some annual herbs, among them anise, caraway, coriander, dill and celery, produce tasty seeds that are used in cookery and flavouring. Harvest these as soon as they start to turn brown but before they fully ripen and scatter far and wide. Cut the entire seed head off into a brown paper bag. Label and date it and store until completely dry, then clean and sort the seeds and store in screw-top glass bottles or well-corked pottery jars.

For drying herbs you will need a few screens which you can easily make yourself: take a frame made from wood or metal and stretch a shade cloth or loosely woven piece of hessian over it. The green herbs can be put directly onto the screen and dried in the shade in an airy shed or garage. For small quantities of herbs, a spread open newspaper will suffice, but be sure to turn the herbs daily and never pack too many on top of each other.

Always dry the herbs in the shade and in our summer heat this will only take a few days. Once they are dry and brittle to the touch, separate the sticks and leaf stalks and rub down the bigger leaves to storable sizes. Have ready-labelled bottles or packets and always work with only one kind of plant, completing its storage before starting the next, or the flavours will intermingle and your effort will be wasted.

Choose airtight storage containers so that moist air cannot be reabsorbed. In the humid coastal regions, herbs can be dried in a cool oven overnight at the lowest heat possible. Never dry herbs in a microwave oven.

I find that after about four months the flavour and goodness of the dried plant have usually deteriorated, so it is best to use up the dried material quickly.

For potpourris the summer flowers can be dried in the same way to keep their colours brilliant (be sure no sun touches them) and if you want whole flowers in your potpourris bunches can be hung upside down from the roof to dry.

The moisture content of most plants is 70 per cent and the aim is to dry the material as quickly as possible to maintain the aroma and flavouring to some degree. A drying period of 3 to 5 days is ideal.

Freezing herbs

Some of the more tender herbs such as tarragon, borage, salad burnet, sweet basil, dill, parsley, comfrey and chives can be frozen satisfactorily and, as these herbs do not really dry well, freezing is a solution if you do not have access to fresh herbs all the year round.

Tie the herbs in bundles with string and blanch in unsalted boiling water for about 5 seconds, holding onto the string so that you can lift them out easily. Cool them quickly by dipping into a bowl of iced water, then fold into foil or freezer bags, labelling each carefully.

If you chop the leaves before packaging they will be ready for use as soon as they are removed from the freezer. A good idea is to put separate recipe amounts in each small bag so that small quantities are available as you need them. They can be placed still frozen directly into the food or sauce you are cooking but if they are to go into salads defrost them beforehand.

Aloe Vera

Family Liliaceae
Species *Aloe barbadensis*
Origin Barbadosis Islands
Plant perennial
Height 70-80 cm; space 1 m apart
Soil sandy, well-drained soil
Exposure full sun
Propagation by small plants called 'pups' that form under the base leaves
Uses medicinal, cosmetic

Hieroglyphics and paintings on the walls of Egyptian temples prove that aloe vera was revered over 3 000 years ago, and in the fourth century BC Aristotle reportedly asked Alexander the Great to conquer the island of Socotra to assure a constant supply of this medicinal herb. Aloe vera gel is a storehouse of nutrients. A stabilised gel or juice is produced that can be taken orally for a number of ailments. The protein contained in aloe vera includes 18 of 20 amino acids found naturally in the body and the nutritional content is rich in vitamins A, B1, B2, B3, B6, C and E.

CULTIVATION As a pot plant aloe vera is most often grown in large terracotta tubs – but remember, in a pot it needs daily watering as it must stand in full sun. Feed twice yearly with a dressing of good compost to ensure vigorous growth. Be sure to shield from frost or cold winds, as it is very tender.

PROPAGATION The plant is sterile and does not produce seeds. It does, however, have a unique habit (among aloes) of propagating itself by forming new, tiny plantlets or 'pups' under its base leaves. Separate the little 'pups' when they are big enough to handle and replant 1 metre apart in well dug sandy soil to which a good dressing of compost has been added. Plant in full sun and water twice a week.

HARVESTING AND PROCESSING Reap base leaves when mature by cutting off with a sharp knife. Remove the bitter skin and you are left with a transparent 'fillet' which can be sliced fresh onto burns or applied to skin ailments, or added to animals' feed.

USES OF ALOE VERA

Medicinal The gel is excellent for application to skin ailments, as it contains anthraquione glycosides and polysaccharides, as well as other components that stimulate the healing of wounds, bile flow, act as a tonic, are antifungal and contain sedative properties. The stabilised juice, bought from health shops or pharmacies, helps arthritis, rheumatism, stomach ulcers, diabetes, high blood pressure, circulatory disorders, indigestion and both constipation and diarrhoea. Gout, kidney stones and inflamed joints all seem to respond well.

Warning: At high dosages the bitter properties are laxative and purgative. The yellow liquid in the outer casings of the leaves contains anthraquiones, which are dangerously laxative. It is therefore essential to use only pharmaceutically processed aloe vera internally in the form of juice. External application of the juice and gel is immediately soothing.

Cosmetic Aloe vera restores the pH balance of both skin and hair, giving a smoother, softer, shiny appearance. Hyaluronic acids in the gel help to rid the skin of toxins, counteracting blemishes and sun spots, clearing clogged facial pores, speeding up circulation and exfoliating dead cells. Products of every description abound, but do check the percentage of aloe vera included in the ingredients – it should be over 50 per cent for it to be effective.

Other uses Aloe vera is an excellent treatment of animal ailments, including arthritis, stiffness and constipation. Skin ailments are soothed by the direct application of the cut edge of a leaf, and a little gel can be added to the animal's food daily – no more than two teaspoons for a large dog and one for a small dog or cat. Horses too can have the gel added to their food, particularly ailing and elderly horses.

Amaranth

Love lies bleeding ● Marog
Family Amaranthaceae
Species *Amaranthus cordatus* ● *A. hypochondriacus*
Origin worldwide, mostly tropical
Plant annual
Height 20-200 cm; space 50 cm apart
Soil any soil, it thrives in waste places
Exposure full sun
Propagation seed
Uses culinary, medicinal, cosmetic

The name *Amaranthus* derives from the Greek *amaranton*, 'unfading'. The beautiful deep wine-red flowers keep their colour and shape for a long time and thus the plant came to symbolise immortality. According to the 17th-century 'doctrine of signatures' the colour or shape of a plant symbolised an ailment or a part of the body. In this case the red colour of the flowers indicated the blood of the patient, thus crushed leaves and flowers were placed over wounds or a decoction of the leaves was drunk to stop bleeding and to build the blood. Modern scientific findings indicate this isn't far wrong!

CULTIVATION Amaranth grows best in full sun, in areas that have been dug over and well composted. Keep seedlings moist and protected, and the sturdy, quickly growing plants will reach maturity in about 6 weeks, from 20 cm upwards. Some varieties grow up to 2 m in height, so you will have red-tinged leaves for a long time in great abundance. The young tender leaves and sprigs are most sought after: remember the more leaves you pick the more it will produce. Once you have amaranth in your garden you will always have it – it reseeds quickly. It is a short-lived annual and will continue up until the first frosts.

PROPAGATION Seed collected in the wild along roadsides or at the edges of fields is the quickest way of getting started. Crush the long fuzzy red flowering spikes and in your hand you will find a mass of tiny black seeds exactly like poppy seeds.

HARVESTING AND PROCESSING All through the growth period, from 10 cm to 2 m. Use leaves fresh.

COMPANION PLANTING Plant with mealies and potatoes.

USES OF AMARANTH

Culinary One of the world's favourite 'spinach' dishes, and a much-loved *marog* in South Africa, the delicious flavour makes it a superb steamed dish and mixed with other leafy vegetables like spinach it is both nourishing and filling.

Medicinal An ancient medicine for blood building. Today's research finds amaranth important for treating anaemia and chronic fatigue as well as chronic and intermittent diarrhoea. Externally it was once used as a wash for ulcers, as a gargle for mouth ulcers as it is astringent and reduces tissue swelling, and to assist in blood clotting after haemorrhaging. So this is an important herb for treating heavy menstrual bleeding, excessive vaginal discharge, dysentery and to clear coughs and coughing up of blood. It can be taken as a tea or as a splash for itching, burning skin too, once it is cooled, or as a soothing lotion to wash wounds. To make a tea, use ¼ cup fresh leaves and pour over this 1 cup boiling water. Leave to stand 5 minutes and strain. Take up to three cups a day for the above ailments.

Cosmetic The astringent action of amaranth is of particular use in oily problem skins. Made into a spritz lotion (see recipe section) it will tighten pores, reduce oiliness, moisten and cleanse the skin; combined with a little apple cider vinegar it is a soothing cleansing lotion for acne and blackheads, and it can be added to the rinsing water for oily hair.

Other uses This is one of the most superb plants for the compost heap and you will always find once you have spread old plants over it that it will reward you with thousands of tender succulent plants that are just waiting to be eaten! It makes a superb liquid fertiliser as well (see recipe section).

Anise

Family **Umbelliferae**
Species *Pimpinella anisum*
Origin **Eastern Mediterranean, Western Asia, North Africa**
Plant **annual**
Height **up to 30 cm; space 30 cm apart**
Soil **light, well-drained, alkaline**
Exposure **full sun, sheltered**
Propagation **seed**
Uses **culinary, medicinal, cosmetic**

Aniseed is a pretty, dainty quick and easy to grow little annual, and has been cultivated for its delicious culinary values for thousands of years. Records of its cultivation in Egypt date back over 4 000 years and in the Pharaonic texts it was recorded as a treatment for toothache, to relieve colic, digestive nausea, sour belching, flatulence and heartburn. The ancient Greeks grew aniseed as a pain reliever and Dioscorides, the Greek physician from the first century AD, recorded that aniseed 'warms, dries, dissolves, facilitates breathing, provokes urine, eases thirst and relieves pain.'

Throughout history anise was used as a flavouring for cakes, known as 'mustace cake' at banquets and weddings and served at the end of the banquet to prevent indigestion and colic after the rich foods (often as many as 12 or 15 courses!). Modern wedding cakes, richly spiced, are derived from this ancient custom.

CULTIVATION Plant in full sun and water regularly.

PROPAGATION Sow seeds sparsely in a shallow drill and keep moist. Protect with a layer of mulch.

HARVESTING AND PROCESSING Leaves can be picked as required, flowers as they open. The seeds ripen at the end of summer. Let the whole plant die off and, once dry, pull the plant up and thrash the seeds off the sprigs by beating bundles over a plastic cloth on the floor. Seal the seeds in a jar. The seeds stay viable and fresh for years.

COMPANION PLANTING Plant between rows of spinach, lettuce and tomatoes.

USES OF ANISE

Culinary The flowers are delicious in teas, cool drinks, punches and sprinkled onto cakes, desserts and into stirfries. The fresh leaves are also edible and can be added to salads and stirfries and to teas and drinks. Our great, great grandparents never cooked cabbage or beans or parsnips without a pinch or two of aniseed. The seeds are also added to cakes, breads, baked puddings, liqueurs and wine.

Medicinal Anise is known for its ability to aid digestion, reduce wind, stop hiccups, ease colic, dissipate bloating and relieve nausea. It is also helpful in countering menstrual pains and respiratory ailments like asthma, spasmodic coughing, whooping cough, bronchitis, pneumonia and even epileptic attacks and heat prostration. Many a nursing mother has sipped cups of aniseed tea to increase her breast milk production (and which benefits the baby's colic too) and anise tea has been found to be beneficial in treating frigidity and impotence and to ease the menstrual cycle. To make the tea, use 1 teaspoon aniseeds and pour over this 1 cup of boiling water. Stand 5 minutes, stir well, sip slowly and chew a few of the seeds. Sweeten with a little honey if liked.
Caution: Do not take anise in any form during pregnancy.

Cosmetic For oily skin, enlarged pores, acne and problem skin, take aniseed tea daily. The same tea can be used as a lotion, a wash, and as a spritz spray to clear the oiliness.

Other uses The whole mature plant, flowers and seeding heads, can be added to cattle feed for milk cows to treat mastitis, and to chicken feed to make the egg yolks more yellow, and to flavour the meat. Aniseed mixed with a little thick mealie meal porridge is an excellent bait in mousetraps. Add the seed to potpourris as an excellent fixative.

Barley

Family **Gramineae**
Species *Hordeum distichon*
Origin **Europe and Mediterranean regions**
Plant **winter annual**
Height **80 cm; sow 2 cm apart**
Soil **well-dug, rich soil**
Exposure **full sun**
Propagation **seed**
Uses **medicinal**

An annual grass grown in winter and cultivated in temperate regions all over the world, barley is an ancient, revered grain that has been part of the diet from the earliest days. Dioscorides in the 1st century AD urged the consumption of barley as a porridge, as a gruel and as a drink for ulcerated sore throats, convalescence and to 'restrain all sharp humours'. By the Middle Ages barley was gradually replaced by wheat, but to this day it remains important for its nutritional content and medicinal value, and is extensively marketed as green barley health products.

Rich in protein, B vitamins and minerals, barley is a hugely important health grain and in the century ahead will become part of a new health regime that is already taking hold. Young and tender leaves can be finely chopped and sprinkled onto food as an energy booster, but the highest nutritional and energy value is in the sprouted seed. In neolithic times the grain was cooked, crushed and pounded into a nutritious milk that built strong bones – barley is now recognised to be important for osteoporosis due to its high calcium and potassium content. A glass of barley water 3 times a week is a superb detoxifier and will restore hair and nails as well as clear a multitude of ailments.

CULTIVATION Water twice weekly once it is established and in midwinter only once a week.

PROPAGATION Sow the seeds in autumn, directly into deeply dug, richly composted moist soil in full sun. Scatter evenly and thickly and rake over the ground to cover the seed. Do not let the area dry out. For indoor sowing all year round, soak 1 cup of barley seed in warm (not hot) water for a few hours. Line a flat tray or dish with a thick layer of cotton wool, or a few layers of flannel. Soak well. Sprinkle the drained seeds evenly over the surface and place out of direct sunlight but near a window. Keep moist. Spray daily with a spritz bottle of water. Use as sprouts and cut the grass with scissors.

HARVESTING AND PROCESSING Reap when ripe and golden – it reaches about 80 cm in height, one ear to one seed.

COMPANION PLANTING Beetroot, cabbages, chamomile.

USES OF BARLEY

Culinary As the seeds begin to sprout, pull them up and eat sprinkled on pizzas and stirfries. As they get taller, push them into a juice extractor with carrot and apple as a health drink. Buy pearled barley from the supermarket.

Medicinal Barley water (see recipe section) is excellent for stomach ailments, sore throats, catarrh, kidney and bladder infections, diarrhoea, hepatitis, high blood cholesterol, children's fevers, cramp, diabetes, for babies to prevent the development of milk curds in the stomach and colic, and for convalescence. A tea can be made of the green leaves and the ears for arthritis, gout, swellings and hay fever. Use ¼ cup fresh green leaves or sprouts and pour over this 1 cup boiling water. Stand 5 minutes. Strain and sip slowly.

Other uses A bundle of dry ripened barley tossed into a pond will keep the water clear and free of algae. A bale thrown into a dam will significantly clear murky water and it is safe for fish and for cattle drinking it – in fact it is a health booster for nature too!

Basil

Family Labiatae
Species *Ocimum basilicum*
Origin India and tropical parts of Asia
Plant annual
Height 40-50 cm; plant 50 cm apart
Soil well-dug, well-composted soil
Exposure full sun
Propagation seed
Uses culinary, medicinal, cosmetic

Basil is one of the world's most loved herbs. It was introduced to Europe from India many centuries ago and, one could say, has never lost its popularity. The Greek word for basil is *basileus*, which means king – and this little 19th-century poem says it all:

Of all the herbs Basil's king
For all the healing it can bring,
For taste and fragrance praises sing
Basil's good for everything!

CULTIVATION Owing to the deep tap roots none of the basils like to be moved. So select the site with care and when transplanting the little seedlings, do so in the cool of the late afternoon and keep the soil moist and shaded around them until they strengthen.

PROPAGATION Annual basil is best grown from seed. Perennial varieties are becoming more and more available through the nurseries and these can be propagated from cuttings. *Ocimum sanctum* (sacred or holy basil) is an ancient medicinal basil from India. Sweet basil is an annual and I sow my first seeds in August for late September planting out and then again in November for a batch to take me right through autumn until the first frosts. Sow the seeds in trays and transplant the seedlings 50 cm apart when they are big enough to handle. Keep them shaded for a day or two with twigs to protect them.

HARVESTING AND PROCESSING Basil is best used fresh (dried and frozen basil loses its flavour). Harvest the leaves as soon as the plant reaches 15 cm in height.

COMPANION PLANTING Plant with tomatoes, summer savory, fruit trees.

USES OF BASIL

Culinary There is no herb that tastes quite so delicious with pizza and pasta as basil, and with so many dishes from fish to summer soups, chicken to sausages, tomatoes to hard-boiled eggs, basil makes the dish! Probably the best-known basil recipe is pesto: there are whole festivals in America devoted to this popular sauce (see recipe section).

Medicinal Used as a medicine since ancient times, basil's remarkable detoxifying properties are well documented. Basil tea is an excellent destresser and detoxifier, as well as for migraines, coughs, peptic ulcers, tonsillitis, mouth infections, hypertension, palpitations, indigestion and delayed menstruation. Use ¼ cup fresh leaves to 1 cup boiling water. Stand 5 minutes. Strain and sip slowly. Use this tea cooled as a lotion. For infected bites and stings, crush a basil leaf and apply to the area. Basil cream (see recipe section) soothes aches and pains and stiffness: excellent for athletes or hikers with cramps or sore backs and feet. Basil vinegar is excellent for sunburn or scalp infections; it helps with psoriasis and eczema too. Use as a splash or add to the bath or hair rinsing water or as a compress on cotton wool.

Cosmetic Perfect for oily problem skins, basil has been used for centuries as an external lotion and poultice, cleanser and toner. As a face steamer, basil is an astringent deep cleanser for oily skin (see recipe section).

Other uses Basil makes a superb spray (see recipe section) against aphids, scale, fungus and white fly. Basil leaves rubbed onto windowsills and counter tops in the kitchen keeps flies away and freshens the air. The Mexicans rub the leaves over horses and blankets to keep insects away, especially the perennial basils.

Bay

Family Lauraceae
Species *Laurus nobilis*
Origin Mediterranean region and southern Europe
Plant tree
Height up to 10-12 m
Soil rich, well-dug soil
Exposure full sun
Propagation layering, cuttings if you are patient
Uses culinary, medicinal, cosmetic

This ancient and revered tree has been used in medicine and in folklore – it is supposed to be a magical tree – since the beginning of time. It was sacred to the Greek god of prophecy, poetry and healing, Apollo, and his temple had a roof made of bay leaves ostensibly to protect against disease and witchcraft and the forces of nature! Perhaps this is why through the centuries a bay tree was planted as protection near the home. In the 17th century the famous herbalist Culpeper believed that 'neither lightning nor the devil will hurt a man who has a bay tree near him'. A wreath of bay leaves was the mark of praise and esteem and excellence bestowed on athletes, poets and achievers across the world.

CULTIVATION All the bay tree requires is a deep hole filled with compost, in full sun, and a deep weekly watering. In its early years it will need some protection from winter frost and it benefits from pruning, trimming and shaping. It loves a squirt of water over its leaves from time to time and benefits from a barrow of compost every spring. Bay is susceptible to sooty scale, so it is advisable to give it a good spray with warm soapy water every now and then. Inspect the leaves carefully for any sign of scale.

PROPAGATION This is a long process and not for the faint hearted. Layering of its new growth alongside the main trunk is perhaps the most successful. Do this by gently bending over a strong new shoot that grows alongside the main trunk (usually these need to be chopped out as they appear, otherwise they make a multi-stemmed forest around your tree). With a hoop of wire press the young shoot down level with the ground, cover a small portion of it with soil and place a stone on top of it. Do not inspect it for a least a year – then cut it off its parent plant and keep it moist. In its second year it will be rooted and ready to transplant.

HARVESTING AND PROCESSING Fresh leaves have a far better flavour than dried ones. Harvest all through the year. Fresh leaves can be preserved in vinegar.

USES OF BAY

Culinary Try a leaf in custard, rice pudding, poaching fish, savoury mince, rice, even mealie meal porridge. Throw a bay branch onto the coals of a braai and tuck fresh leaves into storage jars of rice, sago, lentils, barley and split peas.

Medicinal An ancient medicinal tree, bay has been used as an astringent, digestive, antiseptic plant, formerly used to generate energy and stimulate the digestion and to relieve rheumatic aches and pains. At one time oil of bay was used by pharmacists in soap preparations and in ointments, and also for veterinary ointments, and a special remedy for baldness was once made using the oil and the berries. Today bay is hardly used except by country people who still put a branch of bay leaves into their baths – placed under the hot water tap – for easing muscular aches and pains and rheumatism.

Cosmetic The antiseptic astringent action of bay makes it a good addition to a face or hair rinse, or as a rub into the scalp. A soothing lotion (see recipe section) can be combed into the hair and rubbed into the scalp as a stimulant. My grandmother's bay leaf bath vinegar (see recipe section) was a boon for sore feet, aching muscles and dry or oily skin.

Other uses Twigs of bay pushed into the flour bin or rice container will keep weevils away. Fresh bay leaves deter ants, and folded into winter woollies will deter moths.

Bergamot

Bee balm ● Oswego tea ● Mountain mint
Family **Labiatae**
Species *Monarda didyma*
Origin **North America**
Plant **perennial**
Height **up to 1 m; space 30-50 cm apart**
Soil **rich, moist, well-composted soil**
Exposure **full sun**
Propagation **division**
Uses **medicinal, cosmetic**

Indigenous to North America and introduced to gardens all over the world, bergamot has long been cultivated for its bright flowers, ranging from deep magenta to cerise pink, and deep scarlet to pale pink, as well as its arresting fragrance and taste similar to that of the Italian bergamot orange (*Citrus bergamia*). The Oswego Native Americans used bergamot – Oswego tea – as a cure-all for centuries for treating colds, coughs, bronchitis, sinus, nausea, indigestion, colic and even kidney ailments, insomnia and backache.

CULTIVATION An easy-to-grow perennial, bergamot needs full sun and rich compost-filled soil. It forms a cushion of vigorous stems that flower from midsummer until late autumn. The plant dies back in autumn and needs to be tidied up. It takes frost and heat equally well but, in some humid areas, has a tendency to form mildew on the leaves. New varieties are mildew free and well worth growing.

PROPAGATION Each clump needs to be divided in July, every second or third year. Replant the little tufts 30 cm apart in full sun, in a different part of the garden in well-composted soil.

HARVESTING AND PROCESSING Harvest the flowers and leaves all through summer.

COMPANION PLANTING Plant with beans, beetroot, carrots, peppers, tomatoes.

USES OF BERGAMOT

Culinary Bergamot's most popular use is as a flavourant, using a fresh leaf or two added to a pot of China tea to give it that 'Earl Grey' taste (note: Earl Grey tea is flavoured with the bergamot orange). Bergamot imparts a rich, fragrant flavour when added to rice, samp or barley and is an excellent digestive – add 2-4 leaves while the dish cooks.

Medicinal Tests have proved bergamot to have abundant antiseptic compounds that help to clear respiratory infections and unblock sinus and nasal congestion. Use either as a tea, sipped slowly and hot, or as an external lotion. It's still taken as a health tea in America, served as an after-dinner drink to help digest fatty, rich foods and is an especially important herb for those with liver ailments. To make the tea use 3 leaves or 1 flower head and a leaf in 1 cup boiling water. Leave to stand 5 minutes. Strain and sip slowly. Use the cooled tea as a lotion. Sipped slowly this tea will ease nausea, flatulence, menstrual pain, vomiting and will boost the immune system, lift depression and ease anxiety.

Cosmetic Rich in tannins and the strong antiseptic thymol, bergamot makes an excellent treatment for oily, problem skin. It makes a superb steam treatment and is one of the best herbs to use as a wash or cleansing cream (see recipe section).

Other uses The Oswego Indians used cushions of bergamot on which they stored their baskets of grain during the winter. Dried leaves, crushed and powdered and mixed with equal quantities of khakibos then sprinkled around ants' holes, send ants scurrying. An infusion of khakibos, rue and bergamot makes an excellent spray for mealie bug, aphids and white fly (see recipe section). Bergamot, khakibos and rue can be combined with flour and water to make a herbal incense to keep mosquitoes away from the patio or braai area. Burn in a saucer or tin in a safe place (see recipe section).

Black Seed

The prolific 'black seed' of *Nigella sativa* has been used as both food and medicine for over 5 000 years. The earliest reference to 'black cumin' is found in the book of Isaiah in the Old Testament, and it was found in the tomb of Tutankhamen. Dioscorides recommended taking black seed to treat headaches, nasal catarrh, toothache, chills, scanty menstruation and intestinal worms. Many Eastern and Indian cultures take a few 'seeds of blessing' daily to boost energy, fight off toxins, maintain and restore body heat and help recovery from fatigue or dispiritedness.

This easily grown annual must not be confused with its altogether prettier cousin, *Nigella damascena*, commonly grown as the spring annual 'Love-in-a-mist'. Its seeds do not have the medicinal value of *Nigella sativa*, which has smaller blue flowers and is unobtrusive, with the same feathery delicate foliage.

CULTIVATION In late winter plant seedlings out in full sun, 40 cm apart, and keep them moist. There will be a mass of small pale blue flowers in spring which quickly set seed in balloon shaped pods with fine leaf tendrils.

PROPAGATION Sow the seeds, which look like onion seeds, where they are to grow in autumn in well-dug, well-composted and well-raked moist soil in full sun. Rake over light friable soil to cover them and keep them moist until they are well established. Or sow them in individual compartments in a large seed tray and keep them protected, moist and in the sunlight through the winter. Transplant when big enough to handle. They only transplant well when very small.

HARVESTING AND PROCESSING Let the balloon-like pods dry completely on the plant before reaping and then crush them over a spread of newspaper to collect the masses of black seeds. Store in a glass screw-top jar.

COMPANION PLANTING Plant with field poppies, radishes, lettuce and peas – they all enhance the others' growth.

USES OF BLACK SEED

Culinary Much loved in Mediterranean and Eastern cookery, the delicious spicy flavour of the black seed is enjoyed in almost everything! Versatile and peppery, *Nigella sativa* is an ingredient in curry and spicy mixtures like the much loved Panche phoran, an Indian spice blend that contains seeds of cumin, fennel, fenugreek, mustard and nigella.

Medicinal Taken as a tea with conventional medicine, black seed is found to be extremely helpful in aiding recovery from coughs, colds, 'flu, bronchitis, asthma, hypertension, insomnia, arthritic and rheumatic pain, fever, miscarriage, nausea, vomiting and to clear acne, boils and rashes, and for excessive perspiration. For the nursing mother taking black seed will help lactation and will keep the baby restful and happy. For the elderly and for children black seed boosts the immune system, decreases the length and severity of childhood diseases and will keep colds and 'flu at bay over the winter. Take for nasal catarrh, intestinal worms, toothache, to regulate menstruation and for colic, spasms, stomach ache and flatulence, diarrhoea, fever and as a diuretic for the diabetic. Take as a tea – use 1 teaspoon seeds in 1 cup boiling water. Stand 5 minutes. Stir well and strain. Take 2-3 cups of the tea a day as a diuretic and to increase milk flow in lactating mothers.

Borage

Family **Boraginaceae**
Species *Borago officinalis*
Origin **Mediterranean region**
Plant **annual**
Height **60 cm; space 60 cm to 1 m apart**
Soil **deeply dug, well-composted soil**
Exposure **full sun**
Propagation **seed**
Uses **medicinal, cosmetic, culinary**

According to the history books, borage is said to have given ancient travellers 'courage, joy, and gladness! It comforts the heart to make merry and to give strength and fortitude'. The Crusaders took it with them on their journeys – along with yarrow to stop bleeding and to heal wounds. For these intrepid travellers who had to face famine, bandits and plagues, a 'stirrup cup' – a type of fortifying wine made of borage – was literally their equivalent of Dutch courage. Undoubtedly they would also have taken the dried herb in leather pouches for the journey. Borage flowers are used in the popular Pimms alcoholic drink.

CULTIVATION Borage does best in well-composted soil in full sun – my best specimens grow on the compost heap! It grows up to 60 cm in width – so allow plenty of space.

PROPAGATION Borage grows quickly and easily from seed. It is self-seeding and regenerate rapidly from one plant.

HARVESTING AND PROCESSING Leaves and flowers can be picked continuously, and are only used fresh.

COMPANION PLANTING Bees are attracted to borage flowers. I always have a few rows planted in the vegetable garden amongst the tomatoes, lettuce, chives and strawberries.

USES OF BORAGE

Culinary With its unobtrusive, cucumber-like flavour, borage lends itself to soups, stews and fritters and makes an attractive addition to stuffings and stirfries. I add the exquisite blue flowers to salads and drinks.

Medicinal Borage contains a substantial amount of mineral salts, potassium, magnesium and calcium. It also has the ability to stimulate the adrenal gland to produce its own cortisone, thus opening up the way for further important research. The high quality gammo-linoleic acid present in the seeds – also found in evening primrose – is helpful for menopause changes, premenstrual tension and skin ailments such as eczema, psoriasis and exceptionally dry skin. Borage poultice is probably my most frequently used treatment for bruises, varicose veins and inflamed itchy areas. Borage vinegar (see recipe section) soothes sprains, bruises, etc., or add to the bath and hair rinsing water for an itchy flaking scalp. Borage tea is good for bladder and kidney ailments and colds and flu. Use ¼ cup fresh leaves in 1 cup boiling water. Stand 5 minutes. Strain and sip slowly. Sweeten with honey if liked. Take one cup a day until the condition clears then stop.

Cosmetic Borage can be used as a face pack or cream, smoothing dry winter skin. I add a tablespoon every now and then to the bath under the hot tap to disperse it, to keep my skin really soft. An excellent cleansing cream (see recipe section), I use it to remove heavy make-up after a TV session and find the skin is left soft and wrinkle-free!

Other uses To start off your spring compost, borage is a must as it breaks down immediately, and adds precious mineral salts to the soil. In France dried powdered borage leaves are dug into pot plants twice yearly to give them a boost in spring and in late summer, and often the powdered crumbled leaves are mixed with bonemeal for their potted lemon, orange and bay trees.

Buckwheat

Family **Polygonaceae**
Species *Fagopyrum esculentum*
Origin **Asia**
Plant **annual**
Height **1 m; sow 2-5 cm apart**
Soil **well-dug, well-composted soil**
Exposure **full sun**
Propagation **seeds**
Uses **culinary, medicinal, cosmetic**

An ancient and much revered food, brought to Europe from Asia by the Crusaders, buckwheat has always been one of the world's most important grains. The monks found it to be an excellent medicinal plant and there are records that go back into the 14th century of its versatility in treating many ailments.

I have a continuous supply of the attractive heart-shaped leaves and sprays of tiny white succulent flowers almost all year through. Sow the seeds all year round and watch the butterflies and the bees all around it. At its full flowering stage dig it back into the soil, first slashing it, and let it break down and lie fallow for 2 months. Then, your vibrant, rebuilt soil will be ready for replanting. The importance of the green manure crop cannot be stressed enough as its high mineral content immediately breaks down the soil and returns vital nutrients to the soil.

CULTIVATION An easy to grow, quickly maturing annual. With full sun, well dug soil and a few barrow loads of compost it will literally come up everywhere.

PROPAGATION Sow the seed where they are to grow.

HARVESTING AND PROCESSING Pick fresh leaves and flowers all year round for salads or reap the grain when the little seeds turn dark brown.

COMPANION PLANTING In Europe buckwheat is used as a companion to mealies, each enhancing the other's growth, and next to globe artichokes. It will stimulate the other plant's growth, even in the poorest of soils and it loosens heavy clay soils, so is good for root crops. Do not plant near winter wheat – they retard each other's growth.

USES OF BUCKWHEAT

Culinary Flowers and leaves, cut fresh and added to salads, are the most delicious health-giving snack. As the plant matures, so the tiny dark heart-shaped grains form and while they are still young they can be used, flowers and all, in stirfries, soups and stews. Rich in minerals and vitamins, buckwheat is a health booster and tonic that will restore lost energy and vitality.

Medicinal Buckwheat has a high rutin content, which gives it a powerful effect on the circulatory system. Doctors and homeopaths often prescribe rutin tablets for certain heart ailments, poor circulation, chilblains and varicose veins. Hardening of the arteries responds particularly well to buckwheat's rutin acid content, as do chilblains, cold feet and hands and fragile capillaries. Combined with vitamin C, buckwheat assists in the removal of haemorrhage into the retina of the eye, it lowers high blood pressure and is invaluable for convalescents. To make buckwheat tea use ¼ cup fresh leaves and flowers in 1 cup boiling water. Stand 5 minutes. Strain and sip slowly. Sweeten with honey if liked.

Cosmetic Because of its superb effect on thread veins, buckwheat has long been used as a lotion and astringent cream. Buckwheat lotion (see recipe section) is excellent for coarse pores and as freshening tonic and spritzer for greasy tired skin. Buckwheat cream (see recipe section) is used for cleansing, nourishing and for dry skin on the hands, feet, knees and elbows.

Other uses Add slashed green flowering buckwheat to the compost heap and you'll have a steaming friable, rich and potent heap in no time. As a foliar feed (see recipe section) buckwheat should surely be considered for its inexpensiveness, its easy availability (it can grow all year round except in June and July) and its quick cropping.

Bulbinella

Family **Asphodelaceae**
Species *Bulbine frutescens*
Origin **South Africa**
Plant **perennial**
Height **15 cm; plant 60-80 cm apart**
Soil **any soil, but does well in rich,
    well-composted soil**
Exposure **full sun**
Propagation **pieces of plant break off easily**
Uses **medicinal**

The name bulbinella has confusingly been commonly used (often incorrectly) to name many of this large group of plants. There are several varieties of *Bulbine frutescens*. Some have long, thick, dark green leaves while others have pale, squat leaves that grow in a neat compact plant, but the most common one, found in so many South African gardens as a popular rockery plant, is the yellow-flowered, juicy-leaved bulbinella much loved for its soothing jelly-like juice that can be so conveniently applied with a mere squeeze of the leaf.

I use bulbinella almost daily for all sorts of things. I have it growing outside the kitchen door for quick application for burns, on the front stoep as a potplant for mosquito bites on summer evenings, and in the far corners of the garden for scrapes, cuts, grazes and sunburn. All the farm workers have taken plants home to grow at their houses too! Flat dwellers can grow bulbinella in a pot on a sunny windowsill or in a large tub on a balcony – it is pretty and decorative with its long stems topped with tiny yellow flowers and an absolute joy to grow and use. Bulbinella is South Africa's answer to aloe vera!

CULTIVATION Bulbinella must be one of nature's most remarkable medicine chests all in one, and as it grows so quickly, so easily and so abundantly, no one need ever be without it. It grows 15 cm in height. It thrives in any soil and is used extensively in landscaping, on road islands, rocky hillsides, and in places where little else grows. It likes full sun

and seems to need very little water – but with the odd spadeful of compost and a good watering once a week, it makes a most handsome garden subject.

PROPAGATION A piece pulled off an established plant with a bit of stem will root quickly, and in no time form a cushion of succulent leaves with pretty yellow or orange flowers. Keep the new cutting moist until it reroots.

USES OF BULBINELLA

Medicinal Liberally apply the freshly squeezed juice frequently to burns, blisters, rashes, insect bites, itchy places, cracked lips, fever blisters, cold sores (even up inside the nose), pimples, mouth ulcers, cracked fingers, nails and heels, bee and wasp stings, and sores and rashes on animals. (I have used it on the very sensitive tummies of little puppies for rashes or eczema and it immediately soothed.) No home with children should ever be without bulbinella, as it is an instant first aid remedy for those daily tumbles and scrapes and it stops the bleeding!

Make a bulbinella skin rash or sunburn spread by quickly liquidising 2 cups of bulbinella leaves in about ⅓ cup warm water. Whirl until it is liquefied and immediately apply to the area quite lavishly. Leave it on al long as possible and then sponge off with warm water to which a dash of apple cider vinegar has been added. A thinner lotion can be made by adding 2 cups of warm water to 1 cup of bulbinella leaves. Whirl in a liquidiser for 2 minutes then strain and pour the liquid into a spritz bottle. Spray the affected area frequently until it soothes the rash or sunburn. Make a fresh batch every day.

Burdock

Family Compositae
Species *Arctium lappa*
Origin Europe and Asia
Plant biennial
Height 1,5 m; space 1,5 m apart
Soil deeply dug, compost-rich soil
Exposure full sun
Propagation seed
Uses culinary, medicinal, cosmetic

Burdock has an extraordinary list of traditional uses behind it. The root has been found to assist in removing and eliminating heavy metals from the body, and in today's ever-wider-spreading pollution, this aspect is more important than we think. Used to treat an overload of toxins in the body, burdock was once grown near the coalmines and other industrial sites with heavy dust, smoke and pollution, and was given to the workers as a tea daily.

A robust survivor plant, it appears everywhere in waste ground and on city pavements, along roadsides and in neglected fields, bravely battling the elements, its giant leaves sheltering little field creatures from the storms. 'A brave soldier of a plant,' a Chinese herbalist called it, 'there to soothe mankind's ills.'

CULTIVATION This prolific giant of a herb is a sturdy biennial that will grow to a lofty 1,5 m with its towering flower stem in its second year. It loves a deep compost-filled hole and a long weekly soaking, and thrives in full sun literally anywhere. In its first year its mound of huge leaves spreads 1 m in width and 75 cm in height.

PROPAGATION Easily propagated from seeds encased in burrs that catch onto clothing and animals' fur. Seedlings transplant easily only when they are small as they have a long taproot. It self seeds easily.

HARVESTING AND PROCESSING Leaves can be picked any time and dried for winter use.

COMPANION PLANTING Does well near cabbages, cauliflowers and Brussels sprouts.

USES OF BURDOCK

Culinary The fleshy long taproot can be roasted, sautéed, pickled, boiled, mashed and fried, or roasted to make a coffee. The flowering stalk, just as the flowers are forming, can be peeled and eaten fresh like celery. Young and tender leaves are eaten as a spinach, and Chinese chefs sprout the seeds and use the tender little sprouts in stirfries. Tiny buds tasting like artichoke hearts can be boiled then stirfried, and candied flowering and leaf stalks are a great treat.

Medicinal Burdock's main uses are detoxifying, cleansing, antiseptic and mildly antibiotic. It lowers blood sugar levels, and it has anti-tumour action. It is one of the ingredients in Essiac, the famous anti-cancer remedy made by Rene Caisse, and it contains an ingredient called arctiin, which is known to be a smooth muscle relaxant. Used for gout, fevers, kidney stones; leaf, seeds and root can be made into a tea to alleviate the symptoms of mumps, measles and other infectious diseases. For boils, abscesses, swollen arthritic joints, acne, psoriasis and eczema, a leaf poultice as well as the tea is wonderfully soothing. For sore throats, colds, 'flu, rheumatism, arthritis and stomach disorders, burdock has been used for centuries by the Chinese. To make burdock tea use ¼ cup fresh chopped leaf pieces in 1 cup boiling water. Stand 5 minutes then strain. The root and the seeds can also be added to this tea. Drink two to three cups a day during infection. For chronic ailments take one cup three or four times a week.

Cosmetic Burdock lotion (see recipe section) instantly soothes skin ailments like psoriasis, eczema, rashes, grazes and scratches. Spray frequently onto the area.

Calendula

Family **Compositae**
Species ***Calendula officinalis***
Origin **Eurasia**
Plant **annual**
Height **45 cm; space 30-40 cm apart**
Soil **well-dug, well-composted soil**
Exposure **full sun**
Propagation **seed**
Uses **culinary, medicinal, cosmetic**

A bright and cheerful winter annual that no garden should be without, calendula is a wonderful healing plant. Early records of this herb go back to the Middle Ages when it seems to have been used in religious ceremonies. At that time, when many worshippers claimed that the Virgin Mary was adorned with the golden flowers, monks changed the name of calendula to 'Mary Golde' in her honour. So the common English name 'marigold' was born – and this, unfortunately, is where confusion has arisen ever since, especially in South Africa, where our 'marigolds' are in fact the strongly scented *Tagetes erecta* or African marigold, which does not have the same properties as *Calendula* species. Do not confuse them!

CULTIVATION Full sun and a well-dug bed, rich in compost, will ensure prolific flowering throughout winter and spring.

PROPAGATION Sow seeds from late summer onwards or buy trays of seedlings from the nursery to give you a head start. New varieties are offered as seed and now the common orange variety has been extended to yellow, cream and even a bronzy colour. But it is the orange variety, often single, that has the medicinal value.

HARVESTING AND PROCESSING I keep dried petals for the summer months when it is too hot to grow calendulas. Pick frequently to ensure more blooms. Thread the flowers on fishing line to make garlands to dry for winter use or dry upside down in the shade.

COMPANION PLANTING Plant with basil, cabbages, celery, potatoes and radishes.

USES OF CALENDULA

Culinary Calendula petals give a deep yellow colour to egg and cheese dishes. If fed to farmyard hens and cows, beautiful golden egg yolks and rich-coloured cream and butter are produced. The petals have a slightly peppery taste and can be sprinkled on salads, soups, casseroles and pastas.

Medicinal Primarily used as a skin healer, a poultice of calendula petals is antiseptic and its essential oil compounds will help new tissue form and soothe at the same time. Calendula tea makes an excellent mouthwash for gum problems or after dentistry and tooth extraction. Alternatively, sip slowly to soothe indigestion and as a liver tonic treatment. To make the tea, use ¼ cup fresh or dried flowers petals. Pour over this 1 cup boiling water. Stand 5 minutes. Strain and sip slowly. For an eye wash, dilute the tea with ½ cup warm water – our grandparents used it to help reduce cataract formation and red, tired, sore eyes. Calendula cream (see recipe section) is excellent for treating haemorrhoids, cracked lips, sore nipples, chilblains, varicose veins and leg ulcers.

Cosmetic I make a nourishing cream (see recipe section) for winter-dry feet and hands and massage it into the dogs' feet too. Calendula lotion (see recipe section) can be used as a toner or splash or dabbed on as a lotion. Dry, itchy, flaking skin or aftershave redness, or rashes, grazes or sunburned skin all show immediate results with this lovely lotion. Use calendula bath vinegar (see recipe section) as a dash in your hair rinsing water (and see how it shines!) or add to the bath for dry itchy skin or sunburn, or for rashes and grazes, etc. Use as a foot soak to soothe blisters and calluses and dry, cracked heels.

Other uses Calendula leaves and flowers can be added to the compost heap where they quickly break it down into a rich friable mass.

Californian Poppy

Family Papaveraceae
Species *Escholzia californica*
Origin North-west America
Plant winter annual
Height up to 40 cm; space 30 cm apart
Soil sandy, well-aerated soil
Exposure full sun
Propagation seed
Uses culinary, medicinal, cosmetic

Once, long ago, the hillsides of California were covered in poppies so abundant that the Spaniards called it The Land of Fire and The Golden West. Used for many centuries by Native Americans as a painkiller, particularly for toothache, and as a sedative for young and old, new research is finding this easily grown annual is becoming one of the most important medicinal plants for the 21st century as a natural painkiller and antispasmodic.

CULTIVATION Unfussy as to soil type but it prefers sandy, well-aerated soil. Water twice weekly.

PROPAGATION Sow the seed in autumn where it is to grow. Transplanting can be done only when the seedlings are very tiny. Plant seedlings 30 cm apart in full sun.

HARVESTING AND PROCESSING The flowering tops can be picked as soon as the flowers open. The young leaves are used as well and can be dried for use during summer.

COMPANION PLANTING Good companions are parsley, winter cabbage, radishes and cauliflower.

USES OF CALIFORNIAN POPPY

Culinary Use the petals in salads, fruit salads, stirfries, as a decoration for cakes, desserts and soups, and as an ingredient when baking bread, cakes and biscuits. Added to breakfast muesli or porridge and hot milk it will help to settle an anxious child. Our kitchen gardens astonish visitors when they watch the early morning pickers preparing for colourful salads (see recipe section) and winter soups. One visitor remarked: 'It's like carrying baskets of dazzling winter sunshine into the kitchen.'

Medicinal Although closely related to the opium poppy (*Papaver somniferum*), the Californian poppy is not a narcotic. Instead it contains alkaloids and glycosides that have antispasmodic, sedative, calming and analgesic effects that are safe and sure for treating both the old and the very young. It is used to treat insomnia, hyperactivity, over-excitement, over-stimulation and as a comforting antispasmodic for muscle stiffness, indigestion, and even as a gentle non-addictive hypnotic, tranquilliser and anodyne for all age groups, including children with behaviour problems. New research is finding Californian poppy extracts in a honey-based syrup is extremely beneficial for bedwetting, nervous tension, anxiety, fidgeting, lack of concentration, sleep walking and terrifying dreams in children. To make Californian poppy tea use ¼ cup fresh or dried flowers and leaves and stems and pour over this 1 cup of boiling water. Stand 5 minutes and strain. Take ½ to 1 cups daily for about 10 days, then stop 2-3 days.

Cosmetic Use Californian poppy in the bath as a sleep inducing, calming, end-of-the-day unwinder. Tie 1 to 2 handfuls of flowering tops in a cotton square. Toss into the bath under the hot water tap. Rub with soap and use this to wash the body all over, especially over aching shoulders and feet. For oily hair use Californian poppy vinegar (see recipe section) to clear the oil and tone the scalp.

Other uses The Californian poppy stems contain a latex that has painkilling compounds in it. Native Americans pounded the stems and used them to bind around a broken limb, in both man and animal, as a padding for a splint or as a compress, warmed in hot water over a painful back or aching hip joint.

Caraway

Family Umbelliferae
Species *Carum carvi*
Origin Eurasia
Plant treat as an annual
Height up to 60 cm; space 30 cm apart
Soil light, well-drained, well-composted soil
Exposure full sun
Propagation seed, cuttings
Uses culinary, medicinal

An ancient, revered herb, caraway was once credited with powers to protect against witchcraft. Used in medicines and flavouring by the ancient Egyptians, Romans and Greeks, caraway seeds have been found in the remains of stone age artefacts, in Egyptian tombs and in Mesolithic sites, so we know that its roots go back well over 5 000 years. A small dish of caraway seeds was served at the end of an Elizabethan feast and even today at many Eastern restaurants a small bowl of caraway, fennel, cumin and aniseed is passed around as a traditional end to the meal to aid digestion.

CULTIVATION Easy to grow in well-dug, well-composted light soil; transplant the seedlings if necessary before they reach 10 cm in height. Plant seedlings 30 cm apart. A twice weekly watering will ensure a good crop.

PROPAGATION Sow seeds in situ, about 30 cm apart; keep moist until well established.

HARVESTING AND PROCESSING Seeds can be harvested when ripe and starting to dry; leaves can be gathered when young. Pick seed heads in late summer or when they turn brown. The flowers can be picked at any time. In cooler areas caraway can be biennial.

COMPANION PLANTING A good companion to green peas, radishes and beetroot but keep caraway and fennel apart as they hinder each other's growth.

USES OF CARAWAY

Culinary A favourite addition to cakes, biscuits, sweets, desserts, cabbage and turnip dishes and with cheese, potato and fish dishes, caraway is loved the world over. The lacy flower heads and the leaves can be eaten in salads and stirfries, and when the aromatic seeds form they too can be eaten green or dried added to biscuits, bread and cakes as well as to vegetable dishes, soups, stocks, casseroles, sauces and pickles, jams, jellies and desserts. Caraway roots can be boiled as a vegetable.

Medicinal Caraway is a superb antispasmodic, a diuretic and an expectorant. Caraway can be made into a soothing cough remedy (see recipe section) particularly for children. Caraway soothes the digestive tract, eases wind, colic, bloating and cramps, including period pain, increases breast milk production and eases indigestion discomfort after a large meal. A tea of caraway is excellent for all the above ailments. Use ¼ cup fresh caraway leaves and flowers *or* 1 teaspoon caraway seeds. Pour over this 1 cup boiling water and stand 5 minutes. Strain. Sweeten with a little honey if liked, or add a squeeze of fresh lemon juice. Caraway massage oil (see recipe section) is remarkably soothing for the discolouration and aching of severe bruising.

Cosmetic The oil from the seed is used in mouthwashes and colognes. Caraway makes an excellent skin cleanser. Soak a cloth in warm caraway tea and place over the face to clear away grime, to soften the skin and to refresh. Hold the face cloth over the face and massage well to get the circulation moving. Soak pads of cotton wool in caraway tea and place over the eyes to soothe tired red eyes, and use the tea in a spritz spray bottle as a toner. Caraway is particularly helpful for oily skin as it tones and refreshes immediately. Keep a jar of caraway seeds on the bathroom shelf to add to hot water to rinse the face.

Other uses Removes cooking smells from cabbage and cauliflower. The plant dries beautifully and is ideal for flower arrangements.

Carnation

Family **Caryophyllaceae**
Species *Dianthus caryophyllus*
Origin **Europe**
Plant **short-lived perennial**
Height **45-65 cm; plant 30 cm apart**
Soil **richly composted soil**
Exposure **full sun**
Propagation **seeds and cuttings**
Uses **culinary, medicinal, cosmetic**

An ancient herb used by medieval monks and healers, the fragrant clove-scented carnation – or gillyflower, as it was then known – was much prized as a cosmetic and medicinal herb. Through the centuries it has been treasured in cottage gardens across the world, and can still be found in magnificent variation in some of the old gardens today. The carnation varies in colour from white to the palest pink, deep cerise to red, yellow to salmon and everything in between.

In France one of the most beautiful soaps is still made today using carnation petals (and smelling like a dream) in an ancient recipe that has never lost its popularity. Our grandmothers used carnation water to soften, refine and soothe rough skin. Hybridised carnations today remain one of the world's favourite cut flowers.

CULTIVATION Carnations grow in richly composted soil and reach a height of around 45-65 cm. They need full sun and a deep twice-weekly watering. They need 30 cm spacing between each plant, and I find they tend to sprawl – so a stake or support should be pushed in next to the plant while it is still quite young. If you want bigger flowers, nip off the masses of tiny buds that form, leaving only one or two to mature. Do deadhead the flowers when they go over to encourage more flowers and to prolong the summer beauty well into winter. They do well in big pots too, and a combination of several varieties of dianthus looks stunning if planted together in clumps or between rows of vegetables, as all the dianthus species are edible.

PROPAGATION Small tufts of new leaves form along the stems and these can be pulled off when they are about 10 cm in length with a little heel, and planted in moist, shaded sand-filled trays. Do not overwater, as they tend to rot quite quickly. Once they have rooted, plant them in good rich soil in bags or pots to harden them off before planting out in the garden.

HARVESTING AND PROCESSING Flowers are used fresh only, but can be dried for potpourris.

USES OF CARNATION

Culinary Carnation petals have been used for 2 000 years to flavour wines and drinks; they are made into syrups and used in confectionary in a wide variety of delectable ways. When splitting the flowers and using them for decoration or including them in recipes, remove the bitter white heel at the base of each petal. Use the petals in salads, desserts, fruit salads and drinks. They taste scented and clove-like!

Medicinal The monks made an excellent tonic wine way back in the 16th century to calm highly strung and nervous people. Carnation tonic wine (see recipe section) is an excellent modern tonic for the over-stressed taken just before going to bed or at the end of a hectic day.

Cosmetic Long before carnations were used in cookery, they were used in skin and bath preparations, pounded in egg white as a face mask or boiled with oats as a skin refiner which was rubbed all over the body to cleanse oily spotty skin. Carnation milk soothes sunburn (see recipe section).

Other uses Because of its clove-like scent, carnations can be combined with cloves and clove oils to keep insects out of cupboards. An ancient recipe using carnations and cloves was used by our grandmothers to keep toilets and bathrooms deodorised (see recipe section).

Catmint

Catnip
Family Labiatae
Species *Nepeta mussinii* ● *N. cataria*
Origin Eurasia
Plant perennial
Height 15-70 cm; space 50 cm apart
Soil well-dug, lightly composted soil
Exposure full sun
Propagation division
Uses medicinal, insecticidal

Native to Europe and Asia, introduced and naturalised all over the world, catmint is an easily rooted perennial that is gaining popularity for its insect-repellent and medicinal properties. Much loved by cats, who eat it, roll in it, sleep on it and generally ecstatically envelop themselves in it. No cat-lover should dare to be without a few plants! Versatile catmint has a long medicinal history and has been used for centuries in Europe as a treatment for oily skin and hair.

CULTIVATION There are two main species easily available in South Africa. A larger-leafed variety, *Nepeta cataria* with nondescript white flowers and coarsely serrated leaves of about 2-3 cm in length, grows 30-70 cm in height. The smaller-leafed variety, *Nepeta mussinii*, has tiny pretty mauve-blue or white flowers (var. 'Alba'). It is low growing, never reaching much more than 15 cm in height, with a spreading habit. Catmint needs full sun and good, well-composted soil that needs replenishing every August. In winter the clump can be cut back, removing the old summer growth, trimmed neatly and divided. It needs a deep twice-weekly watering.

PROPAGATION Smaller tufts will root all around the original mother clump. Chop these off with a sharp spade and replant 30 cm apart in a well-composted bed.

HARVESTING AND PROCESSING Harvest all through the year by snipping off little sprigs. Best used fresh.

COMPANION PLANTING Tuck in new plants to protect neighbouring plants from aphids, rust, mealie bug and white fly. It does particularly well with tomatoes, strawberries, green peppers, brinjals, spinach and roses.

USES OF CATMINT

Culinary Long ago, cooks used fresh catmint sprigs wrapped around meat to flavour it and keep it fresh and wholesome. It was also drunk as a tea all over Europe in the early centuries long before ordinary tea was even thought of.

Medicinal Traditionally a tea was used to calm restless children and those who were unable to unwind. Infantile colic, diarrhoea and bedwetting are some of its wonder treatments, as well as delayed menstruation, stress, tension and anxiety. A catmint drink is excellent for colds and flu as it contains vitamin C and does not increase the temperature. It has the ability to increase perspiration, which often helps you to sweat out a cold. To make the tea pour 1 cup of boiling water over 1 cup of fresh catmint sprigs (use *Nepeta mussinii*). Stand 5 minutes. Strain. Sweeten with honey and sip slowly. Externally a lotion (see recipe section) will clear up and soothe cuts, rashes, abrasions, scrapes and insect bites and stings.

Cosmetic As a lotion (see recipe section) it cleanses oily problem skin; added to the rinsing water or combed into the hair it is an excellent way of controlling greasy and unmanageable hair.

Other uses Excellent with garlic in a spray (see recipe section) for aphids, rust, mealie bug and white fly. With the addition of Jeyes fluid, this mixture will get rid of the most invasive ants. Rats and mice are repelled by catmint. Mix dried leaves of catmint with lavender and sprinkle around birdcages and chicken runs to keep rats and mice away. Dried catmint leaves mixed with khakibos leaves can be sprinkled under carpets to keep fleas and ants away or rubbed into the dog's fur to chase the fleas.

Cayenne Pepper

Family **Solanaceae**
Species *Capsicum frutescens*
Origin **India**
Plant **short-lived perennial**
Height **50 cm; space 50 cm apart**
Soil **rich well-composted, well-dug soil**
Exposure **full sun**
Propagation **seed**
Uses **culinary, medicinal, insecticide**

The cayenne or chilli pepper is one of nature's most remarkable medicines – a stimulant, antibiotic and antibacterial food, used with respect from the 16th century. Science has discovered that all the 'hot' foods contain mucokinetic agents, which are reputed to loosen mucus in the lungs thus assisting the respiratory system. Capsaicin, contained in the biting flesh, stimulates the release of endorphins – the body's natural painkillers – to produce a sense of well-being. And that is why chillies, the hotter the better, are one of the world's favourite foods!

CULTIVATION Easily grown in rich, well-composted soil, all the peppers enjoy a long fruiting period. They need a deep, twice-weekly watering and, in the cooler parts of the country with early winter frosts, can be treated as an annual plant. In the hotter regions, most of the bushy cayenne types of chilli can become short-lived perennials that will benefit from winter pruning to enable the spring growth to become more vigorous. Without pruning, the bush become straggly and unprolific with small leaves – so cut it back well, shaping it as you do so. Dig in a spade full or two of compost each spring for a good crop and to give it the nourishment it needs for healthy growth.

PROPAGATION Sow seeds in trays in spring then plant out when big enough to handle in rows 50 cm apart. Keep well watered until they establish themselves.

HARVESTING Pick the fruits as soon as they start to mature. Ripe fruits can be threaded on nylon fishing line and dried for winter use or turned into pickles in either oil or vinegar.

COMPANION PLANTING Plant with lovage, lettuce, beetroot and beans.

USES OF CAYENNE PEPPER

Culinary Cayenne peppers can be used fresh or in the form of dried cayenne pepper or chilli powder. Because the seeds are so bitingly fire-hot, separate them carefully from the flesh to avoid using them. In order to cool a mouthful of heat eat plain yoghurt, bread, a teaspoon or two of sugar, or drink a few mouthfuls of milk. Water will not help!

Medicinal Fresh cayenne, thinly sliced away from those fiery seeds, is being recognised as a stimulant for circulation, varicose veins, haemorrhoids and high cholesterol and is also excellent for hoarseness, laryngitis and tonsillitis, heartburn and indigestion. It can bring immediate relief at the onset of a cold and can also be added to food for easier assimilation. Recently cayenne pepper has been included in medication for gout, rheumatism, migraine, arthritis, aching joints and sinusitis and surprisingly for shingles and high blood pressure too! A compress for bruises and sprains can also be used for rheumatism. Cayenne ointment (see recipe section) is excellent for treating chilblains and aching feet – as long as the skin is not broken! Always test a little on the inside of your wrist before applying cream or compresses, and avoid touching the eye area or any cuts or grazes. Try the following remedy for chilblains: Mix 1 teaspoon of cayenne pepper to ½ cup of boiling water. Mix well, cool and keep in the fridge. Dab on over the chilblains every day after bathing.

Other uses Ants, aphids and fleas absolutely hate cayenne pepper! If you have cats that scratch on your furniture or use the carpet as a sandbox, sprinkle the area with cayenne pepper. Dogs also flee from cayenne pepper and a sprinkling under the sink or fridge will banish cockroaches and fishmoths in no time at all. Mix it with khakibos or marigolds to make an effective insecticide (see recipe section).

Celery

Family **Umbelliferae**
Species *Apium graveolens*
Origin **Europe**
Plant **biennial, often treated as an annual**
Height **50-80 cm; space 30 cm apart**
Soil **deeply dug, richly composted soil**
Exposure **full sun**
Propagation **seeds**
Uses **medicinal, culinary**

Native to the British Isles and Europe, celery is an ancient herb, revered, respected, and cultivated from the earliest centuries, particularly for flavouring food when salt was a rare and expensive commodity. It was used in those far-off centuries to clear the body of excess fluid, toxins and arthritic aches and pains – one is always astonished to find that all our medical progress only verifies what the ancients knew already! Some 3 000 years ago ancient Egyptians ate celery to give them strong bones, strong muscles and fleetness of foot. In the 5th century BC ancient Chinese used celery to slow ageing and treat illness and flush toxins from the body.

CULTIVATION Plant seedlings out 30 cm apart in rows in soil that is deeply dug and compost enriched. I have found that double digging gives me longer stems and I double compost as well as this ensures a mass of juicy leaves and stems for two full years. Plant a second crop within 4 months and do this every 4-5 months all through the year.

PROPAGATION Sow the seed in moist, shaded, sand-filled trays and prick out when they are big enough to handle. Plant the little plants in compost-filled bags, keep them moist and in the shade. Gradually bring them out into the sun for longer periods to harden off before planting out in full sun in well-dug soil.

HARVESTING AND PROCESSING Constantly picking the outer stalks ensures new growth.

COMPANION PLANTING Plant with beans, leeks, marigolds, spring onions and tomatoes.

USES OF CELERY

Culinary A superb detoxifier and cleanser and one of the best diuretics, especially at the festive time of year when we tend to overeat and party too long and too late. Celery added to our salads, soups and vegetable dishes is a quick health boost. Add chopped leaves and stalks at the end of the cooking time, or add finely chopped to sauces, gravies and spreads just as you are about to serve.

Medicinal Seeds, leaves and stems help chest ailments, lower high blood pressure, and act as a superb diuretic, urinary antiseptic, antispasmodic and sedative. Celery's cleansing action on both kidneys and bladder is much respected and this is an effective treatment for cystitis and will improve the circulation to the muscles and joints. For gout, rheumatism and arthritis, celery in all its forms will dispose of the urates that cause the stiffness and pain, as well as reducing acidity throughout the body. To make celery seed tea, use 1 teaspoon organically grown seeds to 1 cup boiling water. Stand 5 minutes. Stir well and sip slowly, chewing the seeds as well. Celery has anticonvulsant properties and the Chinese eat a celery salad daily as a tonic, a cleanser and to bring down high blood pressure. **Caution**: Do not take celery and celery seeds medicinally if you are pregnant or suffering from a kidney disorder. The seeds you buy for sowing are not suitable for medical treatments – use only your own reaped seeds that are organically grown.

Cosmetic Celery leaves make a marvellous cleansing lotion (see recipe section) for oily spotty skin.

Other uses Old celery plants contain excellent minerals that help to quickly decompose compost.

Chamomile

German chamomile
Family **Compositae**
Species *Matricaria recutita* ● *Chamomilla recutita*
Origin **Europe**
Plant **winter annual**
Height **40-50 cm; space 20-30 cm apart**
Soil **well-dug, well-composted soil**
Exposure **full sun**
Propagation **seeds**
Uses **medicinal, culinary**

An ancient, much-loved herb, used since the 14th century as a calming medicine. A winter annual and easily grown in the cooler months, it grows wild all over Europe, Northern Asia and has become naturalised in North America. A perennial variety often cultivated in Europe is the low growing *Chamaemelum nobile*, often called Roman chamomile or lawn chamomile. This is used for chamomile lawns, and, in the cooler parts of South Africa this does fairly well. Both Roman and German chamomile have the same uses.

CULTIVATION Plant seedlings in well-dug, well-composted soil, 20-30 cm apart. Transplant only when small.

PROPAGATION Sow seed in autumn in shallow, sand-filled trays and keep moist at all times. Plant into bags when big enough to handle and put them in the sun to strengthen the seedlings before planting out in the garden.

HARVESTING AND PROCESSING Harvest the flowers as they mature, dry in the shade and store in sealed brown paper bags. The whole plant can be dried by hanging upside down.

COMPANION PLANTING Chamomile is often referred to as the 'plant doctor' as insects do not breed near it and it increases the growth of plants growing near it. It is an excellent companion for cabbages and onions and improves the flavour in both. Wheat grown with chamomile increases its yield.

USES OF CHAMOMILE

Culinary Chamomile's best-known use is in a fragrant, calming tea that can be taken warm or cold. Cooled and added to fruit juices, it is a delicious way of enjoying the benefits of this precious plant, which is particularly good for hyperactive children and those who are stressed, anxious and sleepless. To make the tea, add 1 tablespoon flowers to 1 cup boiling water. Stand 5 minutes, then strain.

Medicinal Long used for stomach upsets, indigestion and anxiety, modern research has isolated various remarkable compounds, like the precious deep blue azulene, salicylic acid – a natural aspirin – and various anti-inflammatory and antiseptic components that promote bile and gastric secretions and act as tonics to the whole system. Chamomile tea is taken for a feverish cold, as a wash or lotion for haemorrhoids and as a douche with superb antiseptic qualities. A compress soaked in the tea is soothing for cuts, grazes, bruises and ulcers. Use as a lotion over eczema, skin rashes, sunburn or allergic reactions on the skin.

Cosmetic Our grandmothers made a rinse with chamomile flowers (see recipe section) to lighten fair hair. It is also an exquisite skin-softening, skin-clearing rinse, a pleasant mouthwash and treatment for tired, puffy eyes. Bath vinegar (see recipe section) made with chamomile is excellent for everything from aching legs to oily problem skin, acne, dandruff, dry flaky skin and rough heels. Chamomile cleansing cream (see recipe section) is especially good for tired, problem or oily skin.

Other uses Dig old plants back into the soil to help break down waste material, and to serve as a tonic booster to poor soil. Fresh green plants added to the compost heap will quickly break down the compost – it is one of the excellent activators that quickly sweetens and warms the compost heap. Add a cup of chamomile tea to an ailing pot plant, or as a tonic booster for those rare indoor plants we treasure. With rosemary, it makes a spray (see recipe section) for mildew, aphids and white fly.

Chervil

Family Umbelliferae
Species *Anthriscus cerefolium*
Origin Europe, Asia Minor, Iran and Caucasus
Plant winter annual
Height 20 cm
Soil well-dug, well composted soil
Exposure partial shade
Propagation seeds
Uses culinary, medicinal, cosmetic

In ancient days chervil was considered so precious that a basket of seeds was found in Tutankhamen's tomb. It has been grown as a flavouring herb in temperate climates across the world; brought into Britain by the Romans, it was revered as a medicine for treating the blood. It was associated with religious penance and Lenten herbs and eaten on feast days.

Every meal during winter should be enhanced by fresh chopped chervil: it literally is one of the most versatile of herbs and can be used as parsley is – lavishly, fresh and frequently. In French cuisine it is one of the much-loved traditional *fines herbes*. Its parsley-aniseed flavour enhances every savoury dish. It acts as a tonic herb, a circulatory herb and a cleanser; it fights infections, is a good diuretic, and will help to lower high blood pressure.

CULTIVATION Prefers well-dug richly composted soil in partial shade (40-50% shade cloth works well). Chervil is a cool weather plant, though heavy frost will kill it. It does well in deep pots provided it is kept moist and shaded.

PROPAGATION Sow seeds in trays in early autumn for winter planting and transplant when big enough to handle, 30 cm apart. It has a long taproot, so it is often safer to sow it in situ, especially under larger herbs so that it can be shaded, as it hates to be transplanted.

HARVESTING AND PROCESSING Harvest can begin when the plants are 6 weeks old. Pick the fern-like outer leaves continuously to encourage abundant growth.

COMPANION PLANTING Does well with dill and coriander to shade it. It enhances the growth of radishes and carrots.

USES OF CHERVIL

Culinary Chop into salads, stirfries, over vegetables, roast meats, sausages, cold meats, chicken, fish and egg dishes. Use it as the French do, in scrambled eggs and omelettes and as the Italians do, sprinkled over pasta and in sauces!

Medicinal Rich in vitamin C, beta-carotene, magnesium, potassium and calcium, chervil tea is a wonderful digestive that will stimulate the whole digestive system, easing constipation, bloating colic and flatulence. It is also an excellent circulatory herb that soothes varicose vein throbbing and discomfort and if eaten daily during the cold months, will ease chilblains and aching cold feet. Use as a poultice over aching joints. Chervil is also a valuable liver cleanser: a cup of fresh chervil tea on those 'off' days will quickly remove that sluggish feeling and act as a safe diuretic. Chervil tea will help to lower high blood pressure. Take one cup on alternate days. To make the tea use ¼ cup fresh leaves. Pour over this 1 cup boiling water. Stand 5 minutes. Strain and sip slowly.

Cosmetic Chervil lotion is an excellent refresher that will discourage dry flaky wrinkles, as well as oily build-up and problem skin. Blended with aqueous cream, for those who do not use soap on their faces, this is the best cleansing cream (see recipe section) I know. Cooled chervil tea makes a soothing wash for the eyes.

Other uses Chamomile, also a winter annual, along with melissa and chervil is still used today by farmers in Europe as a compress to treat hoof rot in cattle and horses. Equal quantities of all three leaves and chamomile flowers are soaked in hot water and then applied to the hoof, bound in place with a leather sock. Usually fresh applications for four days, morning and evening, cleared the problem.

Chives

Family Liliaceae
Species *Allium schoenoprasum*
Origin Eurasia
Plant perennial
Height up to 20 cm; space 30 cm apart
Soil well-dug, well-composted soil
Exposure full sun
Propagation seed and clump division
Uses culinary, medicinal, cosmetic

An ancient and indispensable group of plants, the extensive onion family embraces every variety, from easy-to-grow chives to garlic, spring onions and all types of garlic chives to ordinary onions. With this collection of flavours, shapes and textures (the stronger the taste the more effective the healing power), no other plant variety can match them! Chives and onions, grown and used in China over 6 000 years ago, were introduced to Europe by Marco Polo and since then, the tasty onion family has become an integral part of our daily diet and a natural medicine. Medical facts on the onion family and their therapeutic properties are so well documented that worldwide research now rates onions and chives as the health plants of the century.

CULTIVATION When starting new plants, mix plenty of compost into the soil to get them well established. But once they're thriving, they're not fussy about soil type. Chives die down in winter and at this time they're easiest to dig up, divide and replant. Garlic chives can be divided at any time of the year. Well-dug soil with a good dressing of compost will ensure many years of sturdy growth. Reaping the leaves and flowers constantly produces more flowers.

PROPAGATION Sow seeds at any time of the year, except during the coldest months. When the plants are big enough to handle, plant out 30 cm apart. Keep well watered until plants are established. Divide clumps during winter.

HARVESTING Harvest when the leaves are over 15 cm long by cutting at the base. The spring show of flowers offers masses of pickings. Chives are best eaten fresh.

COMPANION PLANTING Chives and garlic chives are excellent for keeping roses and vegetables free of aphids. Use them as a border along paths and around vegetable gardens – they'll never be attacked by insects. Plant under apple and apricot trees and next to carrots and parsley.

USES OF CHIVES

Culinary Fresh, raw chopped leaves and flowers are mixed into salads, sauces, spreads, cheeses, mayonnaise, dips and stirfries. A favourite way of eating chives is as a garnish over fish dishes, cold meats and cheese omelettes. Mix into cream cheese with a little crunchy coarse salt as an old-time favourite party dip, served with cheese straws or crisps.

Medicinal Chives lower high cholesterol, retard blood clotting, regulate blood sugar, kill bacteria and relieve chest and lung congestion. They act as natural antibiotics, help to boost the immune system and are a superb heart medicine. Researchers now report that the entire onion family helps to kill many bacteria and viruses, even the *E. coli* and salmonella. New tests prove chives are an excellent treatment for tuberculosis, declared almost as effective as streptomycin! So add chives to the diet as often as possible!

Cosmetic Squeeze a drop or two of juice from the stems of chives onto a pimple or infected spot. Constant application quickly clears the offending spot – some beauticians disperse the smell by adding parsley juice.

Other uses Chive insecticide (see recipe section) is used as a spray for aphids and mildew on pumpkins, melons, cucumbers, bergamot, cabbage, beans, etc. This strong, anti-mildew, antifungal spray is excellent for brown rot as well.

Comfrey

Family Boraginaceae
Species *Symphytum officinale*
Origin Eurasia
Plant perennial
Height up to 75 cm; space 1-1,5 m apart
Soil any soil
Exposure full sun to partial shade
Propagation seed
Uses medicinal, cosmetic

An ancient miracle plant, comfrey has a long history. It was brought to Britain by the Crusaders and was taken to America in the 17th century. Thought to be a panacea for many ills, the monks treated the sick and the lame with comfrey with astonishing results. Stories of its healing, bone-building qualities (it is also known as 'knit-bone') abound. When my black labrador was hit by a truck and his pelvis and back legs crushed, I gave him a daily small dose of comfrey tea even while he was in the veterinary hospital and he was able to walk in three months. This is just one of the many comfrey miracles I have witnessed over the years!

The more I use comfrey, the more I am amazed at its remarkable virtues. Lists of components in its leaves, roots and even flowers are astonishing in their diversity. Vitamin content from A to C, B12, E and D, minerals such as the important potassium, phosphorus, calcium, iron, its remarkably high protein content and its breaking-down abilities in the soil as a compost maker are daily being confirmed and augmented.

CULTIVATION Comfrey likes full sun but in very hot areas does well in light shade. It dies down in winter in cold areas. The more water it gets, the bigger it grows.

PROPAGATION Propagation is by pieces of root. Literally any little bits left in the soil after lifting will grow into sturdy little plants in no time at all.

HARVESTING AND PROCESSING Cut the leaves all the time and they can be dried for winter use.

COMPANION PLANTING Comfrey is known as the plant healer so it does well near most plants.

USES OF COMFREY

Medicinal Comfrey's actions are astringent and soothing, healing wounds, fractures, chest ailments and arthritis. When the crushed leaves and roots are applied to an injured limb or arthritic joint, allantoin, contained in the leaves, is quickly absorbed through the skin, speeding up the healing process. Poultices can be made of finely chopped leaves and crushed root and bound over a wound, an ulcer or an arthritic joint. Our grandparents took a cup of comfrey tea to ease chest congestion in bronchitis or pneumonia and also for stomach ulcers and to speed up the healing of broken bones. To make comfrey tea add ¼ cup chopped leaves to 1 cup boiling water. Stand only 5 minutes. Strain. Take no more than twice weekly for chronic ailments; once a day for no more than 10 days for acute ailments. **Warning**: Doctors suggest that excessive internal consumption of comfrey should be avoided because of the alkaloids present in it. But taken in homeopathic doses, comfrey is considered safe.

Cosmetic Comfrey is simply superb in creams (see recipe section), lotions and washes for all sorts of skin ailments. It softens, smoothes and revitalises the skin and is perhaps even more needed today that it ever was, due to our polluted environment.

Other uses Comfrey is a natural fertiliser, compost maker and booster of the soil. With its high protein content, it breaks down quickly and makes a nourishing 'green cocktail' for pot plants and ailing plants that has saved many a day for me!

Coriander

Danya
Family **Umbelliferae**
Species *Coriandrum sativum*
Origin **Eurasia and the Middle East**
Plant **quick annual**
Height **up to 60 cm; space 30-50 cm apart**
Soil **rich, light**
Exposure **full sun**
Propagation **seed**
Uses **culinary, medicinal, cosmetic**

Cultivated for over 3 000 years, coriander seeds have been found in shrines and tombs in ancient Egypt, going back to the 21st Egyptian Dynasty (1085–940 BC) and the ancient Romans, who combined coriander with vinegar and crushed cumin seeds, used it as a preservative over meat, fowl and fish.

The herb reached China during the Han Dynasty (202 BC to AD 9), when it was used as a medicine to treat spreading sores, burns, boils and every other affliction from blindness to lameness.

CULTIVATION Needs full sun and a wide furrow of well-dug, well-composted soil that is kept moist while it germinates and grows. Space seeds 30 cm apart and keep moist and shaded by covering with leaves while the seed germinates. Water twice weekly thereafter.

PROPAGATION Sow seed in situ, 30 cm apart. Sowing seeds every fortnight will ensure a continuous crop. Reap ripened seeds for next season's crop.

HARVESTING AND PROCESSING The first rosette of leaves is picked green and young before the flowering head appears and is used in Indian and Mediterranean cookery as danya. When the primary leaves turn to delicate feathery ones and flowers appear the leaves are no longer picked. Green seeds ripen quickly and the dried clusters of tiny seeds should be collected before they drop.

COMPANION PLANTING A good companion to aniseed, dill and chervil; should not be grown near fennel, as it inhibits seed formation. It will repel aphids but bees and butterflies are attracted to it.

USES OF CORIANDER

Culinary Coriander seeds can be added to all savoury dishes, from curries and chutney to marmalade. Leaves and flowers can be used in salads, sauces and garnishes. The young leaves, called danya, have their own distinct flavour, and this is the part much loved in Indian cookery. An essential spicy flavouring (see recipe section) in many curries and sauces, coriander is as much used today as a flavouring and preservative as it was in those ancient days.

Medicinal Coriander is one of the wonderful digestive herbs. Either a few seeds well chewed or made into a tea will relieve flatulence, colic, heartburn, bloating, griping and belching. It is an excellent herb for nervous tension, nervous upsets, temper tantrums and bad moods. To make a tea use 1 teaspoon coriander seeds, lightly crushed (or use ¼ cup fresh flowers and leaves). Pour over this 1 cup of boiling water, leave to stand 5 minutes, then strain and sip slowly. Coriander seeds can also be chewed to sweeten the breath, specially garlic breath. Our grandmothers made 'fairy sweeties' with coriander seeds dipped into tiny pots of icing sugar which we all delightedly ate, thinking we were consuming fairy food. At Christmas time the children made tiny boxes which they filled with these little sweets and tied with silver thread to await the fairies. And it always was gone on Christmas morning! The fairies must have been thrilled and ever so healthy!

Cosmetic Flowers make a soothing face pack for oily, spotty skin. Steep in hot water to thoroughly warm them and then apply as a face pack. Cover with a face cloth wrung out in hot water and relax for 10 minutes. Rinse in tepid water to which a little apple cider vinegar has been added.

Other uses Leaves, flowers and stem make an excellent insect repellent (see recipe section).

Cornflower

Family **Compositae**
Species *Centurea cyanus*
Origin **temperate regions**
Plant **winter annual**
Height **80 cm; space 50 cm apart**
Soil **well-dug, well-composted soil**
Exposure **full sun**
Propagation **seeds**
Uses **culinary, medicinal, cosmetic**

The folklore that surrounds the cornflower is fascinating. Painters in medieval times used the brilliant blue crushed petals to mix into oils for painting on murals and parchment, and the monks used the petals crushed and in a type of vinegar mixture with egg whites to give the royal blue colour in their calligraphied parchments and scrolls of prayers.

The 12th century herbalist, St Hildegard of Bingen, recommended using crushed cornflowers as wound dressings, as eyewashes and as compresses over slow-healing wounds. Later Mattioli, another herbalist, recommended their use as an eyewash, according to the Doctrine of Signatures, which indicated that a plant's appearance would signify its use (the deep blue colour of the cornflower matching the Anglo-Saxon blue eyes).

CULTIVATION Plant out at the end of July in well-composted, well-dug soil in full sun. Space 50 cm apart; it will reach about 80 cm in height. Water well twice weekly. By the end of November it becomes too hot for this tender annual under the blazing African sun. So save the seeds for next year, pull up the whole plant and dump it on the compost heap.

PROPAGATION Sow the seed in trays from March to early April, then when the seedlings are 10 cm high, prick them out and plant them in individual pots. Keep them moist and protected and during the sunny winter days put them out into full sunlight to strengthen them then plant them out.

HARVESTING AND PROCESSING Pick the flowers as soon as they open – all through the season.

COMPANION PLANTING Wheat, rye and barley rows interplanted with cornflowers will increase their yield.

USES OF CORNFLOWER

Culinary The young, tender shoots of the cornflower are edible and were used in medieval soups, stews and game pots. Slightly bitter, they are at their best lightly stirfried with a dash of vinegar. The petals are delicious in fruit salads and in fritters or sprinkled on custards and ice creams, and added to stirfries, where their exquisite colour gives a most unusual appearance to the dish and their pleasant flavour lends itself to both sweet and savoury.

Medicinal Cornflower tea can be cooled and used as an eye bath for red, tired, sore eyes, and also as a lotion for sunburn, rashes and grazes. Hot cornflowers packed over a bruised wound or graze will help to take the swelling down and heal the area, and strapped over a sprain will greatly assist the healing process, bound in place with a warmed comfrey leaf. There is new evidence that the amino acids in the cornflower support the liver, improving resistance to infection and imparting diuretic qualities to the liver and kidneys. High in magnesium and potassium, this could be a beneficial tonic to the whole system. Cornflower tea is a calming, nerve-steadying treatment for anxiety, grief and stress. To make the tea use ¼ cup fresh leaves, flowers and buds. Pour over this 1 cup boiling water. Stand 5 minutes. Strain and sip slowly.

Cosmetic Added to the bath, cornflower petals are wonderfully soothing and softening for the skin; in a scrub they will cleanse and soften the skin beautifully after winter's dryness.

Other uses Centaurin, tannins and cyanine dyes in cornflower break down compost quickly.

Costmary

Bible leaf ● Alecost
Family **Compositae**
Species *Tanacetum balsamita*
Origin Eurasia
Plant perennial
Height 10-40 cm; space 50-60 cm apart
Soil well-dug, richly composted soil
Exposure full sun
Propagation division
Uses culinary, medicinal, cosmetic

In the Middle Ages, costmary, with its beautifully scented leaves, was used to flavour, clarify and purify ale, hence the name alecost. It was also used as a bookmark in the Bible to keep the pages free of moths and fishmoths and to scent them with a minty camphory refreshing fragrance that helped to keep the congregation awake and free of hunger pangs during long sermons! It was used by the monks in various medicines and also applied to bee stings (many churches kept bees for their honey which the monks used for medicine and to make mead, conserves, wines and jams). Bees feeding on costmary had a delicious honey that was much prized, so most cloister gardens had a large planting of costmary. Costmary was added to the laundry rinsing water, and boiled with lavender to make a fragrant ironing splash to get out all those creases. The fresh fragrance left on sheets, pillowcases and petticoats is nostalgically unforgettable.

CULTIVATION Hardy, perennial, almost a groundcover, forming a lush cushion with 10-15 cm long flat leaves and a midsummer flowering spike of about 40 cm. The flowers are small and nondescript. It will need a deep twice-weekly watering.

PROPAGATION Propagation is by division, chopping off rooted side-pieces and replanting 60 cm apart in well-dug, richly composted soil in full sun.

HARVESTING AND PROCESSING Pick the leaves at any time of the year. Best used fresh but can be dried for potpourris.

COMPANION PLANTING Plant with beans, nasturtiums, pumpkins and radishes.

USES OF COSTMARY

Culinary Use sparingly, as the spearmint flavour can overpower – a little goes a long way! Add a few of the young leaves finely chopped to salads, sweet potato bakes, carrot and pumpkin soups and to your favourite fruit cake! When you are stewing apples or pears or quinces, add a leaf or two to the pot and let it impart its freshness and fragrance to the dish. Our grandmothers added a teaspoon of finely chopped costmary to whipped cream and custard served with desserts.

Medicinal Costmary tea is excellent for coughs, colds, stomach upsets, blocked nose and feverishness associated with a cold. Traditionally this 'Sweet Mary tea' was taken without the honey and the cloves to ease the pain of childbirth and for cramps. To make the tea use ¼ cup fresh costmary leaves. Pour over this 1 cup boiling water. Add 6 cloves. Stand 5 minutes. Strain and sweeten with honey. A poultice of warmed leaves wrapped around a cramping leg and kept warm with a hot water bottle has been a favourite since ancient times. Try stuffing a few fresh leaves into the hot water bottle cover for aching feet and keep the feet on it for about half an hour. It will also scent the bed most appealingly!

Cosmetic An infusion makes a fragrant hair rinse, lotion or spritz that is exquisitely refreshing and skin refining (see recipe section).

Other uses As an insect repellent, the fresh minty fragrance of costmary actually intensifies the fragrance of other herbs, and I have found a combination of tansy, southernwood, basil and costmary very effective against aphids and white fly.

Cumin

Family **Umbelliferae**
Species *Cuminum cyminum*
Origin **Near East, India**
Plant **short-lived annual**
Height **30 cm; space 20 cm apart**
Soil **well-dug, compost-enriched soil**
Exposure **full sun**
Propagation **seed**
Uses **culinary, medicinal**

Cumin is one of the herbs mentioned in the Old Testament in Matthew as a tax payment: 'Woe unto you scribes and pharisees, hypocrites! For ye pay tithe of mint and dill and cumin, and have omitted the weightier matters of the law.' Native to Egypt, cumin seed have been found in tombs and burial chambers dating back thousands of years. Not only was it a much-loved flavouring, but it was grown in medicinal gardens in ancient Egypt and in the Mediterranean area where it was used by the monks to treat the sick.

Widely cultivated from those early beginnings across Europe, cumin's decline in popularity was possibly due to other herbs in the spice trade that were easier to grow and to come by. The ancient Chinese, Indians and Arabs grew protected fields of cumin to use as barter or trade and developed incredible recipes that were handed down from generation to generation.

CULTIVATION It needs well-dug moist soil enriched with compost. Sow the seeds between green peppers and chillies as these crops will protect them and give a little shade. Fine leaved and spindly, cumin is delicate but well worth growing.

PROPAGATION Sow thinly scattered over well-dug moist soil in full sun. Rake the seeds in and cover with a few leaves to keep them shaded during germination.

HARVESTING AND PROCESSING Once the little plants are sturdy, you can immediately start using the leaves and flowers for curries, stirfries and drinks. Allow the seeds to dry on the plant before reaping.

COMPANION PLANTING Plant with green peppers, chillies and brinjals. Cumin enhances their taste.

USES OF CUMIN

Culinary Cumin is one of the important ingredients in curry, in spicy pickles and in sauces, marinades and dips. In Europe cumin seeds are baked in breads, cakes and biscuits and in the Middle East bread dipped into olive oil and then sprinkled with a few seeds of cumin (and coriander and caraway too if liked) is a favourite in many areas. The much loved Za'atar varies from area to area, but this spicy, well-crushed mixture is taken everywhere, stored in little jars. Its basic ingredients are cumin, coriander, caraway, thyme and coarse salt and cardamon, mint and mustard seeds are sometimes added. A marinade of olive oil, cumin and peppercorns, mustard, fresh coriander leaves and lemon juice is superb for chicken, beef, mutton and fish or for those huge flat brown mushrooms.

Medicinal Cumin seeds and fresh leaves and flowers aid circulation and help to clear toxins from the body. In a tea, it is immediately soothing and unwinding, and wonderful for a stuffy nose and sore throat and to treat heartburn, flatulence, colic, bloating, digestive spasm, belching, incessant wind and as a stimulant for the whole digestive process. To make the tea add 1 teaspoon of crushed seeds to 1 cup boiling water, stir well and stand 3 to 5 minutes. Sip slowly and chew the seeds. Indians use cumin tea to treat insomnia, to ease the symptoms of a cold, to bring down fever and relieve arthritic aches and pains. Cumin tea has traditionally been given to a nursing mother to increase her milk production and in so doing it improves the baby's digestion – you just won't have a colicky baby if the mother takes a cup of cumin tea twice a day. In Indian herbal medicine cumin is made into a paste and applied mixed with onion juice to scorpion stings and infected insect bites like mosquito bumps.

Dandelion

Family **Compositae**

Species *Taraxacum officinale*

Origin Europe and the British Isles, now a worldwide weed

Plant perennial

Height up to 30 cm; space 30 cm apart

Soil literally any soil

Exposure full sun

Propagation seeds

Uses medicinal, culinary

One of the world's most common weeds, yet one of the most astonishing healing plants, with an array of health benefits that will take your breath away! It has been used and recorded in ancient pharmacopoeias and herbals in 7th century China and by the 15th century it was well used and listed all over Europe.

The name 'dandelion' was invented apparently by a 15th century surgeon who compared the sharp pointed leaves to the teeth of the lion – *dents de lion* – and amazingly it has the ability with its high mineral content to build strong enamel on the teeth and strengthen the bones. All parts of the plant are effective and safe for use. The root is mildly laxative, a superb liver tonic and an excellent anti-rheumatic. Rich in vitamin A, B, C and D, carotenoids and minerals, especially potassium and calcium, this is one of the very best detoxifying herbs.

CULTIVATION Many people fear that if they once plant a dandelion in their gardens they'll never be able to weed the lawn, but it thrives in a pot and you can nip off the head as the seeds appear. It thrives on neglect, but if nurtured and watered and planted in compost-rich soil, it will grow to 30 cm in height and width.

PROPAGATION Self-seeds prolifically.

HARVESTING AND PROCESSING Pick leaves and flowers all through the year. It's a survivor!

COMPANION PLANTING Dandelion has the ability to exhale an ethylene gas that causes nearby plants to mature and ripen quickly.

USES OF DANDELION

Culinary In the last century cultivated forms with large and tender leaves have been developed. These are the tastiest and, added to salads and even stirfries, give a slight bitterness that is quite pleasant. I chop them with celery and parsley and mix them with lemon juice. Sprinkle this health giving mixture over mashed potatoes, cold meats, soups and roasts. Use dandelion leaves fresh only.

Medicinal Acts as a blood builder, bone builder, joint strengthener and treatment for eczema and infected acne, breaks down gallstones and is extremely helpful for jaundice and liver overload, alcohol abuse and drug abuse. Dandelion also treats high blood pressure. An advantage of its diuretic action and stimulation of bile production (unlike many other diuretics, which cause a heavy loss of potassium) is that the dandelion is so loaded with quickly absorbable potassium you actually gain more! It is recommended to eat three dandelion leaves fresh daily!

Cosmetic Eating dandelion will lighten those dark spots on the hands and clear up acne and oily coarse skin. Dabbed onto pimples and spots, sunburn, coarse pores, rashes and stings, the milky sap will immediately soothe and start to heal the area. Dandelion vinegar (see recipe section) is a refreshing addition to rinsing water or to the bath, as it is tonic and cleansing and is rich in minerals that help to clear dry scalp and condition oily hair.

Other uses Dandelion is so rich in minerals, it makes a superb fertiliser. Its copper builds the soil and ensures cropping. Dig a few dandelion plants back into the soil, and whatever you can spare makes superb compost, enriching the heap!

Dill

Family **Umbelliferae**
Species *Anthemum graveolens*
Origin **Southern Europe, Central and Western Asia**
Plant **cool weather annual**
Height **over 1 m; space 30 cm apart**
Soil **well-dug, lightly composted soil**
Exposure **full sun**
Propagation **seed**
Uses **culinary, medicinal**

The word 'dill' comes from the ancient Norse word *dylla* which means 'to soothe', and bunches of dill were hung over the door to protect the home and ward off evil. Indigenous to Southern Europe, Western and Central Asia, dill has become naturalised in the Mediterranean areas and in the Americas, and is a familiar crop across the world. Revered, respected and much loved, dill seeds were found in Egyptian tombs 5 000 years ago, in burial sites in Rome, Britain and Ancient Greece, and are even mentioned in the Bible in Matthew as a tax payment. A soothing syrup was made of dill by the monks during the Middle Ages to ease colic, indigestion, coughs and colds, 'flu, headaches, spasms and as a diuretic. Modern day research proves all these properties and dill remains a popular crop throughout the world.

CULTIVATION In the heat of the African sun, I have found dill to be better as a cool weather plant that needs watering frequently, so I sow it as a winter annual.

PROPAGATION Sow in individual plugs and transplant into moist, well-dug soil 30 cm apart when the plants are 10 cm high. Keep moist until it is well established then water three to four times a week.

HARVESTING AND PROCESSING Leaves and flowers can be picked at any time. Leave seed heads to ripen on the plant then tie a brown paper bag over them to catch the seeds.

COMPANION PLANTING Plant with lettuce, cabbage, carrots, mealies, cucumbers and tomatoes. Don't plant near fennel as they cross-fertilise and don't let it flower near carrots as it reduces their yield.

USES OF DILL

Culinary The faint aniseed-like flavour of dill combines beautifully with other flavours and a scattering of dill seed over cheese, egg and fish dishes seems to impart a freshness to the dish. Add chopped leaves at the last minute or sprinkle over fish, chicken, mutton, pasta, stirfry and vegetables dishes just as you serve it. Chopped flowers are delicious in stirfries and cooked with stewed quinces, apples or pears, and flowers and seeds can be added to dough in bread and biscuit making, and sprinkled into desserts and salads, and added to soups, casseroles and stews. Traditionally dill is used with cucumber pickles (see recipe section) as a way of preserving summer's bounty. In Middle Eastern cuisine dill water (see recipe section) and dill liqueur is served at the end of a heavy meal to aid digestion. The taste of that silky potion remains in my memory on one gala occasion when a banquet lasted six hours and the tastes and the array of dishes were so spectacular I feared my digestion would never be the same but a sip of the syrupy liqueur put everything to rights.

Medicinal Chewing dill seeds sweetens the breath, and seeds were once chewed during long boring sermons in church to allay hunger pangs, ease digestion and to keep alert! Gripe water – that old-fashioned remedy which can still be bought at your local pharmacy – is every mother's standby for a colicky baby or a fretful, upset child. Dill tea is excellent for tension, upset digestion, hiccups, whooping cough, 'flu, coughs, colds and insomnia, and in nursing mothers will increase milk production. It is a natural antispasmodic, a mild diuretic and will soothe menstrual pains, ease bloating and flatulence. To make the tea use ¼ cup fresh leaves. Pour over this 1 cup boiling water. Stand 5 minutes. Strain and sip slowly.

Echinacea

Purple cone flower
Family **Compositae**
Species *Echinacea purpurescens*
Origin **North America**
Plant **perennial**
Height **up to 60 cm; space 40 cm apart**
Soil **richly composted, well-dug soil**
Exposure **full sun**
Propagation **seed**
Uses **culinary, medicinal, cosmetic**

The world has recently sat up and taken notice of the ancient folklore of the Native Americans who used this beautiful prairie plant to treat everything from colds and influenza to suppurating sores, earache, bladder infections and contagious diseases. Echinacea boosts the immune system so decisively that it is currently being used in the treatment of HIV/AIDS and other diseases affecting the auto-immune system. One of its compounds, echinisen, is an anti-viral agent and another compound, echinacoside, has antibiotic properties, which gives the plant its unique healing abilities.

Varieties range from the bright deep pink 'purpurea' that now flourishes in South Africa, through to tender pinks, mauves and magentas, to the palest yellow, known as *E. pallida*. All types resemble slightly droopy daisies with a hard cone-like centre (which incidentally dries beautifully for flower arrangements), but it is *Echinacea purpurescens* that is used medicinally.

CULTIVATION Needing full sun and richly composted soil to send up those tall, 60 cm flowering heads in late summer, echinacea plants thrive with a good deep, twice weekly watering. They don't like being moved once they are established. They die down in winter.

PROPAGATION Sow seeds in trays of moist sand. Germination is good, especially with last season's seed. The little seedlings can be planted into growing bags as soon as they are big enough to handle.

HARVESTING AND PROCESSING Harvest the mature flowers in midsummer. Pick leaves anytime. Best used fresh.

COMPANION PLANTING Both echinacea and comfrey seem to act like a facelift on slow-growing plants. Echinacea boosts brinjals, green peppers and kale.

USES OF ECHINACEA

Culinary The soft mauvy pink flower petals can be chopped and sprinkled on salads, fruit salads and are exquisite and unusual floating in summer drinks.

Medicinal Tinctures available from the chemist are the easiest ways of taking echinacea. A dose of 10-15 drops taken in water 3 times daily, from March onwards, will do much to prevent 'flu and colds taking hold. And, if taken every 2 hours, at the first sign of symptoms, it will in most cases dissipate the infection. Echinacea tea can be drunk daily as an immune booster for 2 weeks then give it a break. Use ¼ cup fresh leaves and flowers. Pour over this 1 cup boiling water. Stand 5 minutes. Strain. Echinacea and apple cider vinegar (see recipe section) can be used diluted as a gargle, as a mouthwash for ulcers or sore gums, or add a dash to the rinsing water after washing the face to treat acne, oily skins, rashes and spots. Dab onto mosquito bites, stings and insect bites.

Cosmetic My most useful cream for all sorts of little spots and rashes, bites and itches uses echinacea as a base (see recipe section). It is also deeply soothing for dry cracked lips and fingernails. In a bath oil it is excellent for dry skin, while in bath vinegar it is excellent for softening the water as well as for a final rinse when I've shampooed my hair.

Other uses Echinacea combined with comfrey is excellent as a foliar feed. Use it twice during summer and once in late August and watch the amazing luscious growth.

Elder

Family **Caprifoliaceae**
Species *Sambucus nigra*
Origin **Eurasia**
Plant **shrub or tree**
Height **4 m; plant 6-10 m apart**
Soil **deep, well-composted soil**
Exposure **full sun**
Propagation **cuttings**
Uses **culinary, medicinal, cosmetic**

Since the early Egyptians discovered that the flowers improved complexions and soothed skin ailments, the elder has been cultivated for its myriad medicinal properties. Called 'medicine chest tree' in Europe, the elder had been introduced to most parts of the civilised world by the 17th century. These ancient medicines are still used today in rural areas all over the world, and elder trees are still found in cottage gardens everywhere because, it was believed, they kept witches away!

Note that the variegated, or golden elders, are not the correct medicinal plants.

CULTIVATION When planting, dig an extra large hole and mix plenty of compost with the dug-out soil plus a spadeful of bonemeal. Put some of the loosened soil mixture back, then fill the hole with water and allow to drain. Sink the roots deep into the centre of the prepared hole, replace all the soil, firming down as you go until ground level is reached, then make a substantial dam around the tree. Ensure that it receives a deep weekly watering. Every spring dig in a wheelbarrow full of compost around the tree and prune to shape it during July.

PROPAGATION The prunings can be rooted in trays of wet sand as they propagate easily. Cut 15 cm long branches and press hard into the wet sand. Keep moist and shaded.

HARVESTING AND PROCESSING Harvest the flowers when fully open in spring. Flowers can be dried for winter use. Harvest the berries when black and fully ripened.

COMPANION PLANTING Elder protects the whole garden – plant an elder tree in a corner and make the compost heap under it. Onions do well near elder trees.

USES OF ELDER

Culinary Elderflowers can be eaten fresh, sprinkled on to fruit salads, puddings, ice-creams, fruit drinks and punches, and even on to salads, stirfries and pastas. The flowers taste like muscat grapes, the Italians say, and the little round buds can be added to pickles. And, when the jet black plump berries ripen, they can be made into jams, jellies and wine! Elderflower lemonade and elderflower champagne are traditional summer drinks in Europe that are now available branded and bottled.

Medicinal Elderberries have a high vitamin C and mineral content and have been used through the centuries as a tonic for 'flu, coughs, colds, sore throats, anaemia, oedema, neuralgia, insomnia and anxiety. Elderberries are used in tonics and cough medicines in Europe and patent medicines in America. They are made into a gargle for toothache, mouth infections and sore throats, a popular treatment for kidney and lymphatic ailments and an epilepsy treatment. They also treat burns, scalds, erysipelas sores, sore eyes, skin growths, rashes, grazes, flaky patches and sunburn.

Cosmetic Elderflower lotion (see recipe section) smoothes the skin and helps to relieve eczema and psoriasis. Elderflower bath vinegar (see recipe section) soothes sunburned and dry skin. If my hair is dull, I use a little in my final rinsing water after I have shampooed it. Elderflower skin cream (see recipe section) treats dry hands, cracked heels and scaly legs and will soften cuticles and strengthen the nail bed.

Other uses Elder leaf spray (see recipe section) is excellent for deterring aphids and mealie bugs and very helpful for white fly on indoor plants.

Eucalyptus

Family Myrtaceae
Species *Eucalyptus globulus*
Origin Australia
Plant tree
Height 12-18 m; space 10-15 m apart
Soil any soil
Exposure full sun
Propagation seeds, cuttings
Uses medicinal, cosmetic

Originating in Australia, eucalyptus has found its way into most countries around the world in tropical and subtropical areas. But, because of its huge thirst, careful plant management is necessary to prevent ecological problems. Smaller more manageable varieties are now being developed which can be kept pruned to head height and which will not absorb too much water and the suburban gardener can easily keep them in miniature form.

Eucalyptus was first introduced to the Western world in the 19th century because of its insect repelling properties and, as a child, my father, on trips through the country, would point out homesteads surrounded by eucalyptus trees, part of a government project decades before to help to preserve stored grain or the wooden floors of the farm houses, as no ant would cross the eucalyptus barrier.

CULTIVATION These are real survivor trees – they need no attention and no special treatment and will grow anywhere. For today's environmentally conscious world only grow the small pennygums which can be kept controlled, pruned and clipped to manageable heights. They adapt to poor, dry soil or swampy unusual soils and in spite of being such a water guzzler, it has the extraordinary virtue of helping to keep the air clear and will normalise both very poor and dry soil as well as sour brackish boggy areas. Plant your small pennygum or florist gum in a big compost filled hole in full sun and stake the central branch if you want to shape it. Otherwise leave the pretty grey-blue little branches to

spread. All it requires is a weekly watering and pruning to keep it small.

PROPAGATION Seed or cuttings that must be kept moist at all times.

HARVESTING AND PROCESSING Pick leafy sprays any time of the year.

USES OF EUCALYPTUS

Medicinal Eucalyptus oil, easily and relatively inexpensively bought from the chemist, is a worldwide favourite. A few drops in a steaming bowl of water will open a stuffy nose, clear away cold and chesty symptoms and disinfect the sickroom. A traditional Aboriginal remedy for infections, pain relief and respiratory ailments, it also eases arthritic and rheumatic pain and bacterial skin infections. A few fresh sprigs added to your bath will help the muscles relax. A eucalyptus rub will ease aching joints (see recipe section).

Cosmetic A big bowl of boiling water into which a couple of sprigs of fresh eucalyptus leaves have been steeped makes an excellent facial steamer for problem skins. This fragrant steam will open and clear the pores, dissolve oiliness and with its antiseptic, antibacterial properties it becomes an excellent beauty aid.

Other uses To clear a sick building, to get rid of stale germ-laden air, to freshen and clear smoke-filled rooms, sickrooms, toilets and bathroom and kitchen smells, pick a large bunch of eucalyptus leaves. Rinse the leaves to clear dust and pollution. Fill a large jug or vase with water to which you add 2-3 teaspoons of eucalyptus oil, plunge the bunch of eucalyptus leaves into it and watch it act as an air conditioner. It will breathe out eucalyptus oil through the leaves and freshen the room within minutes.

Evening Primrose

Family **Onagraceae**
Species *Oenothera biennis*
Origin **North America**
Plant **biennial**
Height **1 m; space 50 cm apart**
Soil **well-dug, well-composted soil**
Exposure **full sun**
Propagation **seed**
Uses **culinary, medicinal, cosmetic**

Native Americans have used evening primrose since the 15th century, both as a food and a medicine. Evening primrose is tough, drought resistant and one of the easiest of plants to grow. In our climate, the flowers remain open for most of the day with masses of new long pointed buds opening every evening. Evening primrose oil is rich in essential fatty acids and has astringent properties and skin-softening gamma-linolenic acid – a precursor of prostaglandin E – making it an ideal skin treatment.

CULTIVATION In the first year, the leaves form a rosette and plants can be transplanted only while small: once the rosette reaches 15 cm in diameter the single taproot won't tolerate transplanting. In their second year they send up a spike of bright yellow flowers grouped at the top of the stem (the pink- or white-flowered varieties are not the true medicinal evening primrose). Plants do best in good garden soil in full sun. They thrive with added compost dug in around them during their second year, and a twice-weekly watering.

PROPAGATION Once you have your first plant, seeds seem to germinate and pop up everywhere in the garden. Seeds can be collected and sown in seed trays. Keep moist and transplant 50 cm apart as soon as the plants are big enough to handle.

HARVESTING AND PROCESSING Pick flowers in the evening all through the season. Reap the seeds by hanging the plant upside down over newspaper once ripe.

COMPANION PLANTING Good with thyme, rosemary and parsley. They enhance each others' growth.

USES OF EVENING PRIMROSE

Culinary The Native Americans used evening primrose leaves as a spinach; the flowers were cooked in a syrup as a sweet and the root pickled in vinegar as a relish. Sprinkle the ripened seeds over stirfries, salads and soups.

Medicinal Evening primrose capsules are offered in every pharmacy as over-the-counter medicines, and are prescribed by doctors for premenstrual tension, dry skin, high blood pressure and high cholesterol. Many doctors also prescribe it for digestive ailments, as well as asthma and rheumatic disorders. The oil applied externally is helpful for everything from eczema, psoriasis, breast tenderness, itchy rough skin, cramps in the legs and circulatory problems. A poultice of leaves softened in hot water has long been used to ease back pain, rheumatism and arthritis. Evening primrose capsules can be taken daily as an anti-ageing treatment, and bath oil and face creams assist ageing skin and heal dryness.

Cosmetic Evening primrose is beneficial for all skin ailments, refining, moisturising and encouraging new cell growth. Apart from working on the surface of the skin, improving elasticity, softness and strength, external applications of evening primrose extracts and oils are assimilated by the underlying tissues, improving the general circulation. Making your own evening primrose cream (see recipe section) is quick, easy and extremely soothing for sunburn, windburn and dry skin. Evening primrose flower lotion (see recipe section) makes a refreshing splash-on or mist spray that is excellent for refining and toning greasy skin.

Other uses Fling old evening primrose plants on to the compost heap, cover with grass cuttings and leaves and, within a fortnight, the heap will be disintegrating with heat and speed.

Fennel

Family Umbelliferae
Species *Foeniculum vulgare* ● *F. vulgare* var. Dulce
Origin Mediterranean regions
Plant annual or biennial
Height 1 m; space 1 m apart
Soil well-dug, well-composted soil
Exposure full sun
Propagation seed
Uses culinary, medicinal, cosmetic

An ancient, much respected herb, fennel has its roots so firmly embedded in lore and legend that no one is sure who actually used it first. Native to the Mediterranean, where it thrives in the heat and the sun, this easily grown plant had spread into the rest of Europe by the Middle Ages and its medicinal powers were so revered that fennel seeds became a prized trade commodity spreading to India, China and North Africa by the 15th century.

Ordinary fennel (*F. vulgare*), often treated as a biennial, is tough, resilient and prolific. Florence fennel (var. Dulce) is the one that has the swollen bulbous root stalk much loved in Italian and French cooking; this is an annual. Bronze fennel is a beautiful dark maroon, almost black, variety of the ordinary fennel. The dark feathery leaves are particularly beautiful in the mixed border.

CULTIVATION The three different fennels all have the same growing requirements: full sun, good compost-rich soil and a twice-weekly deep watering.

PROPAGATION Fennel seeds germinate quickly and are best sown in seed trays from spring onwards. Keep the seedlings moist and shaded and plant out when they are 10 cm high.

HARVESTING AND PROCESSING Pick flowers and seeds as they ripen. Reap Florence fennel as soon as the bulbous stem is about the size of a tennis ball.

COMPANION PLANTING Don't plant fennel near tomatoes, beans, kohlrabi, coriander, caraway or dill. They dislike one another! Rather grow fennel in the flower border away from the vegetable garden.

USES OF FENNEL

Culinary All the fennels have a pleasant, slightly anise taste that goes beautifully with fish, pasta, cheese and poultry dishes. Finely chopped fresh leaves add a tantalising note to ordinary dressings and dips, and finely chopped stems are superb in salads and stirfries. The flowers are edible and as appealing to the eye as to the tastebuds. The seeds, fresh green or dried, can be added to bread, biscuits, cakes and sprinkled on fish dishes and pastas. Thinly shaved Florence fennel bulb is an appetising addition to salads, stirfries, soups and fish dishes.

Medicinal Fennel is often known as the 'slimmer's herb'. It is an excellent diuretic, flushing out toxins from the body – take 2 cups of tea daily three or four days in a row. Tea made from the leaves and stems reduces the effects of over-indulgence in food and alcohol. It is also excellent for constipation, heartburn, colic and respiratory ailments. To make the tea use ¼ cup fresh leaves or flowers and pour over this 1 cup boiling water. Stand 5 minutes. Strain and sip slowly. Chewing fennel seeds will ease indigestion, flatulence and colic.

Cosmetic Fennel tea is an excellent treatment for oily problem skins. Pads of cotton wool wrung out in the warm tea will reduce puffiness and shadows around the eyes. A deep-cleansing fennel steam (see recipe section) is a wonderfully simple method used by our grandmothers to get the skin really cleaned and refine the pores. After too much partying, a fennel and salt bath is a lifesaver (see recipe section).

Other uses On the compost heap fennel quickly breaks down and with its fibrous stems it aerates the compost heap. Its strong oils make it an excellent foliar feed for pot plants and indoor plants. Add fennel to your dog's diet and sprinkle the seeds under his bedding to repel fleas.

Fenugreek

Family Leguminosae
Species *Trigonella foenum-graecum*
Origin Eastern Mediterranean and North Africa
Plant annual
Height 60 cm; sow 15 cm apart
Soil well-dug, well-composted soil
Exposure full sun
Propagation seeds
Uses culinary, medicinal, cosmetic

One of the oldest medicinal herbs, fenugreek was used by all the ancient cultures. A favourite with both the Egyptians and the Arabs, who not only used the seeds for medicinal purposes but roasted them as a nutritious coffee and ate the leaves as a vegetable. An Egyptian papyrus dating from 1500 BC records medicinal uses of fenugreek for inducing childbirth, treating burns and as a soothing wound dressing and digestive. Dioscorides in the 1st century recommended fenugreek as a treatment for all gynaecological ailments, and Hippocrates, in the 5th century, prescribed fenugreek for inflammations and infections and for treating dyspepsia and ulcers.

The whole plant contains vitamins A, B and C, and a host of minerals. Ongoing medical research suggests that fenugreek may inhibit cervical cancer (it has long been used in China for this); it may be one of the most remarkable of all herbs for reducing blood sugar in diabetics, and it is one of the most well-established plant medicines used to ease colic and abdominal cramps.

CULTIVATION The pungent, oddly shaped seeds are exceptionally easy to grow and can be sprouted as a tasty salad ingredient. For a continuous supply of leaves and seeds, sow a fresh batch every 3-4 weeks.

PROPAGATION Dig over and compost well a spot in full sun and scatter the seeds thinly over the surface. Rake them in and water well. Cover with a light sprinkling of leaves to help retain moisture while they germinate. Take care not to let the area dry out during this stage.

HARVESTING AND PROCESSING Leaves can be picked as soon as the plant reaches 15 cm in height.

COMPANION PLANTING Beans, cucumber, squash, tomatoes.

USES OF FENUGREEK

Culinary The leaves are filled with pungent unusual flavour and can be sparingly sprinkled into salads and stirfries. The seeds have a celery-like spicy taste and are used in chutneys and Middle Eastern confectionery and curries.

Medicinal The nourishing and soothing seeds treat gastric ulcers and gastritis; they induce childbirth and increase breast milk production. Fenugreek may have anti-diabetic properties, as well as lowering blood cholesterol levels. An external warmed paste of crushed seeds is superb for treating boils, abscesses, ulcers, burns and rashes and infected insect bites. Chewing the seeds is an excellent way of freshening the breath and to help restore a dulled sense of taste. Fenugreek lotion soothes rashes, blisters and sunburn; fenugreek tea can be drunk for period pains, for stomach upsets, diarrhoea and fevers, and, importantly, for anorexia as the seeds are so nourishing and will help to stabilise and encourage weight gain in these cases. To make the tea add 1 teaspoon seeds to 1 cup boiling water. Stand 5 minutes and strain.

Cosmetic Fenugreek and sea salt bath is helpful for cellulite, for clearing spots and rashes (see recipe section).

Other uses Fenugreek is a superb green manure crop and compost builder. As a foliar feed it combines beautifully with comfrey to build up flower leaf growth and act as an insect repellent. Fenugreek seeds are a source of yellow dye.

Feverfew

Family Compositae
Species *Chrysanthemum parthenium*
Origin Southeast Europe
Plant biennial or annual
Height 30-60 cm; space 30 cm apart
Soil well-drained, richly composted soil
Exposure full sun
Propagation seed
Uses medicinal, cosmetic

Over the centuries feverfew became known traditionally as the 'woman's herb' and to quote Nicholas Culpeper, the English herbalist in 1653: 'Feverfew is a general strengthener of the womb, it cleanseth the womb, it expelleth the afterbirth, and giveth the woman all the good she can desire of a herb.' It is closely related to tansy and chamomile and was mainly used to treat childbed fever, hence its name. The leaves warmed in hot water were used to ease headaches and bring down fevers, applied externally as a poultice over the forehead and temples.

CULTIVATION Transplant seedlings and rooted cuttings 30 cm apart and keep them well watered until they are established. Thereafter water three times a week.

PROPAGATION Sow in seed boxes during spring and plant out 30 cm apart in full sun when big enough to handle.

HARVESTING AND PROCESSING Pick leaves and flowers at any time.

COMPANION PLANTING Plant with lettuce, spinach, radish, peas, beans and squashes. Feverfew is an exceptional herb in the vegetable garden, chasing aphids, slugs and snails.

USES OF FEVERFEW

Culinary During the Middle Ages fresh feverfew leaves were added to fatty, greasy dishes – the goose was cooked with a little feverfew inside it as a stuffing to 'cut the grease'.

Medicinal Modern research verifies feverfew's analgesic compounds, and that it promotes menstrual flow, reduces fever and that it has anti-rheumatic properties. Feverfew has anti-inflammatory action, the ability to relax the blood vessels and to act as a digestive stimulant and, surprisingly, to expel worms. Tests for migraine and arthritis in Britain and America have shown that one large leaf – or three small leaves – eaten daily on a sandwich for not less than 6 months, would effectively act as a prophylactic. Every 10 days stop taking the herb for 2 days, then continue for another 10 days, or take feverfew tablets available from the chemist.

A bitter tea made by pouring 1 cup of boiling water over less than ¼ cup of fresh leaves could be taken after childbirth to cleanse and tone the uterus, or for painful clotting or sluggish menstruation. Hot feverfew leaves applied as a poultice over boils and abscesses, over suppurating wounds, swellings, bruises and sprains, scratches, sores and insect bites help to clear the inflammation. Feverfew lotion (see recipe section) has been used since those ancient days as a wash for wounds and bites. Tinctures of feverfew can be bought from homeopathic chemists. Take 5 to 10 drops every 15 minutes at the onset of a migraine, and apply a hot towel soaked in feverfew lotion to the head and lie down in a darkened room. **Warning**: Patients taking Warfarin or other blood thinning drugs should not take feverfew as it can affect the clotting rate. Because of its bitter principals, taking feverfew leaves can, in rare cases, cause ulceration of the fine mucous membrane of the mouth.

Cosmetic Feverfew lotion is an excellent treatment for oily acne or spotty problem skin.

Other uses The roots, flowers, stems and leaves are rich in sesquiterpene lactones, volatile oils, pyrethrins and tannins, which act as superb insecticides. I grow masses of feverfew in the vegetable garden and pull up whole flowering plants to make an excellent insecticide spray (see recipe section) for aphids, white fly and red spider.

Field Poppy

Family Papaveraceae
Species *Papaver rhoeas*
Origin Europe
Plant winter annual
Height 50-60 cm
Soil well-dug, lightly composted soil
Exposure full sun
Propagation seed
Uses culinary, medicinal, cosmetic

The wild poppy was revered, 1000 years BC, as a medicine and a food. Fields of wheat in Europe have great swathes of poppies edging them and the ancient Romans looked on the poppy as a sacred flower, dedicating it to their corn goddess Ceres who taught mankind to sow and reap. In the language of flowers the poppy in all its varieties means 'consolation', and that is probably why it was placed around the mummified bodies of ancient Egyptian queens and princesses over 1000 years BC.

At the end of the First World War the field poppy or Flanders poppy became the flower of remembrance in Britain for those soldiers killed in battle on the Fields of Flanders and for soldiers everywhere, the red of their blood symbolised in the red petals.

CULTIVATION Poppies seem to thrive in all sorts of sunny places, asking little attention but a good twice-weekly watering as they grow to their full 50-60 cm height in spring. Once established, they will reseed themselves year after year.

PROPAGATION The little seed capsules bursting with tiny seeds are scattered in well-dug soil that has a little compost added to it, in full sun in early autumn. Keep the area moist until the tiny light green leaves appear during the early winter. In heavy frost protect them with garden fleece thrown over them at night or with a light sprinkling of dry leaves.

HARVESTING AND PROCESSING Pick the flowers when open and reap the seeds when the seed heads are dry.

COMPANION PLANTING Plant with barley, chamomile, cornflower and wheat.

USES OF FIELD POPPY

Culinary Use the seeds on breads and cakes. Petals are delicious sprinkled on fruit salads and desserts, or made into a liqueur like the monks did in medieval times. The petals are exceptionally unusual and exciting served on ice cream and creamy puddings.

Medicinal Poppy petals warmed in hot water were applied during medieval times to rashes, grazes, stings, bites and burns and, applied as a dressing and bound in place by a bandage, are as effective today as they were then. For teenage spots poppy petals are still used today across the world, crushed into a pulp and applied to the acne or pimple. As a wash or lotion for teenage acne and for oily spotty skin, poppy petal lotion (see recipe section) is as popular today as it was in ancient times.

Cosmetic The ancient Greeks and Romans used crushed petals mixed with hot water as a face mask to bring colour to winter-pale skin. There are records of petals being pounded into lard that had been heated and cooled several times to clarify it, and used for dry flaky skin. A modern version is poppy cleansing and moisturising cream, which can be used lavishly on dry flaky areas (see recipe section). I find it excellent for the feet. A scrub made of poppy petals with oats and vinegar is good for dry, rough winter skin (see recipe section).

Other uses Dried seed heads are lovely used in dried arrangements. Some gardeners grow poppies just for their compost heaps and dig in even fresh flowering plants to get that important silica dose into the heap.

Giant Garlic

Elephant garlic
Family **Liliaceae**
Species *Allium sativum gigantium*
Origin **Asia**
Plant **annual**
Height **75 cm; plant 20 cm apart**
Soil **light, compost-enriched sandy soil**
Exposure **full sun**
Propagation **bulbs, sections and seed**
Uses **culinary, medicinal**

Garlic has become so much a part of our daily diet that many a cook cannot even contemplate a dish without it and for those who revel in garlic in all its mouthwatering attributes, the giant garlic is simply bigger and better! One clove of this remarkable, huge garlic is often equal to an entire garlic bulb and its luscious, succulent taste is fast becoming the 'in' food of the decade.

Garlic has been used medicinally since 15 BC. The Romans, Egyptians and the Greeks recorded medical treatments, Louis Pasteur verified garlic could kill bacteria, and scientists continue to record garlic's wonder results in everything from tumour reduction to high cholesterol, acne and high blood pressure reduction, and immune system boosting.

CULTIVATION Bulbs can be planted about 20 cm apart from mid-March to the end of April, giving them the warmth of the autumn sun to set roots and send up leaves. In August a dressing of dolomite can be given to swell those bulbs, well watered in, and perhaps a little more compost before the spring rains. The winter cold and frost will swell the bulb and by spring to early summer luscious large leaves will emerge. Do not use chemical fertilisers or sprays.

PROPAGATION Prepare deeply dug compost enriched sandy loam. Place the bulbs pointed end up about 8-10 cm deep and water well, totally covering the bulb with soil, lightly pressed down. The bulbs must not dry out at this stage as those new little roots need to go deep into the soil before the winter.

HARVESTING AND PROCESSING Once the flowering head topples over and the leaves dry off, it is time to lift the bulbs and to store them in a cool dark shed: as long as the bulbs are kept out of light they can be stored for up to a year.

COMPANION PLANTING Planted near spinach and tomatoes, garlic seems to enhance their growth.

USES OF GARLIC

Culinary Whole books can be written on cooking with garlic! It can be added literally to every dish, from soups to salads, pastas to pizzas, bread, butter, stew, savoury biscuits, spreads, fish, meat and everything in between. The leaves can be finely chopped and added to stirfries.

Medicinal Garlic is able to kill a broad range of bacteria and fungi. It is a natural wide-spectrum antibiotic, building the immune system effectively, especially for those prone to coughs, colds, bronchitis and 'flu. Garlic often clears skin ailments like ringworm, athlete's foot, acne and nail fungus attacks. It helps thin the blood, which reduces the formation of blood clots, and is superb for treating high cholesterol, high blood pressure and sluggish circulation and heart disease. Garlic effectively treats cystitis, sinusitis and crushed fresh garlic is an excellent antiseptic for external and internal application. It helps to prevent free radicals from forming when eaten daily.

Other uses A natural insecticide, very effective for aphids, mealie bugs, white fly and thrips. Give your dog 2 teaspoons of chopped giant garlic twice a week to keep him free of fleas and ticks.

Ginger

Family Zingiberaceae
Species *Zingiber officinale*
Origin Southeast Asia
Plant perennial
Height up to 1 m; space 30-50 cm apart
Soil deeply dug, well-composted soil
Exposure full sun
Propagation division
Uses culinary, medicinal, cosmetic

The Romans carried ginger in their medical supplies when they invaded Britain in AD 431, and it was also prized by the American revolutionaries of 1775 who added it to their food rations as a potion for vigour and fearlessness! Native to Southeast Asia, ginger is now grown mainly in the tropics and probably the best ginger comes from Jamaica – the sea, sun, rain and warm climate together with the lush soil contributing to its glorious taste, no doubt. Ginger is one of the easiest of all plants to grow, and it has the bonus of being attractive in the garden. The only part of the plant used for flavouring is the tuberous swollen root, but the leaves can be used to line salad bowls, and the fragrant white flowers to decorate party drinks and fruit boards.

Note: The ornamental gingers are not edible.

CULTIVATION Ginger needs deeply dug soil with lots of compost, because the roots will stay there for the whole year – and they are voracious feeders! Plant in full sun, although a ginger plant will tolerate some afternoon shade, and give it a twice-weekly deep soaking. Flowers will appear in summer and then all watering must stop from May onwards, to enable the leaves to die down. Don't cut them off; they must die down on their own, returning nourishment to the swollen rhizome.

PROPAGATION Select a firm, succulent tuber with lots of pale green eyes on the knobbly protrusions. With a sharp knife, cut off pieces at their natural 'necks' making sure each has a growing eye. Plant out in spring 30-50 cm apart in well-dug, richly composted soil and keep moist by covering with a thin layer of leaves to shade it. Once it sends up the little shoots, water twice weekly.

HARVESTING AND PROCESSING Ginger can be harvested in July. Carefully fork up the heavy tubers and gently wash them in cold water. I grate freshly harvested rhizomes and store them in brown grape vinegar in a dark bottle – or turn into crystallised ginger or store in syrup.

COMPANION PLANTING Lilies, hostas and elephant ears.

USES OF GINGER

Culinary Try adding thinly sliced fresh ginger to fish dishes or make your own ginger beer with fresh ginger. Marinades, soups and sauces are richly enhanced by this precious spice.

Medicinal Ginger tea is a wonderful treatment for respiratory ailments and nausea – even the nausea associated with chemotherapy. It is excellent for colic, flatulence, poor peripheral circulation, lack of energy, diarrhoea and nervous exhaustion. New medical tests prove ginger helps to lower high cholesterol, as it has amazingly diverse active ingredients from camphene to beta-phellandrene, bomeol and zingerone. To make the tea use 2-4 teaspoons thinly sliced ginger root. Pour over this 1 cup boiling water. Stand 5 minutes. Sweeten with honey if liked. Leave the slices in the cup and chew a little of the root while drinking the tea. Use ginger circulatory cream (see recipe section) for cold hands and feet, gently massaged into the skin.

Cosmetic Use ginger in a footbath to deodorise smelly feet and soften horny skin. Fresh grated or thinly sliced ginger root added to the bath will stimulate the circulation and help to remove toxins from the body. (Ginger can irritate sensitive skins, so always first test the mixture on the inside of the wrist before adding to bath water, etc.)

Other uses Add leftover grated ginger to spent coffee grounds and sprinkle under tender plants to kill snails. Sprinkle ginger powder and cayenne pepper to deter ants and mice.

Ginkgo

Maidenhair tree ● Tree of the dinosaurs
Family **Ginkoaceae**
Species *Ginkgo biloba*
Origin **China**
Plant **tree**
Height **35 m; space 20 m apart**
Soil **a deep, compost-filled hole**
Exposure **full sun**
Propagation **seeds, sometimes layering**
Uses **medicinal**

Native to China and possibly Japan, the ginkgo tree dates back 200 million years at least! It has not existed in the wild for centuries, but survived in Oriental temple gardens and from there was introduced into Europe around 1730 as a pretty, rare ornamental. Some of the oldest specimens are found flourishing in Europe's capital cities, often in heavily polluted areas. I stood under a beautiful fully leafed tree in Central London, fresh and green in its summer dress, while traffic whirled around it, its roots covered by concrete and tarmac to the very edge of its gnarled trunk, and marvelled at its strength!

Medical interest in this amazing tree really only took off in the 1980s although research began in the 1960s, and at present ginkgo is the best-selling herbal medicine France, Germany and Italy have ever recorded, with millions taking the wonder medicine daily! The Chinese also use the fruit from the female tree as a medicine.

CULTIVATION Start the ginkgo off in a deep compost-rich hole, soaked well before planting. It needs full sun.

PROPAGATION This slow-growing tree can be propagated by layering, cuttings or seeds from the female trees.

HARVESTING AND PROCESSING Pick the leaves in summer.

USES OF GINKGO

Medicinal Western interest in this ancient Chinese medicine first concentrated on its mind-restoring abilities, for example Alzheimer's disease and poor circulation to the brain with memory loss and mental deterioration. Then more and more interest took hold as the Chinese pharmacopoeia recorded ginkgo tea has been taken for asthma, wheezing, tight chest and to break down phlegm, for a weak bladder, incontinence, and for cystitis, vaginal infections and discharge, as an anti-allergenic and an antispasmodic. New research shows the importance of ginkgo for high blood pressure and arteriosclerosis in the elderly. Ginkgo has an extraordinary anti-inflammatory action which is of great benefit for auto-immune ailments and organ transplants, as it inactivates the free radicals and increases blood circulation and thus removes toxic build-up. Now it is being used to successfully treat debilitating illnesses such as multiple sclerosis, severe tinnitus, extreme vertigo and irregular heartbeat. Chinese and Japanese folk medicine uses the leaves in a tea for varicose veins, leg ulcers, haemorrhoids and as a soothing poultice.

Ginkgo has an extraordinary inhibiting effect on blood platelet formation which has led to a new area of research, namely PAF or platelet activating factor, which causes the blood to become stickier and more likely to thicken and produce blood clots. With ginkgo the PAF is lessened along with various allergenic and inflammatory conditions that arise. This widespread inhibiting factor is one of the reasons why ginkgo is becoming so important.

The best way of taking ginkgo is in tablet or capsule form bought at the chemist, but it can also be taken as a tea. To make the tea use 4 leaves in 1 cup of boiling water. Stand 5 minutes. Strain and sip slowly.

Goldenrod

Family Compositae
Species *Solidago* species
Origin Europe and Asia, naturalised in North America
Plant herbaceous perennial
Height 50 cm to 2 m; space 30-50 cm apart
Soil any soil
Exposure full sun
Propagation seeds, clump division
Uses medicinal

A strong and brilliant perennial, goldenrod is one of the antique flowers, and as a young physiotherapist I noticed it in the grounds of the hospital where I was training. One of the elderly patients I was treating looked down on the bright yellow bed of tall golden plumes from her window and asked me to pick her a sprig or two for her mid-morning tea. I was intrigued, and she explained it was a childhood herb that helped for a sore throat, upset tummy, and eased kidney aches and pains. I never forgot that introduction and 40 years later I still look at my autumn plumes of gold and marvel at their versatility that too few of us know about. The herbalist John Gerard wrote in 1597 that 'goldenrod is extolled above all other herbs' and medical research proves this. It is a mild, comforting and valuable remedy we have never fully utilised.

CULTIVATION Goldenrod is an invasive plant, but has been used for centuries by farmers to nourish their depleted soil. It is full of enzymes and minerals that put back into the soil all that it takes out. But it needs to be controlled or you'll have a field of goldenrod. It loves compost and well dug soil and needs space. So plant 50 cm apart and water twice weekly. Cut the flowering head once it dries off.

PROPAGATION Sow seed in trays, or divide the clump into many little rooted tufts in late winter, and plant out immediately into newly composted soil. Goldenrod gives a stunning autumn show, specially the 2 metre high *Solidago canadensis*, which has the same properties as the smaller, more fragile *Solidago virgaurea*.

HARVESTING AND PROCESSING It is the flowering heads that are used. As soon as the flowers open pick the long stems and tie in bunches and hang upside down to dry. It is best, however, to use the flowers fresh in a tea.

COMPANION PLANTING Goldenrod attracts ladybirds, lacewings, praying mantises and hoverflies that will devour aphids, mealie bugs, ants and caterpillars. Beans, mealies, pumpkins and squash thrive near goldenrod.

USES OF GOLDENROD

Medicinal The name *Solidago* is derived from the Latin 'solido' which means to join, to make whole. It was used in ancient times by the Saracens as a wound herb and for kidney ailments, which still remains today as one of its most important uses. Goldenrod is used to clear kidney infections, bladder infections, cystitis, chronic urinary infections, and it will ease backache caused by associated kidney ailments. It is an anti-inflammatory, and has diuretic and astringent properties, which makes it helpful in the treatment of arthritis, gout, and as a poultice over wounds and aching joints. It is an excellent antioxidant and has the reputation of flushing out toxins and kidney and bladder stones. Its high saponin content and antifungal qualities work wonders in clearing the candida fungus from the body. For oral thrush gargle 10 times a day with the cooled tea, and for vaginal thrush use a douche (see recipe section) three nights running to clear it. The tea can be taken for sore throats, diarrhoea, catarrh, allergic rhinitis and even for gastroenteritis in children, and a strong tea can be added to the bath to soothe aching backs and joints and soften the skin. To make goldenrod tea use ¼ cup fresh or dried flowering sprigs, pour over this 1 cup of boiling water. Stand 5 minutes, then strain. Sweeten with honey if liked, and sip slowly. Take 2-4 cups daily for acute conditions.

Green Tea

Family **Theaceae**
Species *Camellia sinensis*
Origin **China**
Plant **perennial tree**
Height **up to 2,5 m; space 2 m apart**
Soil **acid, well-dug, well-composted, moist soil**
Exposure **full sun, but requires mist**
Propagation **cuttings**
Uses **medicinal, culinary, cosmetic**

Tea is the world's most popular beverage and yet most people don't consider tea as a herb even though it has been used in Chinese medicine 5 000 years ago. In the 1970s scientists became aware that people who drank green tea seemed to have greater protection against strokes, cancer, high cholesterol levels, high blood pressure, infections and heart attacks. Today any drink that combines flowers or leaves or bark or buds or even seeds is called 'tea', but real tea is *Camellia sinensis*, and it can be black or green or in between, which is known as 'oolong'.

CULTIVATION Like azaleas and camellias, tea needs acid soil and thrives with leaf mould mulches and deeply dug soil. It needs full sun and misty, cool, rainy areas, but can take heat as long as the mist wets their leaves.

PROPAGATION Hardwood cuttings from mature branches, rooted in wet sand and allowed to become strongly established before planting out.

HARVESTING AND PROCESSING Nip off the top 3- or 4-leafed sprig at the tip of every branch.

USES OF GREEN TEA

Culinary For a refreshing cuppa, put 2 teaspoons of green tea leaves in a cup, pour over the boiling water, add a squeeze of lemon juice and sweeten if liked with a touch of honey. Let it draw for 2 to 5 minutes, then strain and sip slowly. Cooled tea can be added to fruit juices, jellies, syrups, cakes, jams and iced teas or to stocks, stews, and even soups for that extra bit of goodness.

Medicinal Green tea's powerfully antioxidant phenols boost the immune system and eases chronic coughs and colds. These antioxidants prevent and repair cell damage that is in the beginning stages of heart disease, cataracts, macular degeneration and other degenerative conditions like cancer. It has been found that green tea has stimulant, antibacterial, diuretic and astringent properties. It also helps to reduce blood cholesterol levels, it has anti-tumour properties and is a general tonic. Dentists are finding that gargling and rinsing the mouth with green tea cuts the risk of tooth decay, as it is rich in natural fluoride.

Caution: Those with irregular heartbeat, pregnant women and nursing mothers should not take more than 1-2 cups daily. And don't forget, even green tea has high levels of caffeine type alkaloids that can to some extent increase the heart rate.

Cooled green tea used as a lotion does much to treat skin cancer. Dab onto the area frequently and dab onto irritated hot itchy insect bites as well. For those with stomach ulcers, sip a little green tea every now and then, no more than a cup a day. In Ayurvedic medicine green tea has been used for centuries as a digestive, a nerve tonic, as an eyewash for eye ailments, as a poultice or lotion for haemorrhoids, swellings and sunburn. For those who are overtired and aching all over, a cup of green tea sipped while lying in a hot bath to which a big pot of green tea has been added instantly revives.

Cosmetic Green tea added to cosmetics helps to preserve them and is an excellent skin refresher. Pour cooled green tea into a spritz action bottle and use this as a refreshing cooling toner (without the honey and lemon). Add green tea to the bath to tone the skin, and mix into aqueous cream to use as a cleanser and make-up remover.

Ground Ivy

Family **Rosaceae**
Species ***Glechoma hederacea*** ● ***Nepeta glechoma***
 'Alehoof'
Origin **Eurasia**
Plant **groundcover**
Height **10 cm; space 30-40 cm apart**
Soil **moist, richly composted soil**
Exposure **shade or partial shade**
Propagation **runners**
Uses **culinary, medicinal, cosmetic**

Native to Europe and Western Asia, ground ivy is naturalised in many temperate regions throughout the world and is an almost forgotten herb that deserves more attention, as its ancient uses have been proved over and over again. There is a variegated form that has the same properties and both have tiny mauve flowers that are edible. This could be called one of the antique plants – it was popular 70 years ago and is now fading into obscurity. Its medicinal role is so important today, I can't believe no one knows about it!

CULTIVATION Shady, moist conditions is what it loves most! But it is a tough little survivor plant that takes a lot of sun and heat and frost, and it literally never needs attention! It spreads evenly and attractively over well-dug, well-composted soil, and does well in both pots and hanging baskets. Ground ivy will form an even green carpet that spreads quite quickly, covering the surface, choking out weeds and covering places where little else grows.

PROPAGATION Propagate by rooted runners cut off the mother plant. Keep them shaded and moist until they start shooting. Then plant out 30-40 cm apart.

HARVESTING AND PROCESSING Pick leaves all through the year. The leaves can only be used fresh.

COMPANION PLANTING It grows under hedges and shrubs carpeting and cooling the soil thus enhancing their growth.

USES OF GROUND IVY

Culinary Fresh leaves can be added to stirfries, salads and soups, and their mild taste combines well with lemon verbena or mint for a refreshing tonic tea. The Anglo-Saxons drank ale traditionally and ground ivy was used to clarify it and flavour it with a subtle flavour. It was grown by the monks and made into delicious minty liqueurs, while a tea was used to bring down a fever. Ground ivy is still found growing outside some breweries and cloister gardens in Europe today. Sprigs of fresh leaves dipped in batter and fried and served with salt and olives are still popular as a snack served with ale. Ground ivy garlands were once wound around the head of an over-imbiber to calm and sober him up and was often grown at a tavern door for this reason.

Medicinal Mainly used as a reliable anti-catarrhal medicine, ground ivy is well known for its cleansing effects on the mucous membranes. It will dislodge thick old mucus from sinuses and nose, and clear old productive coughs and ear infections. It also has tonic and diuretic properties, and is a wonderfully well-tolerated herb that is safe for children and old people. For throat and chest ailments, for any digestive disturbances and acid indigestion, heartburn, colic and gastritis and for sharp diarrhoea, a gentle tea of ground ivy is soothing and calming. A tea of ground ivy has also been taken in the past to treat and prevent scurvy and for kidney ailments, to bring down fevers, for slow, burning urine and to dry up watery stools. In the 16th century it was prescribed for blocked ears, buzzing in the ears and tinnitus and to soothe a hot, fretful baby. To make the tea use ¼ cup fresh leaves and sprigs and pour over this 1 cup boiling water. Stand 5 minutes. Strain and sip slowly. Use this tea cooled as a lotion or splash. Soak pads of cotton wool in it to cleanse oily, problem skin.

Cosmetic Many a medieval lady knew that a lotion made of ground ivy, splashed or sprayed onto the face, would clear oiliness, freshen, close the pores and clear up spots.

Hawthorn

Family **Rosaceae**
Species ***Crataegus oxyacantha*** ● ***C. monogyna***
Origin **Europe**
Plant **shrub**
Height **6-7 m; space 10 m apart**
Soil **plant in a deep, compost-filled hole**
Exposure **full sun**
Propagation **layering and seeds**
Uses **medicinal, cosmetic**

An ancient and very valuable medicinal plant, hawthorn is native to Britain and Europe where, for centuries, it has been a symbol of hope and revered as a medicine primarily for the heart and circulation, but also for kidney and bladder stones, and modern research is finding even more exceptional uses for this old-fashioned hedgerow plant.

Hawthorn is beautiful! Its white blossoms of honey-sweet pungently scented flowers in spring and early summer are edible as are its mass of bright shiny red berries in autumn, and its full green shade in summer and the slender bare branches in winter make it a feature in every garden. It is a shame it has been forgotten and hardly ever finds a place in the nurseries.

CULTIVATION Hawthorns do well in cold areas, with-standing frost and even snow. Water deeply once a week.

PROPAGATION Ripened seeds take almost 2 years to germinate – and by then we've given up! Cuttings from hardwood tips of the branches are also slow and our best propagation method has been layering – that is, taking a long whippy branch and bending it down to touch the ground. Where it touches, scrape away a little bark and loosen and moisten the ground. Hold it down securely by bending a stake over it in a 'U' and hit it well into the ground so that the living branch never loses contact with the soil. In a year's time cut it off the mother tree and leave it for another couple of months: by then it will have established itself and it can be carefully dug up and replanted in a deep compost-filled hole in full sun. Water twice weekly until established.

HARVESTING AND PROCESSING Pick the flowers and berries as they ripen. Both can be dried and stored for winter use.

USES OF HAWTHORN

Medicinal An extraordinary heart muscle relaxant, with antioxidant properties and the precious bioflavonoids rutin and quercitin, both quite rare. It is a cardiac tonic, strengthening the heart, and a blood vessel dilator and an age-old high blood pressure remedy. By increasing the blood flow to the heart muscles it reduces the risk of chronic heart failure and congestive heart failure and degeneration of the blood vessels. So for any heart disease, angina and stress it seems that this amazing herb is the answer. Combined with ginkgo, hawthorn is excellent for memory retention and senile forgetfulness because both herbs increase the blood circulation within the brain. The berries and flowers can be eaten fresh.

Traditionally a diuretic tea of hawthorn flowers or berries was taken for bladder and kidney stones, and for diarrhoea, heavy menstrual bleeding and pains, chilblains, poor circulation and as a tonic for irregular heartbeat. Both the flowers and the berries improve the coronary circulation, reducing the risk of heart attack and angina attacks, and hawthorn helps to normalise blood pressure. To make the tea use ¼ cup of fresh or dried flowering tops, leaves and/or berries. Pour over this 1 cup boiling water. Stand 5 minutes. Strain and sip slowly.

Cosmetic Through the centuries girls have rubbed ripe hawthorn berries into their cheeks and lips to give them colour. They make an astringent lotion (see recipe section) that clears the skin of oiliness and grime, closes pores and freshens.

Honeysuckle

Family **Caprifoliaceae**
Species ***Lonicera periclymenum*** • ***L. caprifolium***
Origin **Southern Europe and the Caucasus**
Plant **perennial climber**
Height **up to 5 m; space 1 m apart**
Soil **any soil**
Exposure **sun and partial shade**
Propagation **cuttings, rooted runners**
Uses **medicinal and culinary**

In China and Japan 'Jin yin hua' has been used for centuries to treat asthma and bronchitis and is listed in ancient Chinese medicine books as the most important herb for bringing down a temperature and taking the heat from infected wounds, abscesses and boils and in dysentery.

Now rarely used in contemporary medicine, honeysuckle is still found in country remedies and in one of the Bach flower remedies to counter feelings of nostalgia and homesickness. Many a country child learned to suck the honey from the sweet flowers – hence its name 'honeysuckle' – and I look back with an ache in my heart as I remember the last day of the school holidays as the little farm children packed their trunks and prepared to say goodbye to their pets as the big station wagon stood ready in the drive to take them so far away to their distant schools. Amidst the cricket bats and tennis racquets I always noticed little bunches of honeysuckle were tied in tin foil to comfort those little farm children that night as they adapted to the noise of the city.

CULTIVATION Honeysuckle needs very little attention: just a weekly watering and regular trimming and tying up over supports.

PROPAGATION Propagate by cuttings or rooted runners and keep moist in bags of compost-enriched soil. Plant out 1 metre apart next to poles, fences, pergolas.

HARVESTING AND PROCESSING Flowers can be picked at any time of year and can be preserved in honey, or in vinegar for the bath.

COMPANION PLANTING Honeysuckle acts as a protective vine to lilies, tuberoses and hyacinths.

USING HONEYSUCKLE

Culinary Add the flowers to fruit juices, fruit salads, stirfries and to honey to impart its delicate fragrance to both sweet and savoury dishes.

Medicinal Honeysuckle has expectorant, diuretic, antispasmodic and anti-inflammatory properties and has been found to reduce blood pressure and to ease catarrh, blocked noses and asthma, and to relieve gout, break down kidney stones, and clear liver ailments and sluggishness. A tea of flowers and leaves is an excellent gargle and mouthwash for mouth ulcers, bleeding gums and sore throats, and in Chinese trials it has been found that honeysuckle has the ability to inhibit the tuberculosis bacillus and to counter infection. Make a tea by pouring 1 cup of boiling water over ¼ cup buds. Stand for 5 minutes, sweeten with a touch of honey and sip slowly. This can be taken at the first sign of a feverish cold, for headaches, shivering and for diarrhoea or gastroenteritis. A thumb length piece of stem can be added to the tea for aching joints, rheumatic fever and the acute stages of rheumatoid arthritis, and the all-over ache associated with 'flu and fever. Take 2-3 cups during the day.

Cosmetic Honeysuckle lotion (see recipe section) will soothe hot, inflamed, sunburnt skin and rashes and is excellent for oily problem skin too. Honeysuckle bath salt (see recipe section) imparts an exquisite fragrance to the bath and can be used as a scrub for cellulite areas.

Other uses The flowers dry beautifully for potpourris.

Horseradish

Family **Cruciferae**
Species ***Armoracia rusticana*** (=*Cochleana armoracia*)
Origin **Europe and Western Asia**
Plant **perennial**
Height **30 cm; space 40 cm apart**
Soil **rich, well-composted soil**
Exposure **full sun**
Propagation **seeds, division, root pieces**
Uses **culinary, medicinal, cosmetic**

During the Middle Ages horseradish was used for a variety of ailments, and was grown in apothecary or medicinal gardens cultivated by monks and priests for their local community. It was only much later that it gained popularity as a culinary relish. For the average garden three or four clumps are all that's needed to keep a household stocked with horseradish all year through. My grandmother used an age-old horseradish poultice recipe to ease the pain of aching rheumatism, sore, stiff joints and aching feet.

CULTIVATION A deeply dug, well composted bed in full sun, laced with extra manure, and a little piece of root, is all that's needed. Dig 15 cm deep holes and place the little root, or crown, at the bottom. Cover with more compost and flood the bed. Flood the bed with water three times a week and within three to four weeks you'll be able to pick the first full tender leaves for a salad.

PROPAGATION Dig up the clumps in autumn – make sure the bed is moist and friable so as not to break the roots. Lift carefully and save the smaller roots for replanting. Separate the old crowns into smaller bits and replant about 40 cm apart.

HARVESTING AND PROCESSING In spring, dig out the whole clump, using a large fork. Cut off the biggest roots to use for horseradish sauce and replant the smaller roots.

COMPANION PLANTING Planted under fruit trees and near potatoes, horseradish deters soil-borne diseases. I find I only need one horseradish plant at each end of a potato row. Planted under mango and apple trees, it helps prevent mildew, brown rot and fungus development.

USES OF HORSERADISH

Culinary Peppery, pungent and tasty, a single young leaf, finely chopped, is all that's needed to spice up a salad. Older leaves become very peppery, but give extra bite to sauces and curries. However, it's the roots that are mostly used to create delicious and easily made condiments. Freshly grated and sprinkled sparingly over rich foods (or grated in vinegar), it stimulates the digestive process. Older roots need to be peeled with a potato peeler first, but avoid inhaling the fumes as they can cause discomfort and watery eyes. **Warning**: Over-eating horseradish may cause irritation of the stomach lining.

Medicinal Horseradish has antiseptic, antibiotic, diuretic and expectorant properties that make it excellent for chest ailments and circulation in general. Horseradish syrup (see recipe section) eases coughs, colds, fevers and 'flu. Horseradish ointment (see recipe section) or poultice stimulates blood flow to the area and thus is excellent for chilblains, aching muscles, strains and sore stiff joints, and is used by many arthritis sufferers. It is also excellent as a deep foot massage or as a massage cream for chilled feet before putting on your socks. When the area feels hot or a slight burning sensation is experienced, stop the treatment. Use very cautiously on sensitive skin as it can cause irritation.

Cosmetic Horseradish lotion helps to lighten freckles and brown marks on the hands and arms. Do not use it on the face as it could cause irritation. Our grandmothers applied this lotion twice daily to keep their skin freckle free.

Other uses As a de-wormer for dogs, add ½ to 1 tablespoon grated horseradish to their food. I use a horseradish spray (see recipe section) to clear mildew on squash, roses and bergamot.

Lavender

Family **Labiatae**
Species ***Lavandula* species**
Origin **Mediterranean regions**
Plant **perennial**
Height **30-120 cm**
Soil **dry, well-drained**
Exposure **full sun**
Propagation **seed, cuttings**
Uses **culinary, medicinal, fragrance**

Lavender has never been so popular as it is at present. No garden should be without a bush or two and new varieties are constantly being developed by serious growers worldwide. The genus *Lavandula* consists of over 30 species. The natural habitat of most of these plants is in countries bordering the Mediterranean; others are found in the Sahara region towards Arabia and even as far as India, and some come from Europe. For many years confusion in the naming of the lavenders has reigned, but recently a 'Classification of Lavandula Species' has clearly defined the different groups. The nomenclature is now accepted worldwide: in spite of common names like French lavender, Spanish lavender, Dutch lavenders, each has the correct Latin name for clear identification, and old names are being faded out.

1   *Lavandula angustifolia* var. 'Hidcote'
    English lavender

This name has been loosely given to cultivars with linear leaves, revolute margins and a flowering spike that is either compact or interrupted – and which are the commercial lavender oil producing crop grown predominantly in England and France. It thrives in the northern hemisphere and struggles in the heat and dryness of the southern hemisphere. Until recently we named all our long flower spike lavenders *L. angustifolia*, but now, with the new nomenclature, realise our English-type lavenders that were once named *Lavandula angustifolia* are in fact **not** *L. angustifolia*, but have *L. angustifolia* parents and so are now named *L. intermedia*. There are several *intermedias* with different growth habits and sizes of flowers. In commercial growing two are favoured above the others: *L. intermedia* var. 'Margaret Roberts' and *L. intermedia* var. 'grosso'.

2   *Lavandula intermedia* var. 'Margaret Roberts'

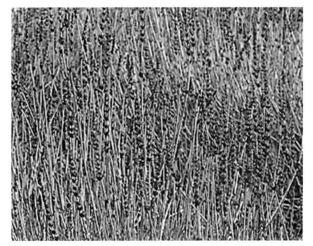

Parents are *L. angustifolia* and *L. latifolia*. This has produced, for our own conditions, a superb perpetual-flowering long flowering spike lavender that has cross-pollinated, as the Labiatae family easily does; a tough, weather-resistant lavender that withstands winds, frost, heat, drought and even poor soil conditions. Known as 'Margaret Roberts' or 'Herbal Centre Giant', this wonderful 1,5 m wide and 1,5 m high lavender is the best cut flower and its intense fragrance makes it superb for cosmetics, oil extraction, bath products, soaps and for medicinal and culinary use and to my mind is the best of all the lavenders for the southern hemisphere. Space 2 m apart. *Lavandula intermedia* var. 'grosso' is another similar lavender also grown for its oil that does well in the southern hemisphere but is far smaller and flowers only once a summer.

3 *Lavandula dentata* French lavender

This group of lavenders, with their obviously dentate or toothed leaves and their typical short, thick flower topped by a little cluster of bright mauve bracts, originated in North Africa, Spain, Madeira and the Cape Verde Islands, but France was the first to cultivate it and it came into England and the rest of Europe via France, so became known as French lavender.

In old gardens you can sometimes still find the smaller-flowered green dentata from which the new bigger-flowered *Lavandula dentata* var. *candicans* has arisen. This has grey dentate leaves, larger, thicker and more prolific than its parent *L. dentata* var. *dentate*, and its flowering head is thicker and longer. A new form has stabilised at the Herbal Centre, which we have named *L. dentata candicans* var. *maxima*. It is bigger and more vigorous, with thumb-length flowers, and a green-leafed form has emerged. Possibly its parent is *L. dentata* var. 'Royal Crown', with longer, more elegant flowers, often thumb length, and like its parent, *L. dentata*, it remains green and neat all year round. We have named it *Lavandula dentata* var. 'Elegans'.

The dentatas cannot be used medicinally, but are wonderful garden subjects, *flowering continuously*, and excellent cut flowers that can be used in potpourris and bath products, and with selected clipping are becoming favourites with landscape gardeners, especially coupled with standard Iceberg roses. Space the dentatas 1 m apart.

4 *Lavandula allardii* Dutch lavender, Hedge lavender

This is a virtually non-flowering large shrub, 1,5 m in height, with wide, flat, grey foliage with a distinct partially toothed margin, that is assumed to be a hybrid between *Lavandula dentata* and *Lavandula latifolia*. It was discovered as a seedling in France in about 1890, and from there went to Holland where it was used as a hedge and for cut-flower greenery, and known as 'loof'. It is tough, weather resistant and simply charming cut as topiary or a neat hedge. Long-lived and reliable, it occasionally flowers and its fragrant leaves are rich in camphorenes and last well in both the vase and potpourris. This lavender is not used for oils or medicinally. Space 1-1,5 m apart.

5 *Lavandula spica* Hedge lavender, Blind lavender, African pride

A larger form, similar to Dutch lavender; also one that hardly ever flowers. This one is commonly found throughout South Africa; a similar blind lavender called 'Devantville' grows along the Mediterranean coast between Spain and France. This is the best tall hedging variety, grey and smooth-leafed, with the occasional toothed portion of leaf. Bunches of leaves in the bath scent the water beautifully and rubbed on furniture will keep flies and mosquitoes at bay. Use in potpourris and mix into furniture wax. Big handfuls of African pride are used daily in our kitchens and tea garden rubbed over countertops and tables to chase the midsummer flies.

Lavandula dentata

Lavandula allardii

Lavandula spica

6   *Lavandula latifolia* Grandmother's lavender, Spike lavender

Originating in Europe, France, Spain, Italy and the Balkans, this is the lavender our grandmothers used in sachets and in washing linen and for drying the linen on. Originally brought to South Africa by my grandmother from Scotland over 100 years ago, this grey-leafed branch-stemmed really old-fashioned 'spike lavender' has the best fragrance I know and grows reliably and easily from seed, which is rare as most lavender seeds are notoriously erratic in germination.

It forms a neat cushion about 75 cm wide and 30 cm high: from midsummer, long branched stems arise in midsummer with grey-mauve interrupted whorls all along the stem – and the butterflies love it! Not as spectacular as the other lavenders, but its fragrant flowers and leaves make it extremely valuable. This lavender is also known as spike lavender and produces 'oil of spike' – a stronger smelling oil.

7   *Lavandula stoechas* Spanish lavender

'Stoechas' is derived from the Greek name for the Stoechades Islands off the Mediterranean coast of France. This group of lavenders is found in Spain, North Africa, Algeria and in the Azores, as well as in parts of Asia. These lavenders were known during the Middle Ages, when they were used as antiseptic washes and in oil production, but *L. angustifolia* and *L. intermedia* have proved to be superior, so now the stoechas lavenders are used only as cut flowers and in potpourris.

Spring and early summer flowering only, when their display is stunning, the neat, fine-leafed grey-green bushes nevertheless look attractive all year round and can be neatly clipped after the flowering period to shape them until next spring. A cone-like flower topped by a colourful little fan of 'rabbits' ears' marks the stoechas group. Most grow as a bushy shrub about 80 cm high.

There are literally dozens of varieties of stoechas lavenders, even a yellow one called *Lavandula stoechas viridis* and a pure white compact one called *Lavandula stoechas* var. 'Snowball' and a brown one called 'Sugar Plum'.

Trials at the Herbal Centre prove 'Marshwood', 'Avonview', 'Papillon', 'Purple Crown' and 'Helmsdale' to be most spectacular, with the smaller, rounder new cultivars of 'Devonshire Dumpling', 'Kew Red', 'Pippa White', 'Plum' and 'Sugar Plum' as fascinating 70-50 cm neat mounds of colour along a path that look good all year round. Landscapers should note that 'Avonview' has a good midsummer flowering period.

8   *Lavandula canariensis* and *L. multifida* Fern leaf lavenders

This is a totally separate group of lavenders, named *Pterostoechas*. All have fern-like leaves and virtually no fragrance. They are winter and spring flowering. New varieties are developing with bright purple flower tips to long stems, named 'Sidonie'

and 'Blue Canaries', from their original parents, *L. canariensis* and *L. multifida*. Spectacular planted en masse, these unusual lavenders are exhibiting cold- and heat- and drought-resistant qualities that could gain them a place in landscaping. Plant them 1 m apart. They do need attention – their long flowering heads once past their prime need to be cut back and the plant trimmed and they can look tatty at the end of summer.

CULTIVATION All lavenders need full sun, well-dug, well-composted soil and a deep weekly watering – twice a week in hot weather – to get them started. I replace my bushes every 3-4 years, once they get straggly and the flowers become smaller. Cut back by a quarter when pruning; when planting space them 1 m apart, with 1,5 m for *Lavandula spica* and *Lavandula allardii*, and 2 m for Margaret Roberts Herbal Centre Giant.

PROPAGATION Cuttings rooted in wet sand. Propagation by seed, which needs to be watched and nurtured, is notoriously difficult, except for Grandmother's lavender.

HARVESTING AND PROCESSING Leaves can be picked all year round; flowers when fully open. Lavender dries beautifully so there is an extensive industry around lavender – from cut flowers to dried leaves and flowers for sachets and potpourris.

COMPANION PLANTING Most insects dislike lavender and in the garden lavender keeps other plants free of aphids, white fly and mildew. Circle the vegetable garden, the chicken run and aviaries and line the kitchen path with lavender to deter cockroaches, rats, mice and fleas.

USES OF LAVENDER

Culinary Surprisingly, lavender is a delicious flavouring and is becoming the real gourmet flavour of the new century. It does, however, need to be used sparingly as it has a strong camphor-type overtone, and the only type of lavender you can use in cooking is *L. intermedia* (in the northern hemisphere *L. angustifolia* is used). Add lavender flowers to biscuit dough, shortbread mixes, cake and pancake batter, to fruit syrups, ice creams, cool summer drinks (see recipe section), fish sauces, pasta, rice dishes and to baby carrots, sweet potatoes and squashes.

Medicinally Lavender essential oil has been researched for decades and has been found to have no toxicity. It alleviates and reduces pain, it has significant antispasmodic, antibacterial and antiseptic qualities, and it calms nervous excitability and anxiety, and relieves stress. It helps ease sore throats, rheumatic aches and pains, depression, headaches, sleeplessness and skin ailments. Add 3 drops of lavender essential oil to the bath or on the pillow. In a superb antispasmodic cream (see recipe section) lavender proves to be indispensable. This is excellent for stiff neck, stiff shoulders, sore back, and arthritic stiffness and pain, bruising and grazes, scratches and insect bites. To make lavender tea use ¼ cup fresh flowers and pour over this 1 cup boiling water. Stand 5 minutes. Sip slowly for all the above ailments.

Cosmetic Lavender in the bath – a small bunch tied in a face cloth – is soothing, calming and unwinding. Use as a scrub with a little soap (I use lavender glycerine soap with the fresh lavender and it is infinitely soothing). Lavender unwinds, relaxes and cleanses problem skin. Lavender vinegar (see recipe section) is excellent in the bath, as a hair rinse, and a cleanser and toner. A special lavender bath (see recipe section) will soothe aching muscles, ease tension and anxiety and clear problem skin.

Other uses Lavender flowers under skirting boards and carpets and behind cupboards will chase ants, fleas and cockroaches. Sprigs of lavender rubbed onto kitchen counters and windowsills will chase flies and in sachets will keep fishmoths at bay and linen fresh smelling.

Lemon Grass

Family **Gramineae**
Species ***Cymbopogon citratus** (=Andropogon citrates)*
Origin **Southern India and Sri Lanka**
Plant **perennial**
Height **1 m; space 1 m apart**
Soil **deeply dug, well-composted soil**
Exposure **full sun**
Propagation **division**
Uses **culinary, medicinal, cosmetic**

Lemon grass has long been characteristic of Far Eastern cuisines, and its abundant growth and easy propagation have made it a much sought-after herb, which has found its place in gourmet dishes as well as in fragrant toiletries throughout the world. Besides its culinary and cosmetic uses, lemon grass has an amazing array of medicinal properties and is at present being scientifically researched in regard to its effect on the immune system. Amongst other natural constituents, lemon grass contains citral, linalol, geraniol and dipentene. These all work directly on the muscle tissue, circulatory and immune systems.

CULTIVATION Lemon grass needs full sun and benefits from being planted in a good-sized, compost filled hole. Thereafter, except for a twice-weekly deep watering, it will give you no trouble at all. It responds to constant picking and even if cut back quite severely from the centre of each section, the grass continues to grow. It makes a good pot plant too, provided it is grown in a large container filled with rich compost and is kept well watered and fed monthly with a seaweed-based fertiliser.

PROPAGATION Divide by pulling apart the sections. Due to its rapid multiplication, potted lemon grass will need to be divided and planted out in new pots at the end of its second year.

HARVESTING AND PROCESSING Pick the leaves at any time of the year. Lemon grass is best used fresh and all parts of the leaf can be used.

COMPANION PLANTING Excellent with all root crops. It gives flavour to sweet potatoes and protects brinjals, green peppers and tomatoes.

USES OF LEMON GRASS

Culinary Absolutely delicious as a tea – on its own or with fruit juice. Use ¼ cup fresh leaves. Pour over this 1 cup boiling water. Stand 5 minutes. Strain and sweeten with honey if liked. Drink hot or chilled. The chopped base of the leaf cluster is used in Thai cooking and is delicious with cheese, egg and fish dishes and as a flavouring for marinades, oils, sauces and stirfries.

Medicinal Lemon grass stimulates cell regeneration and soothes intestinal infections – it acts on the pathogenic flora and the bacillus of dysentery as well as the mucous membranes. Lemon grass tea is almost a tonic, pleasant and infinitely healing. It soothes fever, colitis, digestive disturbances, muscular pain, poor circulation, skin ailments and stress-related conditions. A strong infusion can be used as a deodorant (see recipe section).

Cosmetic Lemon grass is excellent for treating most skin ailments, including athlete's foot and open pores. It has anti-bacterial and astringent properties, as well as being a fungicide, antiseptic, deodorant and anti-microbial. The easiest way of applying it to both skin and hair is in the form of a lotion. Use the cooled tea (see under 'culinary') as a lotion. A lemon grass footbath and a massage using lemon grass cream is a special treat (see recipe section).

Other uses Lemon grass essential oil diluted in a carrier oil, dabbed on arms and legs, will deter mosquitoes, ticks and fleas and quickly soothe a bite or sting. Lemon grass insect-repelling spray (see recipe section) can be sprayed or splashed over insect-infested plants, or watered over beds where seeds will be sown, to protect them from their many predators. I soak peas and bean seed in the lemon grass mixture before sowing and as a result have bumper crops.

Lemon Verbena

Family **Verbenaceae**
Species ***Aloysia triphylla** (=Lippia citriodora)*
Origin **tropical America**
Plant **shrub**
Height **up to 2 m; space 2 m apart**
Soil **a deep compost-filled hole**
Exposure **full sun**
Propagation **cuttings**
Uses **culinary, medicinal, cosmetic**

One of the world's favourite herbs, with midsummer sprays of tiny, delicate mauve-white flowers that are loved by bees and butterflies, lemon verbena has a strong nostalgic scent that exuberantly perfumes the air whenever lightly brushed against. When I was so small that I could hardly reach high enough to pick those fragrant branches, my grandmother showed me how to pick a spray of leaves and immediately push it into the linen cupboard. This is the only herb that dries immediately without mildew.

CULTIVATION Prepare a hole well filled with compost mixed with a little good garden soil and plant in full sun. A graceful shrub, lemon verbena reaches about 2 m high and benefits from heavy pruning. I keep my bushes about 1,5 m in height and width, cutting them back twice a year – in April and November – to ensure a continuous supply of leaves.

PROPAGATION Cuttings can be taken at any time during the summer. Select just the soft green tips, about 7 cm long. Strip off the lower leaves, leaving about 3 notches on the stem, then press 3-4 cm into a tray of wet sand and cover with a plastic tent. Keep moist and sheltered in the shade for about 3 weeks, then remove the tent and never let them dry out. After about 12 weeks, transplant into compost-filled bags and put them into partial sun for a longer period each day until they harden off. When they start to send out side branches plant out in their permanent position.

HARVESTING AND PROCESSING Pick the leaves at any time of the year.

COMPANION PLANTING Plant at the four corners of the vegetable garden to deter aphids and white fly.

USES OF LEMON VERBENA

Culinary The intense citrus flavour of fresh lemon verbena leaves makes this a wonderful culinary herb. My grandmother taught me how to gently rub spanspek or watermelon with a handful of crushed lemon verbena leaves to enhance the flavour. I cook rice with a sprig of lemon verbena – and custards, fruit desserts, steamed puddings and cucumber soup never tasted so good!

Medicinal Lemon verbena is used as a tea all over the world for digestive and nervous upsets, depression, headache, colic, palpitations and heartache. It also helps colds, bronchitis, congestion, cramps, nausea and tired muscles. A cup of lemon verbena tea will help settle a wound-up child. Use ¼ cup fresh leaves. Pour over this 1 cup boiling water. Stand 5 minutes. Strain and sip slowly. Sweeten with honey if liked. Tie a bunch of leaves in a face cloth to use as a scrub over oily problem skin.

Cosmetic Our grandmothers made a massage oil (see recipe section) that soothed aching feet and aided circulation, and gave them the softest skin. Lemon verbena splash, refreshing and cooling, is an invigorating aftershave or after-bath lotion that will help beat the summer heat and clear oily skin (see recipe section).

Other uses Use lemon verbena potpourri to scent and clear the air and to repel moths and fishmoths. Rub lemon verbena over the arms or legs of chairs and over tabletops to keep flies and mosquitoes away. Hang bunches of fresh sprays in stables and near kennels and crush them as you walk past to keep the flies out.

Linseed

Flax ● Flax seed

Family **Linaceae**

Species *Linum usitatissimum*

Origin **Eurasia**

Plant **annual**

Height **50 cm; space 10 cm apart**

Soil **well-dug, well-composted soil**

Exposure **full sun**

Propagation **seed**

Uses **culinary, medicinal, cosmetic**

One of the oldest known plants: in the first century AD the Roman philosopher, Pliny the Elder, wrote: 'What department is there to be found of active life in which flax is not employed, and in what production of the Earth are there greater marvels to us than this?' In 8th century France, King Charlemagne passed a law requiring that linseeds were to be eaten regularly by his subjects in order to keep them healthy, and never before has there been as much attention given to this extraordinary plant as there is now.

CULTIVATION Linseed is a spring or summer flowering annual that matures quickly. When the seedlings are 5 cm high, thin out lightly and quickly replant the pulled seedlings in moist soil 10 cm apart. I plant linseed three times during the summer months to have a continuous fresh supply of leaves and flowers and lots of seeds.

PROPAGATION Dig over a bed in full sun to which a good amount of compost has been added. Moisten the soil lightly and scatter the seeds. Rake in evenly and wet the area well. Sprinkle with dried leaves to shade the area while the seeds germinate, and never let it dry out. Sow the seeds from August to early March.

HARVESTING AND PROCESSING Once the seed heads turn golden, pull up the entire plant and tie bunches together in large brown paper bags so as to collect the slippery little seeds once the seed casings burst.

COMPANION PLANTING Linseed grown with carrots will give the carrots a better flavour and greater size. Planted between potatoes it will keep potato beetles away.

USES OF LINSEED

Culinary Rich in vitamins A, B, D, E, masses of minerals and amino acids, flax seed has got to be one of the most important foods of the new century. Seeds can be added to cakes and breads, muesli and yoghurt and sprinkled onto all savoury and sweet dishes. The pretty blue flowers are edible and look exquisite sprinkled on all savoury and sweet dishes. Flax seed oil can be mixed with a little olive oil and used in cooking. **Note**: Do not use linseed oil for artists or from the hardware shop – that oil is not edible.

Medicinal Modern doctors advise taking linseed as a laxative; 1-2 teaspoons taken whole with water will bulk up and absorb fluid, forming a jelly-like mass that acts beautifully, gently and smoothly, easing all irritation in the whole digestive tract. Because linseed is so rich in mucilage and unsaturated fats, it soothes the chest and all bronchial and respiratory problems. Crushed seeds and leaves made into a tea will soothe all bladder and kidney ailments and a poultice of crushed seeds mixed with warm water makes a superb dressing for a boil, quickly bringing it to a head. Flax seed oil is an extremely important source of essential fatty acids which help to prevent the build-up of fatty deposits in the cells. Many arthritis sufferers swear by a poultice of linseed over swollen aching joints, and a tea made of linseed leaves and flowers quickly soothes sore joints, chronic coughs and bladder infections. To make the tea use 1/4 cup fresh leaves and flowers and 2 teaspoons crushed seeds to 1 cup boiling water. Stand 5 minutes. Strain and sip slowly.

Cosmetic Crushed linseeds can be used as a soothing face pack (see recipe section) for pimples, acne and even rashes and heat bumps.

Other uses In the compost heap flax plants aerate beautifully because they take a while to break down. Young plants tilled into the earth enrich the poorest soil.

Loofah

Family Cucurbitaceae
Species *Luffa cylindrical* • *L. aegyptica*
Origin tropics
Plant annual
Height trailing vine reaching +10 m in length; space 20 cm apart
Soil loose, well-dug, richly composted soil
Exposure full sun
Propagation seeds
Uses culinary, medicinal, cosmetic

Most people are convinced that the loofah comes from the sea, when they see its fibrous inner skeleton, and few know that apart from its bathroom sponge role it has an incredible history of medicine behind its 15 m long vines. Brought from ancient India to China in the T'ang dynasty around AD 616-910, it was revered and respected – the seeds given to the head of the family from generation to generation and used as both food and medicine. The flowers, leaves and young fruits have been eaten by many tribes across the world and used in religious ceremonies and in burial rituals from ancient times, and the seeds were hardly ever sold, but rather became part of an inheritance, which has remained so to some extent today.

CULTIVATION Loofahs need good loose soil with a lot of compost dug in. They need to climb so plant them near a fence or pergola – they become quite heavy when they fruit so be sure it is a substantial fence. Train them up the fence as they grow. They produce a mass of tendrils and masses of yellow flowers. The long squash-like fruits appear from mid summer and will take 2-3 months to mature and they need full sun for the whole day if possible.

PROPAGATION They need steadily warm soil and although seed sown in early spring germinates, I find mid-spring is best. Dig a knee-deep trench lined with several layers of newspaper and a good layer of compost on top of the newspaper. Soak in well then mix the rest of the soil with more compost and fill in the trench to within 10 cm of the top – this is so you can run the hose into it and fill it with water every week. Plant the seeds into the wet soil, 3 cm deep and 20 cm apart and cover with soil and a light layer of leaves to keep in the moisture. Never let them dry out until they are well established thereafter water twice weekly soaking deeply.

HARVESTING AND PROCESSING Leave them to dry completely on the vine – they turn brown and brittle. Then peel away the hard skin, shake out the seeds and you are left with the dry inner sponge.

COMPANION PLANTING Nasturtiums and lavender both help to keep the loofah from being stung.

USES OF LOOFAH

Culinary The flowers can be used in stirfries and soups, or stuffed with savoury rice. The Chinese use the very young fruits, the thickness of the thumb, thinly cut lengthways, dipped in batter and fried. An ancient Indian dish was to pickle the young and tiny fruits with coriander seeds and salt and strong dark vinegar and to serve this with bread and oil. The tips of the vines are still boiled and used as a vegetable today.

Medicinal The Chinese have used loofah tea for centuries to treat pain in the muscles, swollen or sore breasts, aching joints and respiratory infections. Thin slices of loofah soaked in hot water can be used as a poultice. A tea made by adding ¼ cup vine tips and flowers to 1 cup boiling water and left to stand 5 minutes, is an ancient treatment for respiratory ailments, congestion, coughs, pleurisy, bronchitis and a feverish cold. It was often sweetened with honey and two to four cups taken through the day until the symptoms eased.

Cosmetic The soft fibrous inner skeleton is a perfect exfoliator, clearing away oily build-up, dry flaky cells and generally rejuvenating the skin. Used as a sponge with soap, loofah will soften and exfoliate the skin on the feet, knees and elbows.

Lovage

Family Umbelliferae
Species *Levisticum officinale (=Ligusticum levisticum)*
Origin Mediterranean areas and Southwestern Asia
Plant herbaceous perennial
Height 1-1,2 m; space 50 cm apart
Soil rich, moist, cool soil
Exposure partial shade
Propagation seed
Uses culinary, medicinal, cosmetic

Known as the Maggi herb for its delicious meaty, celery-like flavour, lovage has been a much sought after herb, and had a reputation as an aphrodisiac in the Middle Ages. Lovage was much loved by the ancient Greeks as a flavouring for rich food and as a digestive aid. The Romans gathered the leaves throughout the summer and preserved them in vinegar for winter use when the plant dies down completely, and the root was also dug up in winter and grated into warming soups and stews. The monks and priests in those ancient days grew lovage in the cloister gardens, and gave it to weary travellers to soothe and freshen tired feet, and treated the sick with lovage brew to heal infected wounds and grazes, and as steaming brew to ease nausea, vomiting and over-indulgence. In rural areas across Europe lovage seeds steeped in brandy is still used today for over-imbibing – a teaspoon or two added to a glass of warm water and sipped slowly.

CULTIVATION Lovage needs well-dug, richly composted soil and a deep twice weekly watering. It dies down completely during the winter.

PROPAGATION Sow seeds in individual pots in spring. Lovage has a long taproot and doesn't like to be disturbed once it is planted in its final position. Plant out 50-60 cm apart when the plants reach 10 cm in height and mulch around each one.

HARVESTING AND PROCESSING It sends up a tall metre high stem of typically umbelliferae type flowers, which give an abundance of seeds in autumn. Cut down the flowering head once the seeds have been harvested.

COMPANION PLANTING Lovage acts as a tonic to the plants grown nearby and is particularly invigorating on beans and all the capsicums – sweet green peppers and the fiery hot chillis.

USES OF LOVAGE

Culinary Fresh chopped leaves can be added to soups, stews, stirfries, salads and pastas – just a little, as the taste is strong. Crushed seeds can be added to bread dough, pastries and savoury biscuits, rice and couscous or sprinkled onto toast or crackers with cream cheese. The Italians love lovage seed on tomatoes and baked potatoes.

Medicinal Lovage has digestive, deodorising, sedative, anti-convulsant and anti-microbial properties, and is a warming tonic herb for the respiratory and the digestive system. It stimulates a poor appetite, eases colic, treats chesty coughs, is excellent as a gargle for sore throats, treats catarrh, bronchitis and urinary tract infections, and also eases menstrual pains and soothes away painful clots, and promotes scanty, irregular menstruation. It stimulates the kidneys to flush toxins out of the body, it clears problem spotty skin and eases rheumatic pains, and is a strong diuretic. Lovage is a strong herb and to make a tea use only 2 teaspoons fresh chopped leaves to 1 cup boiling water. Stand 5 minutes. Strain and sip slowly. A few seeds added to the tea add a pleasant flavour and ease indigestion if chewed gently. Because of its warming, stimulating effects, poultices of warmed lovage ease swollen aching arthritic joints, improve circulation around the feet and soothe chilblains.

Caution: Those with kidney ailments should not take lovage, nor should it be taken during pregnancy.

Cosmetic Lovage lotion (see recipe section) is an old-fashioned recipe used to treat freckles, spots, oiliness and redness of the face and neck.

Lucerne

Alfalfa
Family **Leguminosae**
Species *Medicago sativa*
Origin **Eurasia**
Plant **perennial**
Height **75 cm; space 1 m apart**
Soil **rich, well-composted soil**
Exposure **full sun**
Propagation **seed**
Uses **culinary, medicinal, cosmetic**

The word 'alfalfa' or 'lucerne' means 'life' in the language of flowers. Pliny the Elder (AD 23-79) recorded that alfalfa was introduced to the Greece by the King of Persia, Darius the Great (550-486 BC), to feed his soldiers in an attempt to conquer Athens. Introduced from Europe and Asia to Africa in the 17th century, lucerne is one of the best fodder plants known to mankind as well as one of its ancient medicines. Lucerne leaves contain vitamins A, B, D, E, K and U. It's also one of the rare sources of vitamin B12 (the only other plant which contains B12 is comfrey). It contains 19% protein (beef has 16%; milk 3%) and has high quantities of calcium, potassium, sodium, magnesium, iron, chlorine and silicon.

CULTIVATION All lucerne needs is a three times yearly dressing of compost and a deep, twice-weekly watering.

PROPAGATION Sow in seed trays filled with moist compost and protect from the elements until seedlings are big enough to handle. Then transplant into larger compost-filled black plastic bags and keep moist and shaded. Once plants are tough and sturdy, gradually increase their daily dose of sun until they can be transplanted into full sun in well-dug, richly composted soil. Space plants 1 m apart as they have long roots which often spread to beyond 9 m. It's this deep-rooted activity that dredges up the minerals from the soil.

HARVESTING AND PROCESSING Pick green shoots and flowers all through the year. Cover the ripe flower heads with small paper bags to catch the tiny seeds. Cut back the spent sprays to encourage new growth.

COMPANION PLANTING Lucerne is one of the most important nitrogen-fixing legumes. It makes an excellent companion around grape vines and fruit trees.

USES OF LUCERNE

Culinary Grow lucerne outside your kitchen door so you can pick leaves and flowers for stews, salads, soups and stirfries. Use only the fresh leaves – avoid wilted ones which can cause bloating and gas in the digestive system.

Medicinal Lucerne tea is an excellent tonic, aiding convalescence and fatigue. And, because of its oestrogenic activity, it is becoming increasingly important as a dietary additive for menstruation and menopause problems. With its energising effect, it is an essential health supplement for those with debilitating illnesses. To make the tea use ¼ cup fresh leaves and flowers. Pour over this 1 cup boiling water. Stand 5 minutes. Strain and sweeten with honey if liked. Sip a cup daily for energy. Doctors in France have used fresh lucerne with winter savory as a resistance-builder to coughs, colds and 'flu, especially for older people. **Warning**: Doctors suggest that those suffering from auto-immune diseases should not take lucerne frequently.

Cosmetic The easiest way to take lucerne is in tablet form, but a tea can also be taken to improve problem skins. Lucerne lotion (see recipe section) can be rubbed into the hair to clear scalp infections or dry scalp and to stimulate hair growth, or applied as an acne lotion.

Other uses A lucerne tea watered into an ailing plant can quickly revive it and promote new growth, or dig chopped, fresh green lucerne into the soil around the plant to give it a quick boost. Prunings will encourage your compost heap to break down at record speed.

Maidenhair Fern

Family Polypodiaceae
Species *Adiantum capillus-veneris*
Origin tropical and temperate regions
Plant perennial
Height up to 50 cm; space 50 cm apart
Soil richly composted, moist, friable soil
Exposure partial shade
Propagation spores
Uses culinary, medicinal

Tricky and temperamental, yet if the conditions are what it likes, maidenhair flourishes! Our grandmothers taught us that maidenhair ferns need moisture, shade and shelter, never to allow a draught near them and never to move them if they are happy. Many years ago I twice took over neglected plant conservatories in different locations and roughly cleared and reshaped beds and pots and troughs and tubs. I opened sealed windows and replaced moss-shaded panes and set sprinkler systems to rights. After the first sprays in both houses a mass of tiny maidenhair spores came up like hairs on a dog's back – in every little nook and cranny, in cracks, in the stone walls, even along rotting rafters. When they were big enough to handle I replanted, repotted, tucked in hanging baskets, and very hastily rearranged them as time was against me. The result: they thrive to this day in draughts, in heat, in bitter cold and quite a bit of rough handling!

CULTIVATION Maidenhair ferns like their roots against rocks, pot sides and walls. They take compost leaf mould and mulching well and can be transplanted and separated into new clumps when full grown with their mass of fronds cut back to allow new growth to be unimpeded. Some of my best specimens grow to 50 cm in height and spread and they love being picked. They love misty sprays and they thrive with moss and moisture.

PROPAGATION Spread mature fronds facing upwards on moist ground, cover with a thin, light layer of compost about 1 cm thick and forget about them. Keep moist, and within 6 months new tiny plants will emerge.

HARVESTING AND PROCESSING Pick the leaves at any time, snipping the thin black stem right at the base.

COMPANION PLANTING Maidenhair fern is a loner – it does not like other plants close to it, but prefers its own space.

USES OF MAIDENHAIR FERN

Culinary The young and tender fronds are edible. Dipped into lightly beaten egg whites and then sprinkled with castor sugar and hung up to dry, the crystallised leaf spray is utterly charming on a wedding cake (in the language of flowers the fern means fascination!) or as decoration on a party dessert with cherries or just fresh in a summer drink. Add fresh fronds to apple cider vinegar for pickles and sauces.

Medicinal Capillaire is an old-fashioned drink made from the mature fronds that is not only an excellent night-time toddy for chills, colds, sore throats and exhaustion, but was once the drink of the courts and served at balls and ceremonies, diluted with iced water. For chest colds and coughs, the Southern Sotho smoke the dried leaves. The Zulus boil up equal quantities of the leaves in water until it thickens slightly and with a little honey mixed into it, to ease a cough and clear a runny nose; take a spoonful at a time. The Tswana and Venda burn the leaves on the fire and inhale the smoke for asthma and chest ailments or boil up the leaves with sugar for children's ailments like coughs, colds, measles or chickenpox.

Cosmetic Maidenhair has great skin softening and soothing qualities. Add fresh fronds to grape vinegar for the bath or add to hair rinsing water if you have a dry scalp.

Other uses Pressed fronds dry beautifully between the pages of an old telephone directory and can be used to decorate cards and pictures. They keep their colour well, gradually turning to pale bronze. Remember to burn the bottom 3 cm of the stem of the fresh frond to give it long-lasting qualities in a flower arrangement.

Melissa

Lemon balm
Family **Labiatae**
Species *Melissa officinalis*
Origin **Northern Africa, Central Europe and the Mediterranean region**
Plant **perennial**
Height **40 cm; space 50 cm apart**
Soil **deeply dug, richly composted soil**
Exposure **full sun, tolerates light shade**
Propagation **division, cuttings**
Uses **culinary, medicinal, cosmetic**

Over 2 000 years ago Greek, Roman and Arab healers prescribed melissa, or lemon balm, for over-indulgence and indigestion, to strengthen the heart and 'against the bite of venomous beasts'. Paracelsus, the Swiss physician, recommended it to renew youth and vigour and chase away melancholy! Over the centuries these virtues have always held good and today melissa is regarded as one of nature's best antidepressants and calming herbs. Its ancient reputation as assisting in dispelling anxiety, depression and insomnia has been substantiated by modern medical research and today medications containing it are found in pharmacies the world over.

CULTIVATION Before planting, dig the soil over deeply and add plenty of compost. Space each clump no closer than 50 cm as each plant will spread into a compact cushion of easily divided, rooted segments. In midwinter, as soon as the first new little crowns of leaves appear, cut the old and straggly leaf sprays back to ground level.

PROPAGATION When a clump is sufficiently large to be divided, use two forks back to back and thrust into the centre of each clump, forcing them apart. Each little part has fine root hairs that transplant easily into moist soil. Thumb length cuttings can be taken at any time of the year except the coldest months and rooted in wet sand.

HARVESTING AND PROCESSING Pick sprigs to use fresh in teas, drinks and cooking – these are best harvested before the tiny flowers develop.

COMPANION PLANTING Melissa attracts bees that help with pollination. It improves the yield and flavour of cucumbers and tomatoes.

USES OF MELISSA

Culinary Refreshingly lemon flavoured, this most versatile herb is lovely in vinegars, syrups, fruit drinks, punches, sauces and garnishes, imparting its minty lemon freshness. Sprinkle chopped leaves over fruit salads, salads, grills and stirfries and add to fish, chicken, pasta, lentil and bean dishes.

Medicinal It treats high blood pressure, helps circulatory problems and calms those who are over-stressed or suffering from insomnia. For indigestion, bloating, heartburn or flatulence, take a tablespoon of fragrant tea several times a day. For excitable, hyperactive children, use the cooled tea as a cool drink base with fresh unsweetened fruit juice. To make the tea use ¼ cup fresh sprigs. Pour over this 1 cup boiling water. Stand 5 minutes. Strain and sip slowly. Frequent use of the tea will help to clear fever blisters and prevent their reoccurrence. New research is finding melissa important in treating panic attacks, restlessness, irritability, despair, fear, nervousness and digestive upsets caused by over-anxiety. For 'flu with muscular aches, chickenpox, shingles, cold sores, headaches, spastic colon, diverticulitis, and colic, especially in babies, melissa is superb. I even use pulped leaves over grazes, stings and rashes.

Cosmetic Melissa freshens, revitalises and cleanses the skin. Use it as a facial steamer for greasy problem skin, in the bath and as a refreshing spritz (see recipe section).

Other uses With its lemony fragrance, melissa is disliked by insects and my grandmother taught me how to rub fresh bunches onto furniture – its oils are thirstily absorbed by the wood. As a spray (see recipe section) it keeps out mosquitoes and flies, and makes fishmoths flee from cupboards.

Milk Thistle

Family **Compositae**
Species ***Carduss marianus** (=Silybum marianum)*
Origin **Europe**
Plant **annual or biennial**
Height **up to 1,5 m; space 1 m apart**
Soil **rich, well-composted, moist soil**
Exposure **full sun**
Propagation **seed**
Uses **medicinal, culinary**

Milk thistle has been used in Europe as a treatment for liver ailments, lactation in nursing mothers and for melancholia, for literally thousands of years, but it is only recently that research has been done on it – and the findings are astonishing! I always marvel at how those old healers *knew* what plant to use: every time they are spot on! Milk thistle contains silymarin, but not until the 1970s did German research discover this remarkable substance and record the test: silymarin protects the liver in a highly effective manner by preventing the entry of toxins through cell membranes, while maintaining its function to reject and prevent damage caused by compounds that are toxic to the liver. It helps wherever the liver is under stress from coal tar drugs, like pain killers, aspirin and codeine, from excess alcohol and incorrect eating, from chemotherapy, and from infectious diseases.

CULTIVATION An easy-to-grow annual, or often a biennial, it will quickly form a huge cushion of exquisitely marked white-veined leaves, prickly and rough, and from midsummer a towering head of shocking pink thistles, often several to a stem, will rise 1,5 m high. The ripened thistle contains the seeds. It thrives on neglect and asks only a deep weekly or twice weekly watering in hot weather.

PROPAGATION Propagation is by seeds. Sow in trays and transplant once they are big enough to handle, into well-composted and deeply dug soil in full sun 1-1,5 metres apart.

HARVESTING AND PROCESSING Harvest seeds once the flower head has dried. Fresh flower heads are used as a tea.

COMPANION PLANTING A stand-alone majestic plant, milk thistle will push aside companion plants.

USES OF MILK THISTLE

Culinary When the flower heads are young and tender, snip off the thorns and boil them as you would globe artichoke. Serve with butter, salt and black pepper and lemon juice. The roots and stalks, peeled and soaked to remove bitterness, can also be cooked, stirfried and thinly sliced or boiled in soups and stews. The seeds can be roasted as a coffee substitute. Beware the prickles.

Medicinal Milk thistle fights hepatitis and cirrhosis of the liver caused by alcohol abuse, stimulates liver repair by boosting protein synthesis and actually scavenging free radicals and counters ingestion of highly toxic substances like carbon tetrachloride or paraffin, or poisonous mushrooms, but it must be administered immediately. Capsules and tablets can be bought from the chemist and for a hangover a 500 mg capsule taken 3 times during the day, can clear the liver immediately. For cancer treatment milk thistle can help to limit the damage to the liver due to chemotherapy and can help to speed up recovery and to clear side-effects once the cycle of the chemotherapy is completed and the patient is undergoing rest and recovery. Boiled young tender leaves were taken as a tonic after an illness and as a drink for hepatitis or biliousness. New research is looking at treatment in newborn infants who have jaundice. A tea can be made of the fresh flowers. Use 1 flower, roughly chopped, and pour over this 1 cup boiling water. Stand 5 minutes. Strain and sip slowly. Take one cup daily; in chronic conditions take 1 cup alternate days. To rebuild the liver take 1 cup daily plus the capsules.

Mint

Family **Labiatae**
Species ***Mentha* species**
Origin **Europe**
Plant **perennial**
Height **up to 60 cm; space 50 cm apart**
Soil **richly composted, moist soil**
Exposure **light shade to full sun**
Propagation **root runners**
Uses **culinary, cosmetic**

The origins of some mints will forever remain a mystery, but there is no doubt that mint in its many varieties has been around a long time. Vials, clay boxes and urns filled with this fragrant herb have been found in ancient burial sites, sacred temples and pyramids dating back to before 1000 BC. Even before the Middle Ages, when mint became so popular, it was used by the Greeks and Romans in bath-houses, as a strewing herb to chase fleas, flies and mosquitoes, in the sick room and during feasts to aid digestion.

The Romans spread mint through Europe, and on into Britain, and from there it spread to the rest of the world. It is now cultivated in many countries across the world as a flavouring, for its superb essential oil and for its insect-repelling properties.

Mint's key actions are: digestive, antispasmodic, increases sweating (and so helps detoxify the body), pain reliever, antiseptic, and stimulates the secretion of bile. Quite a plant, isn't it?

From the earliest recordings on clay tablets mint, in all its varieties, has been loved most of all herbs. If you're a mint-lover just getting started, the following are the best ones, to my mind:

- Garden mint (*Mentha spicata*) is the best known, with green, glossy, crinkled leaves.
- Bowles mint (*M. suaveolens villosa*), also known as apple mint, is a tall, luscious variety with big leaves that are slightly furry, similar in taste to the old-fashioned 'mint sauce' variety.
- Spearmint (*M. longifolia polyadena*) has long, sharp-pointed leaves with an unmistakeable spearmint flavour and fragrance.

- Peppermint (*M. piperita nigra*), dark-stemmed with a low, creeping habit, is the most invasive – but this is the one to help boost exam-time fatigue and help clear thinking.
- Variegated pineapple mint (*M. suaveolens variegata*) is a pretty, low-growing spreading mint with variegated pale creamy markings – this is the most delicious in fruit salads.
- Corn mint (*M. arvensis*), is low-growing, with sharply pointed small leaves, light green and very refreshing in cool drinks.
- Chocolate mint (*M. spicata* var. *piperita*) tastes unmistakeably of peppermint crisp. It makes a wonderful tea and is superb freshly chopped onto chocolate icing on a grand chocolate cake or in chocolate mousse and ice cream.
- Eau de cologne mint (*M. piperita* var. *citrata*) is too strongly fragranced to use in cooking, but, with its purple stems and darker leaves, is exquisite in the bath.
- Cape velvet mint (possibly *M. longifolia*) has tall white flowering stems and a distinct smell of peppermint liqueur. Rare and wonderful. Indigenous to the Cape.

Garden mint (Mentha spicata)

Bowles mint (Mentha suaveolens villosa)

Chocolate mint (Mentha spicata var. spicata)

Pennyroyal (Mentha pulegium)

- Wild water mint (*M. aquatica*) is an indigenous strong spearmint-flavoured mint.
- Pennyroyal (*M. pulegium*), is a compact, low-growing groundcover with whorls of mauve flowers rising on midsummer stems. This is one of the best insect repellents I know – a large shallow bowl next to your patio chair will keep you mosquito free during the summer rains. *This mint is not edible*, but is a superb companion to strawberries, roses, tomatoes, green peppers and brinjals. It is a very strong mint, rich in oils, and if rubbed directly onto the skin could cause irritation. Rub the hands over it and then rub the hands over legs and arms.

CULTIVATION Plant 30 cm apart. Don't plant too many varieties together, as they will cross-pollinate. Mint loves to grow under a dripping tap, in rich, well-dug soil; it is very invasive, so is a good choice for a tub. Dress with compost twice yearly.

PROPAGATION Almost all the mints spread by runners, so new plants can be constantly and easily propagated by digging up rooted pieces. Replant in compost enriched well-dug, moist soil. It is a voracious feeder.

HARVESTING AND PROCESSING Pick leaves at any time of year: the best time is just before the plant flowers.

COMPANION PLANTING Mint improves the growth and flavour of carrots, radishes, beetroot and tomatoes, but because it is invasive it needs a restraining 'collar' of deeply dug heavy duty plastic strips to prevent it taking nourishment from the plants near it. It dies back in winter.

USES OF MINT

Culinary For the creative cook, mint is a fabulous herb. Don't stop at mint sauce (see recipe section) or peas cooked with a sprig of mint: try exciting dishes such as the Bedouins' lentils and cracked wheat cooked with masses of chopped mint, or chopped ginger mint mixed with a little sugar and sprinkled over melon, or iced drinks with chopped mint or make mango ice cream with Eau de Cologne mint, or make a hot toddy on a cold night with brandy, lemon and mint, or chocolate mint on chocolate mousse or sprinkled into hot chocolate drinks – it really tastes like a peppermint crisp!

Medicinal Mint is superb as a general digestive. Chewing a mint leaf will ease nausea, heartburn, colic, flatulence, feverish conditions and even migraines. A cup of mint tea will ease all the above conditions. To make the tea pour 1 cup of boiling water over ¼ cup fresh mint leaves, leave to stand 5 minutes, then strain and sip slowly. The same tea made with peppermint will help you stay alert, keep the mind clear, retain facts, and calm exam-time nerves. It will also clear nasal congestion, unblock sinuses and ease headaches. All the mints have these actions: they are antispasmodic, analgesic, prevent vomiting, promote bile flow, ease sore throats, make an excellent eye wash to remove dust and grit from the eyes (use the cooled tea), cleanse the liver, ease travel sickness and help to clear spotty skin. **Caution**: Do not give mint in any form to babies under 3 years (use melissa instead). Peppermint can reduce milk flow in nursing mothers, so in order to help the baby's digestion, drink melissa tea instead.

Cosmetic Mint makes the best steamer for oily and problem skin, and as a bath vinegar it is a comforting relaxant for aches and pains, poor circulation and problem skin.

Other uses Mint makes an effective insecticide, repelling fishmoths, ants, aphids and mealie bugs (see recipe section).

Moringa

Drumstick tree ● Spinach tree
Family Leguminosae
Species *Moringa oleifera*
Origin Northern India, Arabia
Plant shrubby tree
Height up to 8 m; space 4 m apart
Soil any soil
Exposure full sun
Propagation seed, cuttings
Uses culinary, medical

This extraordinary tree is actually a legume, and as such adds nitrogen to the soil. It thrives in semi-arid areas, producing edible leaves, pods, flowers and roots, as well as an excellent oil from the seeds, which does not turn rancid and burns without smoking. The name comes from the 30 cm long pods, which are used when green in India and parts of Africa to beat the drums.

I have trialled moringa for several years now and have been fascinated with its ease of growing, its attractiveness and its incredible uses. In India it is revered as food, medicine and as a water purifier. Traditionally used in India and Africa for purifying the blood, for building strong bones and teeth and for treating dysentery, diarrhoea and as a diuretic.

CULTIVATION A shrubby, small tree that can grow 4 m in a year. It will be cut down in the frost, but grows so easily that it is worth starting from scratch yearly if it can't be protected. Moringa does well in lightly composted well-drained soil; it is tough and drought resistant and I've seen it grow in roadside rubble close to the coast, and in sandy dunes on Réunion Island and the Seychelles. The top can be cut to encourage side branches so that the fruit, flowers and leaves are within easy reach. It does not like waterlogged roots. It can withstand alkaline soils and brackish water.

PROPAGATION Grows easily from seed and cuttings.

HARVESTING AND PROCESSING The mature seedpods are picked once the outer casing has split and dried.

COMPANION PLANTING Vegetables, especially spinach, lettuces and tomatoes enjoys its light shade in midsummer.

USES OF MORINGA

Culinary The young, tender green pods, leaves and flowers are rich in vitamin C, minerals and iron. The leaves can be cooked like spinach, stirfried or added to soups and stews; the flowers can be eaten raw in salads and fruit salads, and the thinly sliced green pods can be pickled, made into a relish or fried. The bulbous roots can be grated and fried or pickled in vinegar and eaten like horseradish. The seeds can be shelled and roasted like peanuts, or roasted, crushed and pressed to release the exceptional oil.

Medicinal The root is used for heart ailments, freshly grated and added to hot water; oil from the seeds is taken for rheumatism and gout and used in cooking; juice of crushed flowers and leaves will clear blackheads and pimples, applied directly to the area. The leaves and flowers in a tea will stabilise blood pressure, prevent and clear infection of the chest, throat and skin, ease stomach ailments and strengthen the heart. To make the tea use ¼ cup fresh leaves. Pour over this 1 cup boiling water. Stand 5 minutes. Strain and sip slowly. Take 1 cup a day for 7-10 days. Leaves can be used as a poultice over swellings and to ease a headache. In the Philippines moringa leaves are eaten daily to treat anaemia and to ease labour and encourage lactation.

Other uses An exceptionally important use of moringa is its ability to treat and clear river water and water dirty with organic refuse. The inner white seed kernel is crushed and pounded finely and mixed into a paste with water (about 2-3 teaspoons of powdered seed treats 20 litres of water); add 2 cups of water and shake in a screw-top jar for 5 minutes to activate the chemicals. Then pour into the bucket, stir 10-15 minutes, stand for 30 minutes. All the heavy particles and the bacteria will sink and settle and clear water can be drawn off.

Mullein

Family **Scrophulariaceae**

Species *Verbascum thapsus*

Origin **Central and Southern Europe and Western Asia**

Plant **biennial**

Height **up to 1,5 m; space 1 m apart**

Soil **moist, richly composted soil**

Exposure **full sun**

Propagation **seed**

Uses **culinary, medicinal, cosmetic**

An ancient respected and much loved herb, mullein has been an important addition to every cottage and cloister garden since the earliest centuries. Over the centuries it has been known as Aaron's rod, the blanket herb, our lady's taper and the flannel plant, due to the usefulness of the leaves and the metre-high yellow flowered stalks. During the Middle Ages these were dried, dipped in fat and burned as light-providing tapers or candles after dark. The huge, hairy, robust leaves were once used to provide a warm lining in the slippers of noble folk. The monks prescribed mullein for everything from earache, eye complaints and toothache to coughs, scorpion stings, haemorrhoids and everything in between.

CULTIVATION Water two to three times a week. The spectacular yellow flowering spike will only appear in the plant's second year and can reach 1,5 m.

PROPAGATION Sow the tiny black seeds in trays in spring. They germinate quickly and easily. When they are big enough to handle, prick them out and plant in bags in rich soil mixed with good compost. Allow them to mature, gradually moving them out of the shade and into the sun for longer periods each day. When the little seedling is about 12-15 cm in spread plant out 1 m apart in prepared soil in full sun. Once established you must not move the plant as it has a long taproot.

HARVESTING AND PROCESSING Leaves can be harvested when still young and the flowers as soon as they appear on the spike. The flowers can be dried.

COMPANION PLANTING Mullein is excellent with potatoes, carrots and beetroot, and lettuces, spinach and kale all thrive near it. Once it sets seed it can be turned back into the soil to nourish new rows of potatoes.

USES OF MULLEIN

Culinary The pretty yellow flowers make an attractive addition to salads and stirfries. I crystallise the flowers with violets to make fragile and exquisite decorations for cakes.

Medicinal Mullein has been used throughout the centuries as an expectorant, a treatment for catarrh, chest and respiratory problems, tuberculosis and for bladder and kidney ailments. It's also a good wound healer and a remedy for ear infections and haemorrhoids. Rich in saponins, minerals and mucilage, mullein helps to clear mucous from the body, which is why it is so effective in treating bronchitis, pneumonia, dry, persistent coughs, throat infections, earaches and blocked noses. To make mullein tea use ¼ cup fresh leaves and flowers. Pour over this 1 cup boiling water. Stand 5 minutes. Strain and sip slowly.

Cosmetic Mullein makes a lovely soothing cream for sunburn, rashes, grazes, cuts and shaving nicks. Use mullein rejuvenating cream (see recipe section) daily on spots, chapped lips, chilblains, rashes and irritations. For tired feet, cracked skin and dry toenails, soothing mullein foot oil (see recipe section) will quickly restore your hard working feet to their best condition!

Other uses When mullein plants become dry and old, pull them out of the border, burn them and use the precious ash in the compost heap. Rich in minerals, this is a superb ingredient for adding nutrients to the soil.

Mustard

Family **Cruciferae**
Species *Brassica alba* ● *B. nigra*
Origin Mediterranean regions
Plant annual
Height 50 cm; space 30 cm apart
Soil well-dug, well-composted soil
Exposure full sun
Propagation seeds
Uses medicinal, culinary

An ancient, much-loved herb, both the black and white mustards have been grown since medieval times and today are cultivated across the world as a favourite summer crop. Children across Europe from the 17th and 18th centuries planted mustard and cress on trays of wet cotton wool or lint, often carefully spreading the seed to form their initials for fun. When the little seeds sprouted, it was cut with kitchen scissors and eaten on sandwiches or sprinkled on salads. Through the weary winter months the trays of mustard seeds were tended lovingly and placed near a window hoping to catch a little sun. This was often their only green food – so it has always been an important plant.

CULTIVATION Mustard matures quickly and you'll reap lots of healthy leaves before the winter sets in. Sow small batches every 2-3 weeks for a continuous supply of mustard greens.

PROPAGATION Dig over a spot in full sun and add a good supply of compost. Sprinkle the seeds thinly, water well and keep moist. Lightly cover with leaves to maintain the moisture. Water twice a week once they are well established.

HARVESTING AND PROCESSING Pick leaves and flowers as soon as they mature.

COMPANION PLANTING Plant mustard as a 'trap' crop next to cabbage, broccoli and cauliflower – it will entice the cabbage moth away from the vegetables.

USES OF MUSTARD

Culinary For that extra bite, mustard greens are becoming a gourmet food, especially as they are so quick and easy to grow. I always have a tray or two of new sprouts to perk up every meal, and in the garden the abundant flowers and bigger, hotter leaves give zest and health to all my salads and stirfries.

Medicinal For boosting the immune system, mustard greens and flowers are high on the list. Rich in minerals, especially calcium, potassium, iron and phosphorus, and vitamins A, B and particularly C, mustard will fight bronchial infections, ease constipation, ease pleurisy, arthritic and rheumatic pains and with its high alkaline content, it will aid digestion and stimulate the circulation. An all-round tonic herb, mustard is also a valuable diuretic, an excellent anti-spasmodic, and a health boosting drink (see recipe section) can be easily made to treat all the above ailments.

Our grandmothers used a mustard footbath as an amazingly effective treatment for coughs, colds and 'flu, or sip a cup of ginger, honey and mustard tea, which will also ease arthritic pains comfortingly. To make the tea take 1 dessert spoon ginger slices and 1 teaspoon mustard seeds. Pour over this 1 cup boiling water. Stand 5 minutes and strain. Sweeten with honey and sip slowly.

Cosmetic Our grandmothers found mustard leaves and flowers chopped and added to raw oat flakes (not the instant kind) make a superb scrub for oily problem skins. In Mexico mustard leaves are warmed and used as a compress over spots and rough areas. Mustard leaves can burn sensitive skins, so try a small patch first.

Other uses Mustard is a valuable green fertiliser. Pull up spent and drying mustard plants and dump them on the compost heap. They help to break down compost and aerate it. Grow a row of mustard and just before it sets seed, dig it into the soil. As a green manure crop mustard is vital in re-establishing depleted soils.

Myrtle

Family **Myrtaceae**
Species **Myrtus communis** ● **M. c. nana** ● **M. c. variegata**
Origin **Eurasia**
Plant **shrub**
Height **up to 1,5 m; space 50 cm to 1 m apart**
Soil **deeply dug, richly composted soil**
Exposure **full sun**
Propagation **cuttings**
Uses **culinary, medicinal, cosmetic**

Ancient legend dedicates myrtle to Venus, the goddess of love. In past centuries brides carried myrtle sprigs in their wedding bouquets and wore it in their hair to depict love and devotion. With origins in the Mediterranean and parts of Asia, this evergreen shrub has been introduced throughout the world, where it has adapted to a wide diversity of climates.

With its small, dense, glossy, dark green leaves and a summer abundance of tiny white flowers and fat round buds, myrtle responds beautifully to clipping, pruning and sculpting into any shape, including a round topiary ball. It can also be trained into arches, espaliered up a wall, or clipped into hedges. It tolerates winter frost and is always neat, attractive and eye-catching with uniform growth.

CULTIVATION Myrtle is easily cultivated, but slow growing. Plant in a deep compost-filled hole or in a large container in a sunny position, and give it a deep weekly watering. Other varieties of myrtle are equally easy to grow and attractive all year round, such as small myrtle, *M. communis nana*, and variegated myrtle, *M. communis variegata*. They too make a magnificent hedge as they do not die back. They are resilient to all sorts of weather, from searing cold to blazing heat waves and unrelenting drought and are good at the seaside, resisting salt winds and buffeting storms.

PROPAGATION Myrtle is easily propagated by cuttings, which can be taken at any time of the year except the coldest months.

HARVESTING AND PROCESSING Fresh leaves and flowers can be picked at any time of the year. Dried leaves and seeds are excellent in potpourris.

COMPANION PLANTING It makes an excellent hedge around the vegetable garden. Its strong oils deter aphids and white fly.

USES OF MYRTLE

Culinary Myrtle flowers and berries are used in cooking; the stems are also used as skewers, giving a delicious taste to lamb or pork roasted over coals. And when grilling chops and sausages, throw a few fresh sprigs of myrtle on the fire to impart an elusive, wonderful taste and aroma. Remember, it is a strong herb so use fresh myrtle sparingly. Dried berries are a good pepper substitute and can be ground in a pepper grinder.

Medicinal Antiseptic and antibacterial, myrtle has been used throughout the centuries as a wound lotion and as a compress over bruises and sprains and contused varicose veins. With its astringent properties, it was also used to reduce haemorrhoids, usually in the form of a cream (see recipe section). The cream can also be extremely soothing over strains and sprains and, for hikers, to ease those aching feet! Myrtle lotion is soothing for eczemas and other skin ailments.

Cosmetic Myrtle vinegar (see recipe section) is excellent for aching legs, toning circulation and easing cramps, and when diluted with rainwater, it helps to refine oily skin problems as a lotion or rinse as it has astringent properties. Myrtle has long been used as a rinse to promote growth and shine of dark hair. Fresh myrtle sprigs are an invigorating addition to bath water. It has cooling astringent properties as a skin wash.

Other uses Myrtle is excellent for pests such as aphids, white fly and red spider. The strong, pungent, refreshing oils make it an ideal insect repellent and as myrtle benefits from pruning and shaping with clippers, all the sprigs and branches can be constantly put to good use. Myrtle makes an excellent potpourri to keep fishmoths, ants and moths out of your cupboards. Mix dried sprigs with cloves and clove oil.

Nasturtium

Family **Tropaeolaceae**
Species *Tropaelum majus*
Origin **Peru**
Plant **annual**
Height **30 cm; space 30 cm apart**
Soil **sandy**
Exposure **full sun to light shade**
Propagation **seed**
Uses **culinary, medicinal, cosmetic**

Native to Peru, nasturtiums are cultivated lovingly all over the world thanks to their easy germinating, large and prolific seeds, and are now found in temperate regions across the world. It has become naturalised in many places, flourishing in moist roadside ditches, along streams and anywhere hospitable. Nowadays it is widely cultivated as a salad herb, both for its bright red, orange and yellow flowers, and for its succulent peppery leaves.

Its general name *Tropaeolum* comes from the the Latin word 'tropaeum' meaning trophy or victory. In the Middle Ages, soldiers wore helmets with a small brim and carried round shields. After the battle was won, their opponents' shields, swords and helmets were removed and hung on trees and fences to display their victory. The nasturtium's round leaves look like shields and their upside down flowers look like the helmets – so it became the victory flower. The leaves and flowers have been used in ancient Andean medicine as a strong disinfectant and a wound healer and were also used on the battlefield as a poultice over wounds and as a disinfectant wash.

CULTIVATION Survives in most soil types; prefers sandy soil.

PROPAGATION Plant two seeds together in lightly composted well-dug soil, 30 cm from the next two seeds and keep moist.

HARVESTING AND PROCESSING Pick leaves and flowers as required; seeds when ripe. Seeds can be stored in vinegar.

COMPANION PLANTING Broccoli, all cabbages, mealies, tomatoes, cucumber, broad beans, radishes and fruit trees.

USES OF NASTURTIUM

Culinary Pickled in vinegar, fresh green nasturtium seeds make an inexpensive substitute for capers and are delicious in cheese sandwiches, served with cold meats, mixed into cream cheese and chopped into mayonnaise. This pickle makes a much appreciated gift for the gourmet (see recipe section). Leaves and flowers can be used in salads.

Medicinal Nasturtium was used in the 17th century to treat scrofula, which is the tubercular infection of the lymph nodes. Ground seeds have purgative properties and were used to treat worms in both children and animals. An infusion of the leaves will increase bacterial resistance, easing emphysema and clearing nasal and bronchial phlegm and the same brew can be used as a treatment for skin infections. My grandmother taught me to chew the peppery nasturtium leaf at the first sign of a sore throat. It can also be made into a tea. Use ¼ cup leaves and flowers and pour over this 1 cup of boiling water. Stand 5 minutes, then strain. Add a squeeze of lemon juice. This infusion is taken as a natural antibiotic – nasturtium is rich in vitamin C, has antibacterial properties and increases the resistance to bacterial infections. It clears both nasal and bronchial catarrh, and stimulates the coughing up and clearing of phlegm in emphysema. Nasturtium makes an effective wound wash – pour 1 litre of boiling water over 1 cup of leaves and flowers. Leave to cool to a comfortable warmth, then strain and use as a wash, or soak bandages in it and apply as a poultice to draw infections out. Warmed leaves can also be heated in hot water and applied directly to the wound, bound in place by a crêpe bandage.

Other uses Grow nasturtiums in greenhouses as a trap crop for white fly and aphids or use in a spray to repel white fly and mealie bug (see recipe section).

Neem

Family Meliaceae
Species *Azadirachta indica*
Origin India
Plant tree
Height 15 m; space 20 m apart
Soil any soil
Exposure full sun
Propagation seed and soft wood cuttings
Uses culinary, medicinal, cosmetic

The extraordinary and versatile neem is considered to be one of the most important trees known to mankind. Its traditional uses, its chemistry, and its pharmacology have been extensively studied and all parts of this beautiful tree are used. The National Research Council's spokesman, Paul Hoversten, in 1982 said that 'the neem tree may eventually benefit every person on the planet. It may usher in a new era of pest control, provide millions with inexpensive medicine, cut down on the rate of human population growth and perhaps even reduce erosion, deforestation and the excessive temperature of an overheated globe'.

Neem has been part of Ayurvedic medicine which can now be found in pharmacies and health shops across the world. **Warning**: Do not confuse neem with its close relative, the poisonous and invasive Seringa or Persian lilac (*Melia azedarach*), a favourite street and garden shade tree.

CULTIVATION The neem cannot take low temperatures and I have found it to be a slow growing tree that takes a long time to get started in my high-altitude area. It needs full sun and a big deep compost-filled hole with a weekly soaking while it is young. Cover it from winter cold for the first few years. It seems definitely to prefer low altitudes.

PROPAGATION Propagation is by seed and soft wood cuttings, but it has to be fresh seed sown 4 weeks after harvesting.

HARVESTING AND PROCESSING Pick leaves and seeds any time of the year.

COMPANION PLANTING Neem is a natural protector to any plant that grows near it.

USES OF NEEM

Culinary Used as a spinach the leaves are often added to other spinaches and with olive oil, onions and curry it makes a nutritious and healthy dish. The small oval fruit is added to stews and stirfries and cooked in syrup as a tonic.

Medicinal The entire tree is useful. The young tender branches are used as chewing sticks to keep the gums and teeth healthy. The seeds contain a rich and potent, strongly smelling oil, margosa oil, that is antifungal, anti-inflammatory, antiseptic and antiviral. It is also used to treat leprosy and it has contraceptive qualities that are being researched at present. The bark and the root made into a tea are traditionally used to treat jaundice and other liver disorders, intestinal parasites, stomach ulcers and malaria, and the seeds have been used as a tea to treat bladder, kidney and prostate ailments, and in a cream to apply to haemorrhoids. A tea is made of the leaves for swollen glands, sprains and bruises, and used as a poultice for eczema, to reduce fevers, rashes, boils, to lower blood sugar levels, to treat wounds and ulcers. It can be used as a wash or lotion and the leaves as a poultice. To make the tea use ¼ cup fresh leaves. Pour over this 1 cup boiling water. Stand 5 minutes. Strain and sip slowly. **Warning**: Do not give neem to children under 4 years or to the elderly.

Cosmetic Margosa oil is used as a hair dressing and to stimulate hair growth. Neem hair rinse stimulates hair growth and rids the scalp of nits, dandruff and dry itchy scalp.

Other uses The wood of the neem tree resists insect attack and so is used for all kinds of building. Grain can be stored quite safely in boxes with neem branches and leaves as neem has a low toxicity to humans! Leaves and seeds boiled up in enough water to cover them for 20 minutes and then cooled overnight and strained, make a superb all-purpose insect spray.

Nettle

Stinging nettle
Family **Urticaceae**
Species ***Urtica dioica***
Origin **temperate regions worldwide**
Plant **hardy perennial**
Height **up to 1 m; space 1 m apart**
Soil **any soil**
Exposure **full sun**
Propagation **rooted pieces off the clump**
Uses **culinary, medicinal, cosmetic**

The word nettle comes from the old English word *noedl*, which means needle and refers to the needle sharp burning of this famous stinging plant. Its Latin name, *Urtica*, comes from *uro*, which means to burn – those bristly hairs contain formic acid that causes the skin to burn. Always wear gloves when near stinging nettle, and immediately apply bulbinella or aloe vera juice and gel to the area to soothe the irritation.

Nettle is an ancient herb that has had its place in myth and magic, in history and in the pharmacopoeias of the world. The coarse fibres in the stems were used to make some of the first fabrics known to mankind. Nettle sprigs were placed in milk buckets to protect the milk from witchcraft and nettle bundles were used to 'flail' the limbs – in religious ceremonies and for medicinal purposes.

CULTIVATION A waste ground weed, nettle is tough, resilient and adapts to all types of soils but thrives in well-composted soil in full sun, spaced 1 metre apart. It sends up tall spires of leaves with tiny green sprays of flowers.

PROPAGATION With a sharp spade chop off pieces of rooted stock and branches and replant immediately into moist, well-dug soil.

HARVESTING AND PROCESSING Pick fresh leaves and sprays (wear gloves!) and cook as a spinach. Nettle is best used fresh and cooked immediately.

COMPANION PLANTING Rich in nitrogen and chlorophyll, nettle is valuable in the compost heap as it breaks down organic material quickly. Potatoes, tomatoes and horseradish grow quickly and healthily near nettles. Nettle intensifies the oil content of peppermint, sage and marjoram.

USES OF NETTLE

Culinary Steamed as a spinach and added to soups, stews and casseroles, nettle is a vitamin and mineral rich, body building tonic herb. Add it to stocks, gravies and soups (see recipe section) for extra strength, energy and vitality.

Medicinal Nettle's key action is cleansing and detoxifying, which is why it is essential for gout, arthritis, poor kidney function and fluid retention. Because of its diuretic action it increases urine flow and often dissolves blockages in the urethra. Nettle is also an anti-allergenic and will ease hay fever, asthma, eczema and insect bites and is also used to treat anaemia, to improve breast milk production, and to reduce an enlarged and painful prostate. Nettle tea purifies the blood, helps expel kidney stones and aids in anaemia and sciatica. It has also been used to treat internal haemorrhage, dysentery, bronchial catarrh, jaundice and infertility. To make nettle tea for all the above ailments use ¼ cup fresh sprigs and leaves and pour over this 1 cup of boiling water. Stand 5 minutes, then strain and sip slowly. Take 1 cup daily for 10 days. Give it a break for 4 days, then resume, or take 1 cup alternate days for chronic conditions. In acute conditions, e.g. gout, take 1 cup 3 times a day for 4-5 days then stop once the condition has cleared.

Cosmetic A nettle hair treatment (see recipe section) improves the texture and colour of the hair and will prevent hair loss, encourage new growth and clear dandruff and oily hair.

Other uses Stems and leaves are used to make cloth and paper. Nettle spray (see recipe section) makes an excellent repellent for aphids and mildew, and can be used as a green fertiliser for pot plants.

Oats

Family **Gramineae**
Species *Avena sativa*
Origin **Northern Europe and Asia**
Plant **annual**
Height **80-100 cm; space 10 cm apart**
Soil **well-dug, composted soil**
Exposure **full sun**
Propagation **seeds**
Uses **medicinal, culinary**

Originating in Europe and Asia, oats is grown as a commercial crop all over the world. An ancient grain, oats has never lost its popularity and now 21st-century research is finding it to be a hugely important food and medicine. Did those healers in the 7th and 8th century know that too? Our grandmothers gave us a bowl of oats porridge at the end of an overexcited day or when we had a cold or 'flu. Sweetened with a little honey and milk or a touch of cream stirred in, it was every child's favourite and we all settled down nicely after that.

CULTIVATION Oats needs well-dug soil in full sun and a good twice weekly watering.

PROPAGATION Sow oat seed in well-dug, well-composted soil in full sun. I sprinkle the seed haphazardly all over the well-dug soil and then I rake it in and immediately set sprays on it to keep it moist. Water it daily in the early days as it starts to germinate. Sow oats as a winter crop in autumn.

HARVESTING AND PROCESSING When the little sprouts are 4-6 cm you can pull them up and include them in your salad or in a tea, or allow to ripen fully before reaping. The grain can be threshed and the straw kept for tea.

COMPANION PLANTING Grow oats near the compost heap to use as a mulch for strawberries in spring. Pull up the whole matured plant, chop roughly and lay around the strawberries; then a year later, clear the mulch away for the compost heap. I interplant oats and red clover. Each will boost the other's mineral content and prevent and control eelworm infestation. Oats benefits broad beans, cabbage and onions.

USES OF OATS

Culinary I add oats as a thickener in casseroles and stirfries and I make pancakes, biscuits, crunchies and fritters with never a failure. In winter there is nothing better to start the day than my oats health breakfast (see recipe section).

Medicinal Oat straw and oats contain many important minerals, alkaloids, vitamins B1, B2, D and E, as well as substantial quantities of carotene. Oats has long been used as a restorative tonic, for both physical and nervous exhaustion and stress, helpful in times of grief and anxiety. Now oat straw is proving to be excellent for building strong bones, a great boon for osteoporosis sufferers, degenerative diseases like multiple sclerosis, thyroid deficiency, depression, panic attacks, recurring colds and 'flu, and lack of energy. The high silica content in oats helps skin ailments like acne and greasy skin, and oat bran is a superb constipation remedy, as well as having anti-thrombotic action. The grain and the bran both literally sop up high cholesterol: recent research has found that including oats porridge (not the instant kind), oat bran and a daily cup of oat straw tea in the diet can drastically bring down high cholesterol levels. For women going through menopause, oat straw assists in oestrogen deficiency. To make oat straw tea use ¼ cup chopped oat straw and pour over this 1 cup boiling water. Stand 5 minutes. Strain.

Cosmetic Our grandmothers used oats softened in warm water as a mask for problem skins and as an exfoliating scrub, and the cooled tea as a lotion to soothe sun and wind-burnt skin.

Other uses Oats stores nitrates in the soil, which will benefit crops in the future. Oat straw used for horse and cattle bedding is extremely valuable for rebuilding tired, depleted soils and can be dug in straight from the stables.

Olive

Family **Oleaceae**
Species *Olea europaea*
Origin **Mediterranean regions**
Plant **tree**
Height **up to 10 m; space 10 m apart**
Soil **any soil**
Exposure **full sun**
Propagation **cuttings**
Uses **culinary, medicinal, cosmetic**

A much-loved evergreen tree, grown for its fruit in Mediterranean countries and in other countries that are hot and dry, the olive was first cultivated in Crete around 3500 BC, not only for its oil-producing fruit, but for its leaves which were used to disinfect and wash wounds, soothe burns, clear infections and rid the body of parasites. The ancient Greeks revered the olive as a symbol of prosperity and used the oil in cooking and as an oil for their lamps. The ancient Romans planted olives throughout Italy, and oils from Tuscany and Umbria are still considered to be amongst the best in the world today. From the earliest days infused oils were used as medicine and with foods, and the olive leaf was added to the oil by the monks and used as wound dressings and for burns. For too long we have forgotten about the relatively unsung virtues of the olive leaf, and it is only recently that medical research has tested olive leaf extract with astonishing results.

CULTIVATION Olive trees thrive in heat, drought, winds and arid conditions with no attention whatsoever. They withstand cold and frost and icy winters, demanding nothing but a weekly watering. Start a tree off in a large, deep hole filled with good compost mixed with topsoil. Soak the hole so that the moisture goes deep down before planting. Stake the tree while it is young to keep it straight.

PROPAGATION Root cuttings in wet sand – they will take several months to root. Fruiting begins usually after 6-7 years. Seed that has ripened on the tree can be sown in bags, but takes 2 years to germinate.

HARVESTING Leaves can be gathered throughout the year and the fruit when ripe in midsummer.

USES OF OLIVE

Culinary Olive oil is one of the oldest culinary oils. Medieval monks stored their oil in crocks and jars away from the light and prescribed it to patients as part of their daily diet to encourage the healing process: today's research finds the oil with the leaf infused a unique combination of valuable health boosting minerals, oils and vitamins, which tastes good as a salad oil and a cooking oil.

Medicinal Extracts of olive leaves which contain olearopein, a strong antiviral and antibacterial, lower high blood pressure, improve the whole circulatory system and also have the ability to lower blood sugar levels – olive leaves have been taken to treat diabetes for centuries. A tea of the leaves has now been found to be an excellent diuretic, a comforting and energising treatment for chronic fatigue syndrome and for multiple sclerosis, as well as for dizziness, disorientation, cystitis, viral attacks, high fevers and feelings of utter depression and helplessness. A poultice of leaves crushed in the oil treats rashes, grazes and slow healing wounds. Olive leaf tea lowers blood pressure, can increase natural immunity and treats ME and chronic fatigue syndrome; and partially dried leaves in olive oil balance the fats in the body and lower high cholesterol. To make the tea use ¼ cup fresh olive leaves and sprigs. Pour over this 1 cup boiling water. Stand 5 minutes. Strain and sip slowly. Take 1-2 cups a day for any of the above symptoms. After 10 days give it a break for 2-3 days then continue for chronic ailments.

Cosmetic Olive oil will moisturise dry skin and makes an excellent stretch mark massage oil.

Oregano & Marjoram

Family Labiatae
Species *Origanum* species
Origin Mediterranean regions
Plant perennial
Height up to 60 cm; plant 50 cm apart
Soil light, well-drained soil
Exposure full sun
Propagation division
Uses culinary, medicinal, cosmetic

Created by Aphrodite as a symbol of happiness, marjoram was a popular nuptial herb and brides wore it in their hair and carried sprays of it in their bouquets. The Romans used marjoram and oregano oil as a massage oil and oregano oil was used in ancient Egypt as an embalming herb.

Perennial and undemanding, the varieties range from a golden compact creeping variety, *Origanum aureum* (lovely in tubs or edging pathways), to a tall, prolific white-flowered variety often called Greek oregano, and a smaller more compact version, *Origanum vulgare*. The ordinary knotted marjoram, *Origanum marjorana*, has upright bushy growth with sprays of tiny white flowers and pale leaves with little seeds that form the knots. Not as strong or as pungent in flavour as the other oreganos, marjoram makes a neat border – it needs to be cut back hard twice yearly to keep its shape neat, whereas the other oreganos tend to sprawl and some form excellent groundcovers that send up pink or white flower sprays in midsummer.

CULTIVATION All the oreganos withstand frost and make excellent container plants and, due to their pungent oils, are free of insect infestation as well as mildew and wilt. Watering need only be twice weekly in hot weather – remember they originate in the hot mountains of the Mediterranean region.

PROPAGATION Cuttings can be easily made by pulling off mature woody sprigs and rooting them in wet sand.

HARVESTING AND PROCESSING Leaves, sprigs and flowers can be picked at any time of the year.

COMPANION PLANTING Plant the low-growing golden oregano next to strawberries – the fruit ripens perfectly on its living mulch. Excellent with green peppers, paprika, brinjals, okra, green beans and artichokes.

USES OF OREGANO

Culinary With their spicy, pungent, strong and distinctive flavour, marjoram and oregano are ideal for fritters, cheese and egg dishes, pasta and pizza, meat and fish dishes, casseroles, soups and stirfries.

Medicinal Both marjoram and oregano are superb digestive herbs. They are also excellent for colds, 'flu, anxiety attacks, menstrual cramps, nausea and exhaustion. Sprigs of any variety warmed in hot water and applied to a badly bruised area will soothe and disperse the haematoma. The same compress, or marjoram massage cream (see recipe section), is infinitely soothing for a stiff neck and arthritic and rheumatic aches and pains. Chew a sprig of oregano to sweeten the breath, ease toothache and clear mouth infections.

Cosmetic Oregano or marjoram face steamer is an excellent treatment for oily problem skin. Save the cooled, strained water for the bath, or use as a wash for tired, smelly feet. A deodorising lotion (see recipe section) can be used as an underarm wash or as a rinse for oily hair after shampooing. This same brew can be added to the bath as a relaxant or applied to varicose veins. It also makes an excellent rinse for the dog after shampooing.

Other uses Due to their high oil content, these pungent herbs lend themselves to insect-repelling sprays and drenches (see recipe section). Use chopped sprigs and clippings dug fresh into the soil to act as a 'green manure' around fruit trees in particular. The oils act as a repellent to ants and aphids and, at the same time, add valuable minerals to the soil.

Oregano   *Marjoram*

Paprika

Hungarian pepper
Family **Solanaceae**
Species *Capsicum annuum*
Origin **tropical America**
Plant **annual**
Height **50 cm; space 50 cm apart**
Soil **well-dug, well-composted soil**
Exposure **full sun**
Propagation **seeds**
Uses **culinary, medicinal, cosmetic**

Commonly known as Hungarian pepper, the paprika we know today was probably a Turkish native brought into Hungary in the 15th or 16th century when the Turks conquered Hungary and allowed some Bulgarian farmers to settle there. They were the first to cultivate the new red pepper – mild and sweet and full of flavour. Soon the Hungarians started to include it in their diet and it became so popular it was known as their national spice.

Paprika contains an unusually high amount of vitamin C and this is probably why it is so important in boosting the immune system to resist winter colds and 'flu. In Hungary children sprinkle paprika powder in their milk when suffering from a cold.

CULTIVATION The plant reaches about 50 cm in height and is beautifully decorative in the garden – the zbig elongated fruits are showy and fascinating as they change from bright emerald green to the fiery red colour we are so familiar with. A sturdy annual, it will bear fruit right up to the first heavy frosts and the seed saved from the largest and most brilliant of the fruits can be sown again the following year with no fear of deterioration in quality.

PROPAGATION Seeds sown in trays in early spring and planted out when they reach 10 cm in height, 50 cm apart in compost-rich, well-dug soil in full sun and a deep twice weekly watering, will ensure a prolific crop.

HARVESTING AND PROCESSING Pick the fruits when fully ripe and bright red at the end of summer.

COMPANION PLANTING I grow paprika as part of an unusual red and green garden bed that also includes parsley, sweet basil, tomatoes and strawberries (see page 8).

USES OF PAPRIKA

Culinary The Hungarians have perfected the art of cooking with this delicious spice and although we sprinkle our grills and pastas with the powdered, bottled, bright red spice, it is so delicious using your own fresh paprika you could become as fond of the sweet yet pungent, richly flavoured spice as the Hungarians are (see recipe section).

Medicinal Rich in vitamins and minerals and the precious vitamins A, C and beta carotene, paprika is used all over the world to boost the immune system, ease a sore throat and stop a constant cough. No medicine shelf in Russia, Hungary or Czechoslovakia is without a bottle of paprika. In rural areas it is still used today to clear wounds, scratches and grazes by sprinkling into the washing water, and taken with milk to stimulate sluggish bladder and kidneys. Medical science has proved that the brilliant red colouring is an important anti-cancer food, it contains a small degree of the fiery capsaicin which is present in large quantities in most of paprika's cousins, the peppers, and so helps to ward off colds, 'flu and strengthen the whole immune system.

Cosmetic The beautiful red colour of freshly ground paprika was once used in a cream to brighten the complexion of those who lived under the sunless skies of the long dark winters. Girls would have experimented with lip creams as well, adjusting the amount of powder in it to deepen the colour. **Warning**: Paprika is mild enough to be used in this way, but do not ever use cayenne pepper or any chilli powder: it will burn the skin badly.

Parsley

Family Umbelliferae
Species *Petroselinum crispum*
Origin Mediterranean
Plant biennial
Height 10-15 cm; space 30 cm apart
Soil well-dug, well-composted soil
Exposure full sun
Propagation seeds
Uses culinary, medicinal, cosmetic

One of nature's most amazing plants, used throughout the world from the early centuries: parsley is literally a multivitamin in a leaf! A mere half cup of chopped fresh parsley contains more beta carotene than 2 large carrots, more vitamin C than 2 large oranges and 20 times more iron than one serving of liver! And even 10 times more calcium than a cup of milk! The Romans ate parsley as a deodoriser and after-orgy refresher (it still is used today to mask the smells of rich foods and alcohol), it was used in the Middle Ages by the monks to treat everything from hair loss to plaque, respiratory ailments to gout, and it has to this day never lost its popularity.

CULTIVATION Parsley needs at least 7 hours of full sun a day, with a rich, well-composted soil and a good watering two or three times a week. Both the flat leaf variety and the more common moss curled parsley have the same requirements and both thrive from constant picking and trimming – the more you pick the more it grows.

PROPAGATION Sow seed in trays and transplant into bags when big enough to handle, transplant once they are sturdy and about 4 cm in height. Space about 30 cm apart. Cut off the flowering head to prolong its life, but should you want seed, let it ripen and scatter and a mass of little seedlings will appear, waiting to be transplanted.

HARVESTING AND PROCESSING Both the flat leaf variety and the more common moss curled parsley thrive on constant picking and trimming at all times of the year. Cut off the flowering head to prolong its life.

COMPANION PLANTING Planted under roses, parsley is said to deter aphids. Next to beans, tomatoes, broccoli and spinach it is a growth enhancer; next to strawberries it is superb, giving support and protection to their berries as they ripen and repelling fruit fly and aphids as well.

USES OF PARSLEY

Culinary Parsley is the world's favourite herb – of that one can be sure! Because of its somewhat mild taste it is used on every savoury dish and salad the world over. As a garnish, as a flavour and as a health giver there is surely no more versatile herb than parsley. Added during the last moment of cooking to everything from omelettes to casseroles, roasts, soups, fish and poultry, cheese dishes and stirfries, there literally is no dish that parsley does not enhance.

Medicinal Used through the centuries as a diuretic herb and in the treatment of gout, arthritis and rheumatism, parsley is as effective today in our fast-lane lives as it was then, for cystitis, fever, delayed menstruation, flatulence, nausea, 'liverishness' and the control of high blood pressure. A plus for men with prostate problems, and, for bloating and painful bladder infections: just eating fresh parsley helps, and 1-2 cups of parsley tea sipped throughout the day will bring swift relief. To make the tea use ¼ cup fresh leaves. Pour over this 1 cup boiling water. Stand 5 minutes. Strain and sip slowly.

Cosmetic Because of its high vitamin content it naturally tones the skin and brightens the eyes, while vitamins A and C and its phosphorous content ensure elasticity, healing and toning throughout the body. Fresh parsley eaten daily will do much to clear the skin, break down oiliness and heal acne and pimples. A simple parsley lotion or bath is an instant toner (see recipe section).

Pennywort

Gotu kola (a related species, *Hydrocotyle asiatica*)
Family **Umbelliferae**
Species *Centella asiatica*
Origin **Native to India, Australia, Southern Africa and parts of South America**
Plant **perennial groundcover**
Height **up to 30 cm**
Soil **any soil**
Exposure **sun and shade**
Propagation **runners**
Uses **medicinal, cosmetic**

Rich in glycosides, fatty acids, amino acids, vitamins B and C, a variety of minerals, particularly calcium, magnesium and sodium, and flavonoids, sugars, pectin and resins, pennywort has been used in Indian and Chinese medicine since the 12th century. The Zulu caretaker at our seaside cottage taught me how to use pennywort to cure bad sores by applying warmed leaves over them as a poultice.

When I delved further into French and Chinese pharmacopoeias I found they used it to treat leprosy and other serious skin ailments too. Now I grow great swathes of pennywort and send a 4 kg bag of fresh leaves to France bimonthly, as they find our pennywort the best skin and beauty treatment and use it in exclusive cosmetics, ointments, medicines, capsules and lotions.

CULTIVATION The long trailing stems or runners send down roots and these can be planted easily by pulling them of the plant. I start it off in rich, well-composted soil that is kept moist and shaded until the nodes have rooted. Thereafter a good twice weekly watering is all it needs. A few spades full of compost in autumn and again in early summer will ensure a spread of lush, brilliant light-green leaves.

PROPAGATION It can be propagated by rooted nodes that establish themselves within three weeks to a month, and pieces can be easily propagated at any time of the year.

HARVESTING AND PROCESSING Pick the leaves all through the year and use fresh.

COMPANION PLANTING Pennywort is a superb ground-cover and makes an excellent living mulch under fruit trees, vines and shrubs.

USES OF PENNYWORT

Medicinal Pennywort is a superb tonic for nervousness, stress, schizophrenia, epilepsy, amnesia and helps to promote mental calm and clarity and relieve tension. It is credited with antiseptic, diuretic, digestive and anti-inflammatory properties and is used as a treatment for eczema, psoriasis, cellulite infections, dermatitis and leprosy and to speed up the healing process after surgery and reduce scar formation. The juice of the leaf stops allergic skin irritations, and soothes heat and nappy rashes and sores on babies. For swollen rheumatic and inflamed arthritic conditions pennywort tea brings great relief. Use 3 fresh leaves in 1 cup boiling water, stand 5 minutes and strain. Take 1-2 cups daily. It also treats bedsores, poor circulation, hepatitis, urinary tract infections, common colds, sore throat, tonsillitis, peptic ulcers, constipation, fevers, fibrocytic breasts, lupus, anal fissures, cirrhosis of the liver, periodontal conditions, tuberculosis, measles, venereal diseases and pleurisy. Swellings, spider veins, varicose veins, phlebitis and ulcerative conditions of the legs are all greatly improved not only by drinking pennywort tea, but by applying a poultice made of warmed leaves or pennywort lotion (see recipe section). This is a true wonder plant!

Cosmetic Practically all skin problems respond to pennywort and it stimulates hair and nail growth. Pennywort lotion (see recipe section) is excellent for treating sunburn and dry skin and gives elasticity back to ageing skin.

Other uses Pennywort is a superb natural foliar feed.

Pyrethrum

Family Compositae
Species *Tanacetum cinerariifolium*
    (=Chrysanthemum cinerariifolium)
Origin Europe
Plant short-lived perennial
Height 20-40 cm; space 40 cm apart
Soil well-dug, lightly composted soil
Exposure full sun
Propagation seeds
Uses medicinal, insecticide

Pyrethrum originated in Dalmatia, but it is now extensively cultivated as an excellent natural insecticide commercially in Africa, Central Europe, the Far East and America. Ancient Chinese herbals indicate pyrethrum was used as an insect repellent over 2 000 years ago! Pyrethrum contains pyrethrins and cinerins, which are poisonous to aphids, red spider, white fly and codling moths, but can also affect bees and ladybirds. So sprinkle the crushed flowers over affected plants in the early evening or use as a spray just as it gets dark as the bees and the ladybirds do their fly-away home trick!

Pyrethrum will form a cushion of pretty greyish leaves and in spring and summer will send up sprays of white daisy flowers which contain the precious oils. When using pyrethrum extracts wear gloves – remember it is toxic and can kill fish and helpful insects.

CULTIVATION Plant out 40 cm apart and water twice weekly.

PROPAGATION Sow seeds in trays and plant into bags when big enough to handle. Allow seedlings to grow to a good size before planting out 40 cm apart.

HARVESTING AND PROCESSING Dry the flower heads in the shade when they are fully mature.

COMPANION PLANTING A row of pyrethrum interplanted with pennyroyal at the edge of the patio will help repel mosquitoes and flies. Plant pyrethrum near roses, tomatoes, brinjals, sweet peppers and under windows and beside doorways to repel ants.

USES OF PYRETHRUM

Medicinal Although pyrethrum is no longer used as a medicine in most parts of the world, the Chinese in some rural areas still use the root to treat fevers and inflammatory conditions. Modern research today finds the flowers have certain natural antibiotics, which can be isolated and research is ongoing.

Insecticide Crumble the dried flower heads, mix with powdered rue and use this potent powder to sprinkle down ant holes, along skirting boards (I mix in baby powder talc here, as ants hate talc – equal quantities of each) and along paths and under the ferns to get rid of slugs. It will also get rid of cockroaches, fleas and bedbugs, and is non-toxic to mammals. Our grandmothers used pyrethrum flowers tied in a tight bunch, about 10 of them, dried and then dipped into saltpetre, placed in a flat wide tin or a terracotta pot-plant saucer and lit. This alternative to a mosquito coil works beautifully outdoors or on the patio during an evening braai or picnic. Pyrethrum spray is excellent for indoor plants (see recipe section).

When the active ingredient in pyrethrum is extracted it is toxic to humans and animals. It is safest to wear gloves while working with pyrethrum but when used whole and fresh or dried and not chemically processed, it is non-toxic to mammals. The great advantage is that it does not accumulate in the environment or in the bodies of grazing animals. Kenyan growers have been cultivating pyrethrum for many years and trials here at the Herbal Centre prove it does well in Southern Africa, so why is it not grown commercially more often? This is an important environmental programme we should be paying more attention to.

Raspberry

Family Rosaceae
Species *Rubus idaeus*
Origin Europe to Asia
Plant perennial
Height up to 1 m; space 50 cm apart
Soil well-dug, well-composted soil
Exposure full sun
Propagation runners
Uses culinary, medicinally

The raspberry has been a favourite household remedy for centuries, and its best-known use has been as a tea to prepare for childbirth. Warriors in the early centuries took raspberry leaves with them to use as a wound wash and to treat 'soldiers' diarrhoea', which plagued them on the long journeys and battles fought in adverse conditions. Medieval monks prescribed raspberry leaf tea for sore throats, rheumatic pains, for eye ailments and as a cleansing diuretic. Medical research today proves these ancient treatments were indeed correct, and today raspberry is still considered as an important treatment in childbirth the world over.

CULTIVATION Although it is essentially a cool climate plant, certain varieties like Autumn Bliss do quite well under hot and dry conditions. They need to be supported as the metre long fruiting stems are soft and pliable, and they need space between each plant as masses of new little tufty plants will push up from the roots all around the mother plant. Cut the fruiting branches back to ground level in winter. Give a good dressing of compost and water once a week until the new growth pushes through then water twice a week.

PROPAGATION Dig out rooted new shoots when they are about 10 cm high. Immediately replant 50 cm apart in well-composted wet soil. Keep wet until the plants recover, thereafter water 2 to 3 times a week.

HARVESTING AND PROCESSING Leaves can be picked at any time of the year, except in the coldest months when the leaf sprays are cut back. Fruits ripen in midsummer and bear right up until the late autumn sets in.

COMPANION PLANTING Raspberries love garlic and yarrow, both improve the taste and yield and both deter beetle attack. Do not grow raspberries near potatoes – the potatoes may succumb to potato blight more easily – or near youngberries – each will compete for space to the detriment of the weaker crop.

USES OF RASPBERRIES

Culinary Raspberry juice is still one of the best tonics and it is rich in vitamins A, B, C and E, an exceptional array of easily assimilated minerals and enzymes and is a superb antioxidant. Never was a health food so delicious! Raspberry coulis, made by heating and mashing sugared raspberries, is one of the best laxatives and digestive tonics and young and old love it. Try serving it on hot oats porridge with a little natural yoghurt. Raspberry vinegar (see recipe section) is superb as a salad dressing – and as a gargle, diluted with a little warm water!

Medicinal A syrup of raspberries and raspberry vinegar was used through the centuries to treat diarrhoea, mouth infections, indigestion, rheumatism, to clear mucous after colds and coughs, and to flush the kidneys and bladder. Raspberry leaf tea is taken in late pregnancy to prepare for labour. Take 1 cup daily in the last month of pregnancy and drink raspberry tea during labour (but do so with your doctor's consent). To make the tea add ¼ cup fresh leaves to 1 cup boiling water, leave to stand 5 minutes, then strain. **Caution**: Take the tea in the **last month only, never in early pregnancy**. The same tea is an effective uterine stimulant.

The leaves also have astringent properties and make an excellent mouthwash and gargle for mouth ulcers, throat infections and gum ailments. Apply the same tea regularly on pads of cotton wool to treat varicose ulcers or use as an eyewash for conjunctivitis – bathe the eyes 5 or 6 times a day with the cooled tea or make into a lotion (see recipe section).

Red Clover

Family Leguminosae
Species *Trifolium pratense*
Origin Eurasia
Plant short-lived perennial
Height 30 cm; space 30 cm apart
Soil well-dug, well-composted soil
Exposure full sun
Propagation seeds
Uses culinary, medicinal, cosmetic

Clover is a well-known invasive weed that is native to Europe and Asia and has been introduced as a fodder crop all over the world. The three-lobed leaves were associated by medieval Christians with the Holy Trinity and the monks used it medicinally to treat all sorts of ailments. They also believed the crescent-shaped leaf markings indicated that the plant could be used to treat cataracts. There has been little research done on clover generally in spite of its rich folklore and ancient claims that it reduced the size of cancerous tumours. Fresh flowers for medicine are still sold in market places in rural Europe today.

Ancient uses included using crushed flowers and leaves on bee and wasp stings and mosquito bites and rashes, and for change of life in rural women clover was considered to be a vitally important herb.

CULTIVATION Red clover needs full sun and well-dug, well-composted soil with a good weekly watering to thrive.

PROPAGATION Sow seeds in spring, spacing 30 cm apart, or propagate side pieces from the clump. In cold areas sow seed annually, as it dies down and becomes untidy, especially if you are constantly reaping the flowers.

HARVESTING AND PROCESSING Pick the flowers as soon as they open. The flowers can be dried.

COMPANION PLANTING Plant red clover with apple trees, grapevines, tomatoes, grazing grasses, cabbages, cauliflowers, Brussels sprouts and broccoli.

Keep away from camellias and gooseberries as it may cause the buds and the fruit to drop.

USES OF RED CLOVER

Culinary Flowers can be added to salads, stirfries and drinks. A delicious combination is clover flowers, celery, green peppers and mushrooms in a quick and easy stirfry supper dish, or cook the flowers with rice and ginger for party fare. Everyone loves it!

Medicinal Sweet and pleasant, clover was once considered to be a gypsy food but because of its reputation as psoriasis and eczema treatment and an anti-cancer herb and with its possible oestrogenic activity, it has become more and more popular. A douche was used to treat vaginal itching and infections and as a wash and a lotion. The tea is also still taken today for bronchitis, coughs and colds, sore throat (also used as a gargle) and for whooping cough, arthritic pains and swollen lymph nodes, painful breasts, for all the symptoms of menopause and as a compress to the site of a tumour as well as crushed warm flowers held over the area. To make the tea use ¼ cup fresh clover flowers and pour over this 1 cup boiling water. Stand 5 minutes. Strain and sip slowly. Take 1-2 cups daily for no more than 10 days. Give a 3-4 day break then start again.

Cosmetic Red clover lotion and cream are excellent for oily skin, spots and pimples, and as a splash or spritz for rashes, sunburn and rough, dry skins (see recipe section).

Other uses Red and white clover has been widely cultivated for centuries as a fodder crop and as a nitrogen-fixing crop that is ploughed into a barren field just as the flowers start. Clover clippings are rich in the important trace mineral boron and if these clippings are dug into the soil around ailing, yellowing plants, it acts as a tonic. Clover is a nourishing companion to grasses for milk cows and the milk is richer and creamier.

Rocket

Salad rocket • Roquette
Family **Cruciferae**
Species *Eruca vesicaria* (=*E. sativa*)
Origin **Mediterranean regions**
Plant **annual**
Height **60 cm; space 50 cm apart**
Soil **well-dug, well-composted soil**
Exposure **full sun**
Propagation **seed**
Uses **culinary, medicinal, cosmetic**

The ancient Romans valued rocket for its pungent leaves, flowers and seeds, using it extensively in their banquets and in medicine. Right up to Elizabethan times, rocket was made into a syrup with honey and lime to treat coughs, even chronic ones, and chest ailments. The crushed seeds were used to treat bronchitis and, added to other herbs – possibly comfrey, mullein or sage – were used as an expectorant to clear the chest. Then, strangely, it fell out of favour and virtually disappeared from kitchen, monastery and apothecary gardens for 200 to 300 years. Not until the last decade of the 20th century, when the Italians started using it in 'designer salads', did rocket regain popularity right across Europe.

It will grow to about 60 cm in height and bears a wealth of spicy, pungent, meaty-tasting leaves and a mass of small, creamy, four petalled flowers that look like little propellers and are marked with fine brown veins.

CULTIVATION Rocket is a semi-hardy annual that readily seeds itself. Once it is established in your garden, you'll always have it. All it requires to flourish is a position in full sun, fairly well-composted soil and a twice-weekly watering.

PROPAGATION Collect seeds when the little elongated pods dry and sow them from spring to early autumn. Rocket seed can be sown in seed trays and the little seedlings planted 50 cm apart in moist soil. Keep the seedlings protected and shaded until they are established. They don't like to be moved once they are established.

HARVESTING AND PROCESSING Pick the leaves and flowers often to keep it at its succulent best. It can only be used fresh but the more you pick the more leaves it produces.

COMPANION PLANTING Rocket acts as a tonic to tomatoes, raspberries and onions, chives and garlic chives – they enhance the taste in one another.

USES OF ROCKET

Culinary The classic, ancient way is to prepare rocket with olives, cheese and vinegar and to serve it with plain dry biscuits – and that takes some beating. Add the leaves and flowers to salads (see recipe section) and sauces, steam them with onions or celery, or serve them with a rich white sauce over baby potatoes or leeks. When the flowers are just starting to open, use the tender flowering heads in a stirfry or sear them in hot olive oil and add them to roasted vegetables or grilled fish. Sprouted rocket seeds are delicious served with grills or sprinkled over pasta.

Medicinal The syrup used by the Romans to treat coughs and chest colds would have been similar to the one I use (see recipe section), with crushed green rocket seed pods, lemon juice, honey, sage leaves and rocket leaves. The seeds have been used through the centuries as a poultice to treat bruises and sprains. Crushed petals were also used to treat skin blemishes by pounding them into a pulp and spreading the softened mixture over the area, squeezing the juice so it covered the blemish completely.

Cosmetic The astringency and pungency of rocket leaves refines and closes oily pores, leaving the skin soft and cleansed. The juice of rocket stems and leaves is still used in rural areas across Europe to treat itchy, inflamed spots, insect bites and irritating rashes. Monks also used rocket seeds, crushed and pounded into olive oil, to treat broken nails and calluses.

Other uses Layers of old rocket plants on the compost heap provide immediate heat.

Rose

Family **Rosaceae**
Species ***Rosa* species**
Origin **Europe and Iran**
Plant **perennial**
Height **up to 1,5 m; space 1,5 m apart**
Soil **a deep, compost-filled hole**
Exposure **full sun**
Propagation **cuttings**
Uses **culinary, medicinal, cosmetic**

*'Roses are God's thoughts of beauty taking
form to gladden mortal gaze, bright gems of
the earth, in which perchance, we see what
Eden was – what Paradise may be!'*

The rose is without doubt the most loved flower on earth! It has inspired gardeners, lovers, poets, artists, musicians and the hardest, most cynical, and the most depressed person, lifting them momentarily by its sheer beauty and fragrance to the place where the angels are.

CULTIVATION All roses need full sun, richly composted, deeply dug soil and twice yearly composting and a deep twice weekly watering. I only grow roses organically as I use the petals for cosmetics, medicines and food – so fertilisers and sprays are strictly forbidden.

PROPAGATION Cuttings can be taken at any time of the year. Grafting is essential for serious rose growers – graft onto strong brier root stock.

HARVESTING AND PROCESSING Harvest the open flowers all through spring, summer and autumn.

COMPANION PLANTING The underplanting of catmint (*Nepeta mussinii*) and winter savory (*Satureja montana*) is an excellent way of keeping aphids away, as well as white fly, scale and even to some extent black spot. A border of marigolds, such as lemon drops, is an added bonus and I interplant these with parsley and strawberries to make a very defined border. After pruning in July I dump around each rose never less than 2 buckets of good rich compost after I've cut back and tidied up the catmint and winter savory. Then I let the hose run in for a deep watering.

USES OF ROSES

Culinary Just sprinkling rose petals over a salad is so easy and so festive that I grow roses in the kitchen garden for just this purpose. Particularly delicious are the old English roses like the Margaret Roberts rose, the multi-petalled bloom is tender and fragile and the perfect 'food for the gods'.

Medicinal Roses have been used since ancient times for treating everything from rheumatism to coughs, aching muscles to epilepsy. A rose brandy hot toddy can be taken at the first sign of a cold (see recipe section); rose petal tonic eases stress, tiredness and exam-time tensions as well as being a tried and tested tonic for those emerging from a long illness or a period of depression. Rose petal tea is an old-fashioned recipe for treating bladder ailments, coughs and colds, indigestion, insomnia, tension, premenstrual tension and period pains, anger and despair. To make the tea use ¼ cup fresh rose petals (use only flowers from your own organically grown roses – never from sprayed or fertilised bushes). Pour over this 1 cup boiling water. Stand 5 minutes and strain. Sweeten with a little honey and sip slowly.

Cosmetic Our grandmothers made rosewater, rose lotions, and even rose creams to soothe, soften and moisturise the skin. Some of those recipes are still made today: rosewater, used as a splash-on or spray over the face and neck and as a freshener in a spritz bottle on a long hot journey; rose and glycerine body lotion, used as a massage oil for dry skin, after the bath, or rose foot ointment, used on cracked heels and around cuticles and on dry calluses (see recipe section).

Roselle

Rosella • African mallow • Natal sorrel

Family **Malvaceae**
Species *Hibiscus sabdariffa*
Origin **India and Malaysia**
Plant **annual**
Height **up to 80 cm; space 1 m apart**
Soil **sandy, well-drained soil**
Exposure **full sun**
Propagation **seed**
Uses **culinary, medicinal, cosmetic**

There is a definite resurgence of interest in the health benefits of this much-neglected, easily grown plant. The first records of the leaves and calyxes found for sale go back to 1687 in Java, where it was sold as food rather than as a medicine. It gained popularity from Mexico to Australia during the 17th century. (Interestingly enough, back in 1895 the Australians shared seed with the Californian Agricultural Experimental Farms hoping to promote a jelly industry, but this failed – a pity, as roselle is so similar in taste and nutritional content to the cranberry and much easier and more prolific to grow.)

For the past decade I have grown roselle at the Herbal Centre, where it has attracted much interest. With its extraordinary amino acid and vitamin C content, medical researchers are now looking at using it to treat TB and chronic chest ailments. But what's truly astonishing is that it was used to clear chest ailments and sore throats centuries ago!

CULTIVATION Roselle is a warm-climate annual that sows itself prolifically once it likes its position. It needs sandy, well-drained soil and full sun. Space the pretty red-stemmed bushy plants 1 m apart as they grow to about 80 cm high and 60 cm wide. When you plant out the young seedlings, dig in some compost and, other than the twice-weekly watering, forget about them!

PROPAGATION Sow the seeds in moist sand in trays and transplant when they are big enough to handle. Take care not to let the soil dry out. I sow my first crop in early August, planting out in late September, and then a second crop in October for planting out in December. As soon as it gets cold, the crop dies.

HARVESTING AND PROCESSING Pick the calyx – red, bright and crisp – once the petals of the typically hibiscus-like cream flowers have died off. Peel the calyx away from the marble-sized seed capsule and use fresh or dried.

COMPANION PLANTING I partner it – as the West Indians do – with cassava, mealies and chillies. All enhance each other's growth and keep each other aphid and mildew free. Underplanted with creeping oregano, we've had a bumper crop of flowers and very big calyxes over the last four summers.

USES OF ROSELLE

Culinary Food industries across the world are considering roselle, with its brilliant red colouring, as a substitute for tartrazine and other coal tar dyes currently in use. The dark trilobate leaves, which have a sour taste, are delicious in salads as are the flower petals. Cool drinks have been made with roselle syrup for many decades and are known commercially as 'karcade'.

Medicinal Rich in a vast array of amino acids, high in calcium, potassium, riboflavin, iron and vitamin C, roselle is excellent for coughs, colds and 'flu if taken as a tea twice daily and used as a gargle for sore throats. To make the tea use ¼ cup fresh or dried calyxes. Pour over this 1 cup boiling water. Stand 5 minutes. Strain, sweeten with a little honey, and sip slowly. A lotion (see recipe section) made of the fibre-rich stems, flowers and leaves has been used for centuries as a wash for rashes, insect bites and stings, and for sunburn in many tropical countries.

Cosmetic The high mineral and amino acid content makes roselle very effective in treating oily skin and acne. Roselle soap (see recipe section) is excellent for problem skin.

Rosemary

Family **Labiatae**
Species ***Rosmarinus officinalis***
Origin **Mediterranean area and Southern Europe**
Plant **perennial**
Height **up to 1 m; Tuscan Blue almost 2 m;**
    space 50 cm apart
Soil **any soil**
Exposure **full sun**
Propagation **cuttings**
Uses **culinary, medicinal, cosmetic**

Legend has it that rosemary was the bush that sheltered the Virgin Mary when she rested during her flight into Egypt. Some say she dried her cloak over the bush, and in reverence the flowers took on its beautiful blue colour. Known as the herb of remembrance in ancient times, rosemary was used at weddings, funerals and christenings, and was one of the 'strewing herbs' laid on floors to be walked on, thus releasing the antiseptic fragrances and oils. During the Great Plague, rosemary was one of the herbs made into little posies, called tussie-mussies, that were carried and sniffed to keep not only bad smells but also the plague itself at bay.

CULTIVATION The beautiful 'McConnell's Blue' rosemary is the best variety for its tough showy growth, and in the last four years I have clipped and trained my white rosemary (*R. officinalis* 'Albus') into marvellous metre-high clipped hedges. The low-growing Huntington carpet (*R. o. prostratus*) and the beautiful creeping rosemary 'Irene' form excellent groundcovers for hot, dry areas like rockeries and slopes.

New varieties are the stiff, coarse-leafed, long-stemmed very tough 'Tuscan Blue' rosemary that has come from Italy. For palest blue flowers and finer leaves, 'Severn Sea' and 'Benenden Blue' rosemary form dense, attractive bushes up to 1 metre high that clip well. 'Major Pink' is a sprawling pink-flowered rosemary that has masses of flowers, much loved by bees. There are new pink forms becoming available – *Rosmarinus officinalis* 'Roseus' and a slight variation on 'Major Pink' called *Rosmarinus officinalis* 'Majorca Pink'.

The astonishing 'Tuscan Blue' makes an extraordinary tight high hedge and, with regular clipping and a weekly watering, offers landscapers much scope. Left to send up its virtually branchless 1,5 or even 2 metre high stems topped with bright blue flowers, it never fails to draw comment. We trialled this rosemary for five years and find it adapts beautifully to South African conditions, including intense heat, drought, hail storms, frost and bitter winter winds. It is a true survivor!

'McConnell's Blue' rosemary

Creeping rosemary 'Irene'

PROPAGATION Thumb length cuttings rooted in moist soil. Occasionally seeds, but germination is slow and erratic.

HARVESTING AND PROCESSING A wonderful evergreen – pick at any time of the year and use fresh.

COMPANION PLANTING Beans, carrots and cabbages thrive near rosemary. It repels carrot fly and cabbage worm and discourages slugs and snails. Grow rosemary as a protective hedge around the vegetable garden.

USES OF ROSEMARY

Culinary I use masses of the beautiful blue flowers – pulled out of their hard little calyxes – in salads and drinks and to decorate snacks. Use sprigs with roast lamb and pork; skewers made of rosemary twigs stripped of their leaves are an excellent way of imparting a marvellous flavour to sosaties for the braai. I also use twigs on the braai itself, for even the wood smoke permeating the meat imparts a marvellous flavour – and it keeps mosquitoes away!

As a general guide, 2 teaspoons of finely chopped fresh leaves are sufficient in any dish. Rosemary has a strong taste, so use sparingly!

Medicinal Rosemary's key actions are anti-inflammatory, stimulant, energiser and astringent. It is primarily a circulation herb, long used as a leveller of blood pressure as well as an energy-giving and uplifting natural treatment. It has received glowing reports as a treatment for rheumatism and arthritis, diabetes, chronic pain, circulatory disorders, and to aid recovery after long-term stress. This may be due to its abundance of calcium, which is easily digested and used by the body. A cup of rosemary tea daily, for no more than 10 days, is the standard way of treating most ailments, especially stress-related ones. To make the tea add 1 thumb length sprig to 1 cup boiling water. Stand 5 minutes and strain. Sweeten with a little honey and sip slowly.

Rosemary is one of the herbs that is often prescribed by homeopaths and herbalists for people who, although they are not seriously ill, are over-stressed and are 'failing to thrive'. A cup of rosemary tea on alternate days – or daily for 10 days – will restore energy and a positive outlook. Rosemary is also valuable for treating depression and anxiety and even vertigo and epilepsy, and to improve concentration and memory and ease headaches and tension. My grandmother's much-loved recipe for rosemary wonder water (see recipe section) – a tonic, a pick-me-up, and a convalescent's revitaliser – literally warms the cockles of the heart!

'Tuscan Blue' rosemary

'Severn Sea' rosemary

Cosmetic A rosemary hair rinse (see recipe section) gives sheen, lustre and body to damaged hair and encourages and stimulates its growth. Rosemary also has a refining effect on the skin and the famous 'Queen of Hungary's Water', made in the 14th century for Queen Isabella (still so beautiful at the age of 72 that the King of Poland proposed to her!), is still used today (see recipe section).

Rue

Herb of grace
Family **Rutaceae**
Species *Ruta graveolens*
Origin **Southern Europe, Mediterranean region**
Plant **shrub**
Height **up to 1 m; space 1 m apart**
Soil **well-drained, richly composted alkaline soil**
Exposure **full sun**
Uses **medicinal, insecticide**

Rue is an ancient herb used in the earliest centuries in ancient Greece and Rome to induce abortion and strengthen the eyesight. This strong-smelling woody perennial shrub was once found in every cottage garden and in the cloister gardens of churches across Europe. Through the years it has been used to treat respiratory and heart ailments, to draw boils and abscesses, relieve tiredness and anxiety, menstrual pain, epilepsy, worms, fevers, ringworm, convulsions, snakebite and rabies! And the ancient healers painted it on their doors as a sign that they were medicine men and women. Rue has an appalling smell! Use with caution!

CULTIVATION It prefers moderate temperatures and grows best in fertile, well-drained alkaline soils, but will grow in poor soils. For the hardiest plants, with more aromatic leaves, little irrigation is needed. Protect the plant against excessive cold in winter; prune back at the end of winter.

PROPAGATION By means of seed or stem cuttings taken at any time of the year. Use small, strong shoots and root in a sandy medium that must be kept moist. Transplant cuttings 1 m apart in well-dug, well-composted soil. Seed must be fresh and germination is usually slow.

HARVESTING AND PROCESSING Sprays of leaves and flowers can be picked at any time of the year.

COMPANION PLANTING Rue and basil cannot grow together. Rue planted near compost heaps and cattle stalls will chase flies. Plant in rows of tomatoes and under fruit trees to deter fruit flies. It is a strong insect repellent that can be used to surround the herb and vegetable garden to protect crops.

USES OF RUE

Medicinal Once a weak tea of rue was used to treat arthritis, rheumatism, asthma, fever, high blood pressure, heart palpitations, to stimulate the muscles of the uterus and to encourage the onset of menstruation. In ancient medical history rue was used by the monks as an eye compress and to treat hysteria, epilepsy, vertigo, cramps and colic, intestinal worms in humans and animals, multiple sclerosis and Bell's palsy. Rue contains rutin, which helps to absorb vitamin C and strengthen the walls of blood capillaries. A tea is used to treat poor digestion, bronchitis and headaches. Rue lotion is used as a drawing poultice for abscesses and a rolled-up bruised leaf will soothe an aching tooth. The oils present in rue can cause an allergic reaction to people with sensitive skins and a small area should be tested first. If no reaction occurs within 10 minutes further treatment can be applied.

Warning: Rue is a very strong, toxic herb that must only be used under professional medical supervision. **Large dosages of rue can be poisonous and rue oil can cause death. Never ever use rue during pregnancy**. Fresh leaves frequently cause allergic skin reactions. I have picked bunches of rue to use as an insecticide, and on a hot summer afternoon carried them across my arm. Within minutes great hot inflamed itchy weals appeared which lasted a couple of hours. If this happens, immediately wash the area with cold water into which a little apple cider vinegar has been added and spread on lavish amounts of crushed bulbinella or aloe vera gel.

Other uses Rue makes an exceptional spray for mildew, fungus, aphids and anything that doesn't budge with normal sprays. Bunches of pungent rue hung in the house keep flying insects away. Lay branches of rue sprigs as a worm repellent around strawberries and use around plants to deter aphids, moths and ants. The roots of rue produce a beautiful red dye.

Sage

Family **Labiatae**
Species *Salvia officinalis*
Origin **Mediterranean region**
Plant **perennial**
Height **30 cm; space 50 cm apart**
Soil **sandy, well-drained soil**
Exposure **full sun**
Propagation **cuttings**
Uses **culinary, medicinal, cosmetic**

The Latin name means 'safe' or 'in good health' and this was the herb the ancients believed enhanced mental clarity and relieved the dullness of age and the illnesses that accompanied it! There are literally hundreds of sages, so get to know the true medicinal and culinary ones carefully. The mauve-flowered variety is the common sage but at the Herbal Centre we have established a pure white-flowered sage as well as a pale pink one that simply appeared one day in our trial beds. Nurseries are now introducing them so snatch them up when you find them, as both are tough and robust and excellent for South Africa's hot summers and icy winter winds. Pineapple sage (*S. elegans*) grows to 1 m high and has a fresh, sweet, pineapple fragrance and taste and a mass of deliciously edible red flowers. Cleveland sage (*S. clevelandii*) grows to an exuberant 1 m high bush, pungently fragrant with great bunches of grey mauve whorls that dry beautifully. Fruit sage (*S. dorissiana*) is the giant woolly sage with big heart-shaped leaves and a glory of edible pink-magenta flowers late in winter. At 1,5 m this is the biggest of all the sages.

CULTIVATION Sage will thrive in sandy, well-drained soil in full sun. After the spring and early summer flowering, prune and tidy up the bushes and replace them every 4-5 years. The tricolour and purple sages are very tender and apt to die off if not carefully watched. Pineapple sage will die down in winter and send up new shoots in spring from a sprawling cushion of fibrous roots. Divide it in midwinter and cut back and cover with compost.

PROPAGATION Cuttings root easily in wet sand. Seed can be sown in boxes. The seedlings must be planted out in bags until established before they go into their final position in the garden.

HARVESTING AND PROCESSING Pick leaves and flowers at any time of the year. The leaves dry well but are best used fresh.

COMPANION PLANTING Sage is a marvellous companion plant for tomatoes, beans and grape vines. Sage leaves make a superb mulch for grapes and will ensure a sweeter crop.

USES OF SAGE

Culinary Sage's camphor, pine and citrus oils give it that pungent, powerful taste, so use it sparingly. Young tender leaves of ordinary sage are best in food. The flowers are edible too. Avoid the tricolour, variegated and purple sages as they are far too camphory in taste to use in cooking.

Medicinal Antiseptic and antifungal, sage heals sore throats, mouth infections, coughs and colds, rough skin, acne, rashes, indigestion, irregular menstruation and memory loss. Its oestrogen content helps the symptoms of menopause. My sage cough mixture (see recipe section) has helped my children and their friends over many a winter. To make sage tea add ¼ cup fresh leaves to 1 cup boiling water. Stand 5 minutes. Sweeten with honey. **Caution:** Don't take sage for long periods – as with all herbs taken for medicinal purposes there needs to be a break for their effect to be beneficial.

Cosmetic Sage lotion is an excellent deodorant and, in combination with apple cider vinegar (see recipe section), makes a cleansing lotion for oily skins and blackheads.

Other uses A big pot of gently simmering water containing fresh sage sprigs (use enough water to cover) will disinfect the whole house and deodorise cooking and pet smells.

Salad Burnet

Family **Rosaceae**
Species *Sanguisorba minor* ● *S. officinalis* (Greater burnet – not often found)
Origin **Europe, Asia**
Plant **perennial, short lived**
Height **20-45 cm; space 50 cm apart**
Soil **well-composted, well-dug soil**
Exposure **full sun**
Propagation **seed**
Uses **culinary, medicinal**

Salad burnet is an ancient herb that somehow has lost its popularity, and is only regaining it gradually now. Once planted as a fodder crop for sheep and cattle, because it remains green all year round and is more nutritious than grass, it provided green grazing for milk cows, even in the snow.

In medieval times the monks made a soothing lotion of salad burnet leaves for skin eczemas, rashes, sunburn, itches, scratches and grazes, and steeped the leaves in wine to hopefully relieve drunkenness. This custom probably encouraged innkeepers and drinking saloons to grow salad burnet at their doors and on the pathways leading into the building to encourage drinkers to over-imbibe as a 'cure' was at hand!

The name 'Sanguisorba' comes from the Latin word for blood, 'sanguis', and 'sorbere' which means to absorb and its traditional use since the Middle Ages was as a poultice to staunch blood and treat wounds. With its legendary wound-healing reputation and tonic properties, in addition to its fresh cucumber flavour, which enhances salads all year round, salad burnet deserves to find a place in every garden.

CULTIVATION Plant out in full sun, spacing the plants 50 cm apart, in well-dug, well-composted moist soil. Keep well watered to establish, then water 2 to 3 times a week to ensure an abundance of new leaves. Cut flower heads back to encourage new growth and pick the leaves frequently. Salad burnet takes heat, bitter winter winds, frost and even snow. It is a reliable winter salad plant.

PROPAGATION Seeds sown in moist sand germinate readily. When big enough to handle prick out and plant in compost-filled bags and allow to mature in partial shade, gradually moving them into full sun.

HARVESTING AND PROCESSING Use only fresh leaves as salad burnet does not keep its flavour when dried or frozen. The younger leaves are delicious in salads, the older leaves can be used to enrich soups and stews.

COMPANION PLANTING Salad burnet does well with peas, lettuce, broad beans and radishes. It strengthens the crop and gives flavour and fullness.

USES OF SALAD BURNET

Culinary The young leaves are tender, refreshingly cucumber-like in taste and delicious in salads, stirfries, dips and soups. Add the little leaflets, stripped off their main stem, to mayonnaise, sauces, dips, salad dressings or sprinkle as you would sprinkle parsley over grills and bakes and casseroles. Because of its deliciously mild flavour, salad burnet combines beautifully with all sorts of other strongly flavoured herbs and spices and the leaves are rich in vitamins and minerals. It is certainly worth including it as a tonic herb in the daily salad or sprinkled over any savoury dish. My favourite way of eating salad burnet is to include the fresh leaflets stripped off their stems in a good pancake batter and to make large pancakes topped with chicken mayonnaise, sprinkled with fresh salad burnet leaves.

Medicinal A soothing tea can be made by pouring 1 cup of boiling water over ¼ cup fresh salad burnet leaves. Stand 5 minutes then strain. It was once a favourite indigestion tea, and was also taken for diarrhoea. The same cooled tea makes an excellent lotion for skin ailments like eczema, rashes, insect bites and stings, sunburn and haemorrhoids. Pour it into a spritz bottle and spray it over the affected area frequently.

Scented Geraniums

> Rose-scented geraniums
> Family **Geraniaceae**
> Species **Pelargonium graveolens** ● **Pelargonium** species
> Origin **South Africa**
> Plant **perennial**
> Height **up to 1 m; space 1 m apart**
> Soil **light, well-composted soil**
> Exposure **full sun**
> Propagation **cuttings**
> Uses **culinary, medicinal, cosmetic**

The beautiful and varied geranium species, indigenous to South Africa, have spread throughout the world as treasured pot plants. There has been a renewed passion among gardeners for collecting and growing old favourites like rose-scented geraniums, peppermint geraniums and citrus geraniums.

CULTIVATION All varieties need a sunny position in fairly well-composted, light soil. Once established in the garden, they need a thorough watering once a week and a spadeful of compost twice a year. A good pruning in January is essential to discourage straggly growth.

PROPAGATION Cuttings are easy to take at any time of the year, except during the coldest months. Simply pull off a thumb-length sprig, strip off the lower leaves and press firmly into a box filled with wet sand. Keep well shaded and damp, and within a month you'll have a sturdy little plant that can be planted out into a pot filled with damp soil.

HARVESTING AND PROCESSING Pick the leaves at any time of the year for teas, culinary and cosmetic uses. The leaves are rich in oils and are at their best used fresh. The small pink flowers are prolific in spring, and these are edible. Oil for the essential oil industry is particularly favoured and rose geranium oil is becoming a sought-after stress release treatment – harvest the leafy tops all through summer.

COMPANION PLANTING Plant near cabbages to repel the white cabbage butterfly, and edge the vegetable garden with rose geranium to act as a trap for some beetles.

USES OF SCENTED GERANIUMS

Culinary Rose-scented geranium is the only variety of the pelargonium species that is edible, although the peppermint and citrus geraniums add flavour to drinks, desserts, syrups and jams. Use rose geranium leaves in scones, cakes, pancakes (add 1 to 2 tablespoons of finely chopped fresh leaves to the dough of your favourite recipe). Serve with rose-geranium butter (see recipe section).

Medicinal Rose geranium is best known as a relaxer and unwinder. Essential oils are now being used to aid stress, sleeplessness, premenstrual tension, skin ailments, as well as depression and grief. A cup of rose-scented geranium tea is still one of the best medicinal teas, relaxing the whole digestive and nervous system. This tea is excellent for headaches, stiff muscles, nervous cramps and spasms, and that feeling of helplessness and tearfulness. To make the tea use ¼ cup fresh leaves and pour over this 1 cup of boiling water. Stand 5 minutes, then strain. Sweeten with honey if liked.

Cosmetic Rose geranium makes a lovely bath vinegar, or use the fresh leaves and sprigs tied in a face cloth as a scrub with soap for a penetrating skin cleansing and muscle relaxing treatment. Use rose-scented geranium massage cream (see recipe section) lavishly on tired legs and feet and for dry skin on hands and feet.

Other uses Scented geranium spray is ideal for treating stale, smoke-filled rooms. You can also use it for aphids, mildew and thrips on plants. Use the strong smelling citrus- or camphor-scented leaves, the tiny nutmeg-scented leaves, the peppermint- and rose-scented leaves or a mixture of all of these. Foliar spray (see recipe section) made from a mixture of comfrey and scented geranium leaves makes an excellent booster for slow growing plants.

Sesame

Family **Pedaliaceae**
Species ***Sesamum indicum***
Origin **Africa**
Plant **annual**
Height **1,5–2 m; space 20-30 cm apart**
Soil **well-dug, well-composted soil**
Exposure **full sun**
Propagation **seeds**
Uses **medicinal, culinary**

Sesame seeds were found in Tutankhamen's tomb – the seed we have today may have had its ancient beginnings in Egypt along with the pharaohs. In Hindu mythology sesame seed was blessed by the God Yama and from then on it was regarded as a symbol of immortality, appearing in many religious ceremonies and devotions.

Sesame is packed with vitamins A, B and E, iron, calcium, phosphorus and potassium, and easily absorbed protein and is possibly one of the most important foods known to mankind. We need to pay more attention to this delicious food and use it as a daily tonic sprinkled on everything!

CULTIVATION Water twice weekly.

PROPAGATION Scatter unhulled seeds on well-dug, well-composted and well-raked soil in full sun and keep moist until they are sturdy, thereafter water well twice weekly.

HARVESTING AND PROCESSING Perfect timing is essential to catch the seeds, so the whole plant is pulled up just as the seed pods begin to ripen. The plant is then tied in bundles and hung over floors spread with cloth – or nowadays plastic – so that each precious little seed can be caught as the pods burst. Paper packets tied over the ripening heads are another way of catching the seed. Agricultural research has come up with a non-scattering variety that can be picked green and its self-ripening action, although no longer in the field, makes it an economically viable crop.

COMPANION PLANTING Excellent with mealies but never plant near sorghum as it inhibits sesame's growth.

USES OF SESAME

Culinary Used in cakes, biscuits, bread, sprinkled onto stirfries, salads, desserts, muesli, fruit salads, yoghurt and made into that delicious creamy paste called tahini that is used so lavishly in Middle Eastern cookery, sesame really is a gourmet's delight. You can dry roast the seeds in a flat roasting pan in the oven or in a dry frying pan on top of the stove, turning frequently to enhance the flavour. Use the oil for salad dressings and in salsas and stirfries.

Medicinal An ancient medicine for constipation – both the oil and the seeds are still used today. For local swellings, tumours, hard cysts, fissures and skin growths, sesame oil has been used for centuries. Its high vitamin E content will break down scar tissue, clear pus and old infections and chronic eczemas and skin eruptions. Eating sesame frequently will strengthen the nerves and the heart and lower blood pressure and is excellent for liver and kidney ailments and detoxifying an overloaded liver. The seeds stimulate breast milk production in new mothers and the root is made into a tea to treat coughs and respiratory ailments and asthma, dizziness, tinnitus and blurred vision due to anaemia. Make a tea by adding ¼ cup chopped root and 2 teaspoons seeds to 1 cup boiling water. Stand 5 minutes then strain.

Cosmetic Sesame oil is good for dry skin, cracked lips, rough heels, broken nails and soothing for rashes, sunburn and itchy dryness. As a hair dressing for very dry scalp and hair and for burns, inflamed red areas and for keeping a youthful appearance, sesame oil takes some beating! Used as a weekly facial massage the wrinkles literally disappear!

Other uses The drying stalk returns minerals to the soil if dug back in. Scientists have isolated insect-repelling ingredients within sesame's leaves, called sesamins, and are finding that these can be used in the same way as pyrethrins.

Silver Birch

Family **Betulaceae**
Species ***Betula pendula***
Origin **Eurasia**
Plant **tree**
Height **10-25 m; space 5-10 m apart**
Soil **any soil**
Exposure **full sun**
Propagation **cuttings, catkins**
Uses **medicinal, cosmetic**

My Scottish grandmother told us as children of the birch sap she drank (tapped in spring) that was an ancient treatment for rheumatism, bladder and kidney ailments and infections. St Hildegarde of Bingen wrote of the silver birch in her medicinal herbal diaries. Used in Asia and Europe for centuries and in Ayurvedic medicine as a treatment for stomach ailments, skin infections and diseases, silver birch is now being researched for skin cancer, psoriasis, lupus and subcutaneous haemorrhages. The bark, once used for writing on, can be steeped in hot water and used as a compress over skin lesions, acne and rashes and will reduce puffiness in chronic skin problems.

CULTIVATION Tough, frost-resistant and heat and dryness tolerant, the silver birch takes most soils and thrives near forests. To start it off dig a large deep hole and fill it with compost and good rich soil. It is a slow grower, but remember it does eventually become a big tree. Water deeply once a week and enjoy it – it needs no attention whatsoever and its light shade will create a micro-climate beneath it in which violets, primulas and daffodils will thrive!

PROPAGATION Cuttings taken in early spring and rooted in wet sand and ripe catkins crumbled and sown as seeds. Germination is slow and sporadic.

HARVESTING AND PROCESSING Gather the leaves in late spring and summer. Peel the bark at any time of the year.

COMPANION PLANTING Silver birch guards the gentle winter annuals – bulbs, primulas, and in Europe, bluebells, buttercups, foxgloves and forget-me-nots.

USES OF SILVER BIRCH

Medicinal A tea of silver birch leaves will remove toxins, ease arthritis, pains and stiffness, reduce fluid retention, ease skin and scalp ailments, help in weight reduction, invigorate poor circulation, disperse swellings, muscular aches and pains, reduce skin haemorrhages and internal haemorrhages, remove waste products from the kidneys and urine and help to break down kidney and bladder stones. To make the tea use ¼ cup fresh leaves. Pour over this 1 cup boiling water. Stand 5 minutes. Strain and sip slowly. A big pot of leaves, catkins, sprigs and pieces of the silvery bark – about 4 cups altogether – can be boiled in 3 litres of water for 20 minutes. Then cooled and strained it can be used as a spritz spray on skin ailments, used in the bath to stop itch and inflammation and used to massage into the scalp and comb into the hair. For gout and rheumatism and swollen arthritic joints, a poultice of leaves first steeped in hot water and applied to the area as hot as is comfortable, and with a cup of silver birch tea will ease the condition comfortingly. Oil taken from the leaves and the catkins is antiseptic, tonic and anti-inflammatory, and a remarkable diuretic that is safely non-toxic, non-irritant and non-sensitising.

Cosmetic My grandmother used witch hazel and silver birch lotion (see recipe section) to wipe away oiliness and clear spots and marks. The same brew was added to the bath for itchy dryness and rashes. Silver birch oil is used in hair care products and as a massage oil for congested skin and acne. I make a face cream (see recipe section) with silver birch for problem skins and it is immediately soothing. The crude silver birch oil, known as birch tar oil, has been used for some time in men's aftershave preparations, especially for shaving rash!

Soapwort

Family Caryophyllaceae
Species *Saponaria officinalis*
Origin temperate Europe, Asia and North America
Plant perennial
Height 20 cm; space 30-50 cm apart
Soil compost enriched, but grows anywhere
Exposure full sun
Propagation seeds
Uses medicinal, cosmetic

This pretty pink-flowered perennial plant, native to Europe, Asia, Britain and North America, has spread far and wide across the world as a natural soap and as a medicine. It was grown extensively in the Middle Ages for washing clothes and fabrics and for washing sheep's wool just before shearing. Well documented in ancient herbals, sapponaria brew was used in the courts to wash tapestries and carpets.

My own findings are: soapwort lotion eases sunburn, eczema, psoriasis, it helps dry up fever blisters, it soothes inflamed mosquito bites and rashes and hot swellings, and it stops itchiness, and this is one plant I can never be without. The Herbal Centre staff grow it near their houses for grazes and rashes.

CULTIVATION The safest way is to find a large tub or area that can be isolated with a deep collar of heavy duty plastic dug in at least 60 cm deep to restrain it. It will thrive in the poorest of soils and, of course, is breathtaking in its tall heads of pink phlox-like flowers when it has good compost-rich soil. It literally needs no attention and is an excellent waterwise plant, thriving on neglect. I find cutting it back ruthlessly every winter keeps the flowers coming and of course constant picking and digging up of roots and the leafy sprigs only enhances its growth. The key word is *invasive*! So do take care where you plant it.

PROPAGATION Rooted pieces, spaced 30-50 cm apart.

HARVESTING AND PROCESSING Any time of year. The flowers, stem and leaves are *always used fresh*.

COMPANION PLANTING Tough and invasive, it thrives next to anything, but needs to be restrained.

USES OF SOAPWORT

Medicinal Primarily used as a skin treatment for everything from eczemas to rashes, allergy areas, insect bites, sunburn, grazes and scratches, a soothing lotion (see recipe section) will immediately bring relief. The Herbal Centre gardeners and staff grow soapwort near their homes and use it daily for treating all those little skin irritations we are so often plagued with as we work in the gardens and fields. Use soapwort lotion to soothe nappy rash, dab onto eczema areas on the dogs and soak the feet in a soapwort bath to clear foot infections and to soothe tired calloused feet (see recipe section).

Cosmetic Because of the high saponin content in all parts of the plant, soapwort makes a marvellous skin-softening and deep-cleansing soap. Merely take a small bunch of leaves, flowers and stem. Wet thoroughly and vigorously rub between the hands, wetting frequently, until a lather is formed. Use this to wash the face and dab onto problem skin areas and allow it to dry. Then rinse off with tepid water to which a dash of apple cider vinegar is added. It can be used as a scrub over oily problem skin or as a quick and effective skin refining and softening treatment. Soapwort shampoo (see recipe section) gives a beautiful sheen as well as leaving the hair manageable.

Other uses I find my basic sprays are enormously effective because of this exceptional plant. Its saponins are disliked by aphids, ants, flies and even mealie bug, and they are the most important ingredient in the spray because they help it 'stick' to the leaves of the affected plant. Spray soapwort and eucalyptus anti-mosquito spray (see recipe section) into the room or around window sills and under tables, and have the spray bottles ready at the patio or around the pool.

Sorrel

Family Polygonaceae
Species *Rumex acetosa*
Origin Eurasia
Plant perennial
Height 60-80 cm; space 1 m apart
Soil deeply dug, well-composted soil
Exposure full sun
Propagation division
Uses culinary, medicinal, cosmetic

The Egyptians, Romans and Greeks ate sorrel as a digestive aid to relieve bloating or over-indulgence: it was grown outside the banqueting halls ready to be picked for quick relief during a feast! The sorrel grown today is exactly the same as it was all those centuries ago – no hybridisation, no change, no development has in any way altered this lovely plant, and it grows with ease just the way it did so long ago. The crushed leaves were traditionally used to treat skin ailments. Long used as an antiseptic, diuretic, laxative and tonic, sorrel is also a remarkable thirst quencher: through the centuries farmers working the fields ate a leaf to keep cool and to slake their thirst – it was known in folklore as the farmer's lemonade.

Undemanding, sorrel spreads into a fairly loose and pretty plant with its large spear-shaped tender leaves. I find the clump grows so prolifically one plant is sufficient for a household. Although it is frost tender there are always new leaves pushing up, which are a great boon for winter salads.

CULTIVATION Sorrel loves deeply dug richly composted soil, full sun and a good twice-weekly watering and given these requirements it will flourish.

PROPAGATION Cut off side portions from the clump and push these sprigs into bags of wet sandy soil. Keep shaded for 2-3 weeks, gradually hardening out in the full sun. I leave my new plants in their bags for at least 2 months before planting them out in the garden.

HARVESTING AND PROCESSING Pick leaves all through the year. Sorrel can only be used fresh.

COMPANION PLANTING Sorrel acts as a trap crop for caterpillars and slugs, so it protects lettuces, cabbages and spinach. Green peppers, peas and beans thrive near it.

USES OF SORREL

Culinary Lemony, refreshing, sour, sorrel is the perfect salad herb. It gives a spark to sauces, soups and fish dishes and is at its best chopped fresh and added at the last moment to the dish. It blends beautifully with nasturtium, tarragon, dill, fennel, chives, and complements potatoes, peas, haricot beans, green beans and stirfried brinjals.

Medicinal The juice from the stems and leaves is an excellent treatment for sores in the mouth, like mouth ulcers and gum ailments. It cools and refreshes the blood, particularly in hot countries and can be taken by women struggling with hot flushes during menopause. For over-fullness after a meal, the Greeks still today make a pleasant tea from sorrel and mint, which is an excellent diuretic tea as well, for detoxification and for water retention. To make sorrel and mint tea use ¼ cup mixed fresh leaves. Pour over this 1 cup boiling water. Stand 5 minutes. Strain and sip slowly. **Caution**: Do not take this often as large doses can damage the kidneys and the oxalic content can prevent calcium absorption.

Cosmetic Sorrel is a centuries-old remedy for acne. Crushed leaves high in oxalic acids were used as a poultice for skin eruptions. Sorrel vinegar is used as a splash or added to the rinsing water after washing the face (see recipe section).

Other uses The juice and crushed leaves and stems remove rust, mould and stains, and my grandmother's mixture of crushed and pounded sorrel leaves with lemon juice and salt is still the perfect cleaner for tarnished silver, copper and brass. Sorrel is excellent for breaking down compost.

Southernwood

Lad's love
Family **Compositae**
Species *Artemisia abrotanum*
Origin **Southern Europe**
Plant **perennial**
Height **50-100 cm; space 90 cm apart**
Soil **well-dug, well-composted soil**
Exposure **full sun**
Propagation **division, cuttings**
Uses **medicinal, cosmetic**

Once a common wild plant over Southern Europe, southernwood was used for centuries by farmers to protect their crops, their homes and their grain. It was once, surprisingly, cultivated for the perfume industry and for herbal medicine, because of its volatile oil, abrotanin, and other strong tannins. During the Middle Ages and the Renaissance, it was used to protect painted canvasses and tapestries from moth and insect damage. In some of the medieval churches southernwood branches were bound around scrolls and parchments and laid in drawers along with the gold-embroidered altar cloths and vestments. Some parchments were made with shreds of southernwood leaves in the actual pulp, which are still visible today, and were sown in the hems of the robes of office for judges, priests and barons to protect the velvet and the embroidered silks from insect damage.

CULTIVATION Plant 90 cm apart. Southernwood is not fussy about soil, but likes well-dug, well-composted soil and thrives with a twice-weekly watering. Cut back at the end of the growing season. It becomes straggly and the lower leaves dry and turn brown, so keep it constantly trimmed.

PROPAGATION By division or cuttings. Where branches touch the ground they root easily and cuttings can be taken at any time of the year.

HARVESTING AND PROCESSING Harvest leaves and sprigs anytime.

COMPANION PLANTING It protects cabbages from aphids and other insects, and repels fruit fly from fruit trees.

USES OF SOUTHERNWOOD

Medicinal The monks used southernwood in the early centuries to treat worms in both children and animals – it was taken as a strong tea first thing in the morning, 2 or 3 mornings running. The same strong brew was used to wash out wounds and a weak tea was taken ½ cup at a time twice daily to ease menstruation, and as a tonic after a long illness, 1 tablespoon of the tea taken three times a day, and is still taken in country districts mixed with honey and lemon juice, one tablespoon of the tea at a time, for coughs, bronchitis, catarrh and mucous congestion. To make southernwood tea pour 1 cup of boiling water over ¼ cup of southernwood sprigs. Leave to stand only 3 minutes. **Caution**: Due to its strong tannins southernwood should never be taken during pregnancy.

Cosmetic Renowned throughout the centuries for its ability to strengthen hair growth, southernwood got the name lad's love because young men used a lotion (see recipe section) made of southernwood dabbed onto their faces to encourage the growth of their beards and moustaches, and combed into their hair to strengthen and encourage its lengthy growth. As a hair rinse it became extremely popular and lad's love vinegar (see recipe section) became a saleable item in pharmacies in the early part of the 18th century. This was added to the hair rinsing water after a shampoo.

Other uses Southernwood is an excellent insect repellent and makes an effective spray (see recipe section). Keep all cut branches for use as insect repellent and in potpourris. It is an ingredient in a very effective spray against aphids; dried and powdered it repels ants. Sprinkle southernwood leaves and talc powder behind books, behind cupboards and under shelving paper – fishmoths hate it!

Soya Beans

Family Leguminosae
Species *Glycine max*
Origin Oriental
Plant annual
Height 40-50 cm; space 50 cm apart
Soil well-dug, well-composted soil
Exposure full sun
Propagation seeds
Uses culinary, medicinal, cosmetic

This extraordinary legume is one of the most important food crops known to mankind, cultivated the world over. For thousands of years it has been known as 'the meat of the earth' and modern science has proved it to be one of the rare sources of complete protein. It was first recorded about 2800 BC by Emperor Shen Nung of China as his country's most important crop and then it spread to Japan and Korea, only reaching Europe around 1712.

CULTIVATION Although there are several varieties, still the most popular soya bean is the old-fashioned edible vegetable bean. The pods grow under the leaves, against the stems, and the more you pick the more they produce. The plant matures slowly and can go right into late autumn. Once the beans are reaped, dig the plant into the soil to revitalise and replenish it or toss onto the compost heap.

PROPAGATION Plant individual seeds in rows in well-dug, well-composted soil in full sun 50 cm apart.

HARVESTING AND PROCESSING Pick as soon as the little beans mature to eat, or leave to dry on the bush.

COMPANION PLANTING Like most other legumes, soya fixes nitrogen from the air into their roots, so helping to recondition poor, depleted soil. Grown between rows of mealies they will control mealie borer and several types of beetles and act as a growth stimulant to the mealie as well.

USES OF SOYA BEANS

Culinary Much ingenuity has gone into creating palatable soya bean foods: all over the world you can buy miso, tofu, soy sauce, tempeh and soya milk. Eating half your daily protein intake in the form of soya could revitalise the whole body, including the heart and blood sugar levels. Sprouting soya beans is an excellent way of including this precious plant in your diet.

Medicinal Superb for diabetics, for treating late-onset diabetes particularly, and for treating menopause symptoms, the coumestrol and the isoflavone content in the soya beans closely mimicking the oestrogen within the body. Soya stimulates the circulation, acts as a general tonic, toning blood and muscles and stimulating sluggish liver and kidneys; it helps to reverse the build-up of toxins due to medication and processed foods within the body. In fact, as soya contains no fat it is good for treating high cholesterol – remember it has a superb alkaline reaction and it can therefore also help to dissolve and remove gallstones. Soya regulates the bowels and lowers cancer risk, particularly during menopause as it replaces lost oestrogen. The Chinese eat a bowl of soya bean soup daily to treat all the above ailments including heart and circulatory disorders and for those with high cholesterol, some of the damage done to the arteries can often be reversed by eating soya frequently.

Cosmetic The ancient Chinese used mashed cooked soya beans as a scrub over problem oily skins, and for teenage acne and pimples this is not only soothing but acts as an exfoliator, gentle yet deeply cleansing. It makes the skin soft and fine textured and removes all oily, coarse build-up.

Other uses It is an extremely important 'green fertiliser' and compost maker. Often grown as a smother mulch, soya chokes out weeds in one season, and ploughed back into the soil at its maturity it will completely revitalise the area. Green soya laid on the compost heap will quickly break it down and add those superb and vital nutrients to it.

St John's Wort

Grace of God • Soldier's woundwort

Family **Guttiferae**

Species ***Hypericum perforatum***

Origin **Europe and Britain**

Plant **perennial**

Height **5 cm groundcover; flowering head 40-50 cm; space 50 cm apart**

Soil **well-drained soil**

Exposure **light shade or full sun**

Propagation **root runners**

Uses **medicinal, cosmetic**

St John's wort is an ancient, much revered herb. Its name comes from the red pigment in the flowers, symbolising the blood of St John on his beheading on 24 June – St John's Day – a midsummer day in Europe when the flowers are at their best. Much has been written about this herb, especially in the last decade, and much confusion has arisen from the many varieties of *Hypericum* that have similar brilliant yellow flowers with multiple stamens, that are borne all summer long. The tiny-leaved *Hypericum perforatum* is the only variety that is used medicinally. This low-growing groundcover was considered to have such magical properties that in medieval times every cottage had a plant or two growing at the door to repel evil and to treat nervous and emotional complaints. By the 19th century it had fallen into disuse, but research has brought it back into prominence.

CULTIVATION Well-drained, fairly poor soil seems to be its favoured habitat. In full sun with a twice-weekly watering it forms a soft, ever spreading groundcover sending up flowering spikes with a mass of tiny yellow flowers from spring to early winter. Cut back the flowering head once it is spent and give a little compost around the edges of the creeping runners in midsummer.

PROPAGATION Creeping rooted runners pulled up and planted in moist rich soil. Keep shaded and protected until they take, then harden off and plant 50 cm apart in well-dug, well-composted soil.

HARVESTING AND PROCESSING Pick flowering heads in summer when they are fully open. The flowers can be dried for winter use. It is only the flowers that are used.

COMPANION PLANTING Excellent with strawberries, green peppers, cucumbers and brinjals. Its closely knit runners act as a green mulch under the ripening fruits.

USES OF ST JOHN'S WORT

Culinary The tiny tender leaves were once a popular salad ingredient, stimulating both gastric and bile secretions. The flower petals are far more pleasant in salads or stirfries and sprinkled onto both savoury and sweet dishes.

Medicinal Some claim this is nature's Prozac! It certainly is one of the most valuable herbs for nervous problems, depression and menopausal problems, easing the symptoms of hormonal change as well as tension, sleeplessness, decreased vitality, nervous anxiety and as a tonic for the liver and gall bladder. It is available in capsule form or can be taken as a tea for all the above ailments. Use ¼ cup flowering heads to 1 cup boiling water. Stand 5 minutes and strain. Sweeten with a touch of honey and take once a day, for no longer than 10 days, then give it a break of 5 days and start again. St John's wort oil (see recipe section) eases cramp and neuralgia and heals wounds and burns. It also has natural antibiotic, antiviral and anti-inflammatory properties. Hypericin is so strongly antiviral that it is being researched for the treatment of HIV and Aids. For arthritic pain, sprains and strains, massage the affected area lavishly with St John's wort cream (see recipe section).

Cosmetic The fresh flowering tops contain high quantities of hypericin, which gives the extracted oil its red colour. This is an excellent skin healer and natural antiseptic. Use the cooled tea as a spritz or add to the final rinse water as a hair and scalp tonic.

Life size

Stevia

Family Asteraceae
Species *Stevia rebaudiana*
Origin South America
Plant perennial
Height up to 1 m; space 1 m apart
Soil well-dug, well-composted soil
Exposure full sun
Propagation seed, cuttings
Uses culinary, medicinal

The sweetest herb in all the world, stevia has only just come to South Africa and in the trials we have found it to be an easy-to-grow perennial – unobtrusive and quite spindly, with several branches bearing pairs of medium-sized leaves. It was used as a sweetener by the ancient civilisations of South America, who knew it as 'honey leaf'. Research on stevia began in 1931 when two French chemists isolated a compound contained in the leaves. They named it stevioside and found it to be 300 times as sweet as sugar! Around 1941 it was grown at Kew and research found it safe for sweetening beer and possibly drinks for diabetics. When the Japanese government banned certain artificial sweeteners around 1954, stevia was used in drinks and confectionary, frozen desserts, chewing gum and sweets. But, strange to say, it has never been fully utilised.

CULTIVATION At the end of summer it produces a spray of tiny whitish flowers that burst into airborne feathery seeds. It rapidly dies down with the first sign of frost and disappears from sight, only to emerge well into spring when the soil has warmed it. Undemanding and quite tough, it thrives on a deep twice-weekly watering. Don't overwater it.

PROPAGATION Propagation is by seed or by cuttings; in its wild state it roots on the branches that have been down-trodden by cattle but it tends to be temperamental.

HARVESTING AND PROCESSING Harvest the leaves all through summer and use fresh chopped or dry. Dry in the shade and store in brown paper bags.

COMPANION PLANTING Celery, chives and radishes.

USES OF STEVIA

Culinary Roughly 1 or 2 leaves are equal to 1 cup of sugar, but this all depends on where the stevia has been grown. Stevia's sweet components are heat stable, so you can bake with it, but it does not caramelise like sugar, nor does it crystallise. A syrup can be added to fruit salads, cakes and desserts, or served with fruit slices and cream, or with fresh lemon juice and iced water added for a refreshing summer drink. Boil 10 leaves in 1 litre water for 15 minutes. Cool and strain.

Medicinal Stevia is being researched for its effects on high blood cholesterol, high blood pressure, blood sugar levels, tooth decay and plaque. It is used now in toothpastes, mouthwashes and as a cosmetic ingredient. It alleviates bleeding gums, soothes sore throats and clears fever blisters due to its anti-bacterial properties, and as a low-caloric sweetener it does not affect blood glucose levels. It is non-toxic and it possibly has a strengthening effect on the heart and cardiovascular system. Make stevia tea with 2 freshly picked leaves, finely chopped. Pour over this 1 cup boiling water. Stand 5 minutes. Stir with a cinnamon stick and sip slowly.

Over the past two years I have been experimenting with a three herbs for chronic fever blisters with very comforting results. Here is the recipe for my stevia tea for fever blisters: use 1 tablespoon elder flowers (fresh or dried), 1 tablespoon peppermint sprigs (*Mentha piperetta nigra*) and 2 chopped stevia leaves. Pour over this 1 cup boiling water. Stand 5 minutes. Stir well and then strain. Sip 1 cup of the tea two or three times a week. The combination of these herbs could clear the *Herpex simplex* virus, which causes fever blisters, from the body.

Strawberry

Family **Rosaceae**
Species *Fragaria vesca*
Origin **Europe**
Plant **perennial**
Height **20 cm; space 30 cm apart**
Soil **well-dug, richly composted soil**
Exposure **full sun**
Propagation **runners**
Uses **culinary, medicinal, cosmetic**

Native to Europe and the British Isles, the strawberry is an ancient medicinal plant that has withstood the tests of time and remains one of the world's favourite fruits. The wild strawberry from which the masses of varieties have arisen was used in ancient times as a treatment for diarrhoea, inflammation of the liver, digestive ailments and as a poultice for skin cancers – leaves, flowers and fruit all being used. The monks in the early centuries used the fruits and roots to cure gout and inflamed rheumatism. They applied mashed berries to skin eruptions – and today's research proves the efficacy of this. I am always astonished at how important those early cures were by today's standards!

CULTIVATION Dig over a bed in full sun with masses of compost, and water twice weekly. I dig in a wheelbarrow load for every 2 metres. Strawberries require no attention except picking the fruit in spring and early summer and replanting the little new runners at the end of summer.

PROPAGATION Soak the bed well and then carefully separating the runners from the mother plants, set them into the ground in rows 30 cm apart and spaced 30 cm from each other. Keep them moist until they have set down roots. Strawberries need to be replanted and the mother plant discarded every 2 to 3 years.

HARVESTING AND PROCESSING Pick the fruit as it ripens. Leaves can be harvested at any time of the year.

COMPANION PLANTING Companion to beans, spinach, lettuce and roses. Pyrethrum grown nearby will keep the strawberries free from aphids.

USES OF STRAWBERRIES

Culinary In medieval times no banquet was complete without a small dish of strawberries rolled in honey for each guest, eaten a berry at a time throughout the meal to aid digestion! Rich in vitamins A, B, C and E, potassium, calcium, iron and phosphorus, the strawberry is a true health food. The best way of eating them is fresh, unsugared, off the plant.

Medicinal The strawberry was once used to treat syphilis, fruit and leaves made into a tea were both drunk and used as a poultice. A crushed strawberry placed over a ringworm infection and reapplied fresh daily has long been used as a natural treatment. A tea made of the leaves is still used today to treat diarrhoea, kidney infections and even diabetes. To make strawberry leaf tea use ¼ cup fresh leaves. Pour over this 1 cup boiling water. Stand 5 minutes. Strain, sweeten with honey if liked and sip slowly. Rich in antioxidants, strawberries destroy many viruses, including *Herpes simplex*, and benefit the whole cardiovascular system. Rich in pectin and fibre, the berries reduce blood pressure, and polyphenols in the fruit and leaves fight cancer.

Cosmetic Mashed ripe strawberries as a face mask will clear acne, soothe rough inflamed areas and sunburn and whiten the skin. Rubbed over the teeth it will whiten them as well and tone the gums. Leave on as long as possible before rinsing to help to remove tartar from the teeth. Strawberry scrub is a fabulous toner and rejuvenator for tired grey skin. Strawberry leaf lotion (see recipe section) is a wonderfully astringent refreshing toner for the summer heat.

Other uses Soil scraped from under pine trees with their mat of needles is superb for preparing strawberry beds. This mulch later makes an excellent addition to the compost heap that rids the soil of cutworms.

Tansy

Family **Compositae**
Species *Tanacetum vulgare*
Origin **Eurasia**
Plant **perennial**
Height **up to 1,5 m (flowering head); space 60 cm apart**
Soil **well-drained, compost-enriched soil**
Exposure **full sun**
Propagation **seed, division of the clump**
Uses **insect repellent**

Tansy is a fabulously strong, showy, aromatic perennial that, although its native habitat is Europe and Asia, has spread throughout the temperate zones of the northern hemisphere on waste ground and alongside ditches and roadsides, almost becoming naturalised. Its name comes from the Greek word for immortality, because it was believed to arrest decay. Tansy was one of the precious herbs used by medieval herbalists, notably St Hildegarde of Bingen in the 12th century, and the monks grew it in the cloister gardens as an insect repellent – apples picked and stored in the monasteries over winter were placed on beds of tansy to keep them worm free and the monks stored their parchments with branches of tansy. It was also cultivated as a worm-expelling treatment, and as a preservative for meat and poultry.

CULTIVATION Tansy grows vigorously in well-drained soils in a sunny place. It loves compost-enriched soil, and will thrive in most climates. The plants grow tall during summer and should be cut back in autumn. Tansy needs to be contained as it spreads very rapidly. Curly tansy or fern leaf tansy (*Tanacetum vulgare* var. *crispum*) has similar uses to tansy, but is not as tall or as vigorous.

PROPAGATION By means of seed sown in spring and autumn or root division. Divide the clump in late winter and set the pieces 5 cm deep and 60 cm apart in well-dug, well-composted moist soil to give them a good start.

HARVESTING AND PROCESSING Leaves appear in early spring and are ready for cutting within a month. The tall flowering head appears in midsummer. Gather flowers when open and dry leaves and flowers in the shade.

COMPANION PLANTING Grow tansy near fruit trees to keep fruit fly and fruit moths away. It can be grown with roses to keep insects away, but grow it behind the rose border as its flowering head becomes very tall.

USES OF TANSY

Culinary Dried powdered flowers were once used as food colouring. Tansy is a bitter herb and was once used very sparingly in stuffings and with pork, poultry and egg dishes. Commercially it was once used to add flavour to sausages, meat pies and to wrap around meat and poultry to preserve it, but its bitter taste made it unpopular.

Medicinal One of the most mineral rich of all herbs, tansy is an ancient healer, used as a wash or lotion (see recipe section) for cuts, scratches, bruises and rheumatism. It remains popular in many rural areas today. **Warning**: Nowadays tansy's potential toxicity is being tested, so do not use it internally or externally without professional guidance. Even external application for lice or scabies is unsafe and it should never be used during pregnancy. The whole plant and especially the oil, which contains thujone and camphor and sesquiterpene lactones, are restricted in some countries, but the fresh plant is safe for use as an insect repellent.

Other uses Tansy's main use is as an insect repellent (see recipe section) for flies, ants, lice and aphids. A green dye for cloth can be made from tansy roots and a yellow or orange dye from the flowers. Mix into the compost heap for its potassium content. Use the flowers in potpourris. If the leaves are rubbed into a dog's coat it helps keep fleas away.

Tarragon

Family **Compositae**
Species *Artemesia dracunculoides* ● *Artemesia dracunculus*
Origin **Russia, Western Asia, Himalayas**
Plant **perennial**
Height **40-60 cm; space 50 cm apart**
Soil **Well-composted, deeply dug soil**
Exposure **full sun**
Uses **culinary, medicinal, cosmetic**

Tarragon was used in ancient times throughout Europe as an antidote for the bites of venomous beasts, including perhaps the dragon – hence its Latin name! Arab physicians used a teaspoonful of fresh tarragon, well chewed, to mask the taste of bitter medicines as, in the chewing, it makes the tongue slightly numb. As a bonus, tarragon restores tired taste buds, giving you a new interest in your food, and at the same time giving your circulation a boost.

Through the years I have found that classic French tarragon (*Artemesia dracunculus*) is a difficult plant to grow, and though the flavour of this finicky French one is superior in every way, I still grow the tough, resilient, prolific Russian tarragon (*Artemesia dracunculoides*). The more you cut, the more it grows – and remember, the longer it is established in one place, the better the flavour!

CULTIVATION Tarragon thrives on neglect. It likes a well-composted soil in full sun and does well with a deep weekly watering rather than a light spray. It dies down in winter. In July I cut back the old growth and dump a few buckets of compost over the bed. It will remain dormant and will survive with a fortnightly watering until mid-August when its new tender growth pushes through.

PROPAGATION Just as its new growth shows above the soil, you can divide it by forking out some of the roots and establishing it elsewhere. Plant it 50 cm apart in deeply dug richly composted soil.

HARVESTING AND PROCESSING Pick the leaf sprays all through the summer. Tarragon can only be used fresh.

COMPANION PLANTING Tarragon improves the flavour of brinjals and green peppers and increases the bean crop.

USES OF TARRAGON

Culinary The secret of cooking with tarragon is to add it to the dish just before serving. I use it lavishly and frequently in vinegars, pickles, salads, sauces, herb butters, roasts and fish dishes. The taste is light, fresh, slightly aniseedy, peppery, and yet subtle. It lends itself to *fines herbes* with parsley, chervil and chives used in equal quantities.

Medicinal Rich in iodine, potassium, vitamins C and A and a host of mineral salts, tarragon has long been used to cure scurvy, as a tonic for those who have become debilitated or stressed out, and as a relief for flatulence, over-acidity and indigestion. The finely chopped root, packed into an aching tooth and around the gum, was an ancient toothache remedy, possibly due to its analgesic properties. Contemporary research has proved tarragon contains the exceptional cancer-fighting compound rutin, while its rich potassium content helps lower high blood pressure. Added to the bath for rashes and grazes, tarragon in apple cider vinegar (see recipe section) is excellent. You can also drink 2 teaspoons in a glass of water twice daily to combat fluid retention. Tarragon vinegar is superb for applying to wasp and bee stings. It helps to reduce swelling immediately, and reduces the itch considerably. **Caution**: Tarragon has mild menstruation inducing properties and should not be taken during pregnancy.

Cosmetic I use tarragon vinegar to clear oily skin and for restoring lustre to tired hair. Add a dash to hair rinsing water after shampooing and massage briskly into the scalp. You'll find it clears dandruff too.

Tea Tree

Family Myrtaceae
Species *Melaleuca alternifolia*
Origin Australian
Plant tree
Height up to 7 m; space 3-10 m apart
Soil most soils
Exposure full sun
Propagation seeds
Uses cosmetic, medicinal, culinary

The name 'tea tree' was given to a great number of plants that were originally catalogued by Captain Cook on his voyages, when he sent his scurvy-ridden sailors ashore to search for any green plant with which to make tea, to relieve their debilitating symptoms. So every plant they picked and tried was listed – tea tree 1, tea tree 2, tea tree 3, and so on, which has caused much confusion! The Australian Aborigines have used the precious leaves in traditional medicine for centuries. It is antiseptic, antifungal, antibacterial; it has strong antibiotic properties and it stimulates the immune system.

I have a tea tree growing outside my bathroom window. When I am very tired, or have a heat rash or aching feet and legs, I reach out and pick off a few sprigs and toss them under the hot-water tap. The oils are immediately released and act with speed to relax and soothe.

CULTIVATION The evergreen tea tree is tough, resilient, hardy and wonderfully prunable. A superb water-wise plant – all it requires is a deep compost-filled hole in full sun with a wide dam around it and a deep weekly watering. It does not like its roots to be disturbed, so dump a barrow of compost onto it in spring, very lightly turn it in and water well. It will thrive in heat, drought and winds and storms but it does not like heavy cold and frost.

PROPAGATION Propagation is by seed – fresh seed is best.

HARVESTING AND PROCESSING Pick the sprays of leaves at any time of the year. The tree can be cut back by two thirds every year for oil production.

USES OF TEA TREE

Culinary Primarily used as a refreshing tea by the Aborigines – it can be used with fruit juice on a hot day to refresh and revive, and added to jams, jellies and fruit punch.

Medicinal Use the crushed fresh leaves to open a blocked nose by inhaling the refreshing scent. Make a tea for both chronic and acute infections like glandular fever, cystitis, coughs, colds, 'flu, bronchitis, as a gargle for sore throats, and as a douche for thrush and itchy hot vaginal infections. To make the tea use ¼ cup fresh sprigs. Pour over this 1 cup boiling water. Stand 5 minutes. Strain and add honey or fruit juice. Take either hot or chilled. The oil, like the fresh leaves, is active against all three varieties of infectious organisms: bacteria, viruses and fungi. It is also anti-inflammatory, expectorant, acts against parasites, but is non-toxic, non-irritant and can be applied directly to the skin for insect bites, rashes, fever blisters, athlete's foot, acne spots, chickenpox blisters, warts, plantar warts and even boils and ringworm.

Cosmetic With its amazing antibacterial, antifungal and antiseptic qualities, tea tree is the most exciting cosmetic ingredient and is used in everything from soaps and shampoos to toothpaste and mouthwashes. Use as a lotion (see recipe section) to dab frequently on oily spotty skin, or use as a spritz spray. Also good for enlarged pores and as a rinse after shampooing the hair.

Other uses Use sprays of fresh tea tree sprigs tied in bundles to rub onto counter tops and window sills to chase flies and mosquitoes, and stand a vase in the kitchen with a few drops of tea tree oil in the water to clear the air.

Thyme

Family Labiatae
Species *Thymus* species
Origin Mediterranean regions
Plant perennial
Height groundcover up to 15 cm
Exposure full sun
Propagation cuttings
Uses culinary, medicinal, cosmetic

Not only is thyme indispensable in cooking but now, as never before, thyme finds itself being tested for everything from its antibiotic principles to its volatile oil, thymol, which is used to cure mouth ailments. Some researchers say it can kill bacteria in 40 seconds!

Thyme was used as a medicine and food preservative in ancient Greece, where it still grows today in profusion. The sheep and goats of Greece were encouraged to graze on banks of wild thyme to make their meat tastier and, in biblical times when people sacrificed animals (often a lamb), the meat was sprinkled with fresh thyme to make it, one assumes, more enticing to the celestial gods.

Of the 150 or so varieties only a few are worth growing here in the heat of our African sun. Through the years I have found these varieties the most rewarding:

- Cooking thyme (*Thymus vulgaris*): Savoury and fragrant, this is the best of all for cooking. It maintains most of its flavour when dried too, so is excellent for salts, 'pinch of herbs' mixtures and oils. This is the most well-known thyme.
- Lemon thyme (*T. citriodorus*): This sometimes comes in a variegated or golden form and has a strong lemony scent and flavour. It makes a neat round mound and creeps most beguilingly as it matures. Excellent as a tea and in desserts, syrups, jams and preserves. Its close cousin, silver posy or silver lemon queen (*T. citriodorus*), has lovely silvery foliage.
- Creeping thyme (*T. serpyllum*): Excellent as a groundcover, this is the most prolific of the creeping thymes and it is a good one for repelling insects, planted under roses, between tomatoes and beans, or it can be used to cover seats and banks. It is best used in sweet dishes.
- Bressingham thyme (*T. coccineus; T. alba*): These are adorable low, creeping decorative thymes with tiny pink or white flowers. I use them between stepping stones or in low walks where they creep charmingly. They are excellent used as insect repellents, but not as flavourings and tend to be more delicate in growth habit.

Lemon thyme (Thymus citriodorus)

Bressingham thyme (Thymus coccineus)

- Doone Valley Thyme: Has a mass of pink flowers and forms a low prolific mat of sprigs. Use as an insect repellent or as a lemony flavouring.

....

CULTIVATION Low, shrubby and tough, all the thymes need well-drained soil and full sun. They make superb pot plants, but do need a sunny balcony or windowsill. All the thymes will withstand drought, heat, frost and strong winds. In August's first warmer spring days, prune the old growth back, dig in a few spadefuls of rich compost and water well. Within a month there will be a tender mass of new little shoots, just begging to be plucked for that spring soup or delicious stirfry!

PROPAGATION Easily propagated from cuttings. Thumb length sprigs pressed into wet sand root easily, or chop off pieces of the clump.

HARVESTING AND PROCESSING Thyme is at its best fresh, but also dries well. Sprigs tossed onto newspaper in the shade and turned daily, dry in three days. Rub through a coarse sieve and discard the little sticks.

COMPANION PLANTING Thyme repels cabbage fly, white fly and aphids. Plant near onions, cabbage and brinjals. Plant the creeping thymes under strawberries and tomatoes.

USES OF THYME

Culinary If I had to choose only one herb with which to cook, I am sure it would be thyme! It gives everything pizzazz, be it fish, scrambled eggs, chicken stuffing or baked potatoes! It gives that boost so needed if you're striving for healthy, tasty food without monosodium glutamate, and if you're cutting back on salt, reach for the thyme. Thyme also breaks down fatty foods in the body, so include it in poultry stuffings, stirfries, stews, casseroles, roasts and cheese dishes.

Medicinal Thyme – in a tea or aromatherapy oil, especially the lemon thymes – is antiseptic and antibacterial, soothing sore throats, coughs, colds, allergic rhinitis, hay fever, back pain, aches and pains, poor digestion, scabies and lice, ringworm and thrush, athlete's foot, chest ailments, in particular asthma and bronchitis, hangovers, insomnia and poor circulation, and stimulating the body's production of white blood corpuscles to resist infection. Thyme has antiseptic, expectorant and antispasmodic properties. It soothes fungal and inflammatory conditions and is now claimed as one of the anti-ageing herbs. For thyme tea, use the lemon thymes or creeping thyme (*Thymus serpyllum*). Add ¼ cup fresh sprigs to 1 cup boiling water. Stand 5 minutes. Strain, squeeze in a little lemon juice and sip slowly.

Cooking thyme (Thymus vulgaris)

Creeping thyme (Thymus serpyllum)

Cosmetic Thyme is tremendously effective for acne and problem greasy skins, as well as dandruff and itchy scalp. A lotion can be made from lemon or creeping thyme (see recipe section). A lemon thyme steamer is particularly good for clogged greasy skins and large pores (inhale deeply at the same time as the oils have a marvellous effect on the lungs). Place 1 cup of lemon thyme sprigs in a large bowl, pour over this 1½ litres of boiling water and with a towel tent over the head and the bowl, steam for 5 minutes.

Other uses Mixed thymes make a superb deodorising potpourri (see recipe section) and spray for white fly and aphids (see recipe section).

Turmeric

Family **Zingberaceae**
Species ***Curcuma longa (=Curcuma domestica)***
Origin **native to southern Asia and India**
Plant **perennial**
Height **70-80 cm; space 1 m apart**
Soil **rich, loamy, moist soil**
Exposure **partial shade**
Propagation **cuttings from the rhizome**
Uses **culinary, medicinal**

Much loved in southern Asia where it has been a favourite in Indian cookery, particularly in curry mixes, it is only during the last two decades that turmeric's therapeutic actions have been researched and understood. In recent times there has been an upsurge of interest in foods that have health benefits like lowering high cholesterol, cancer prevention or that have anti-inflammatory actions – and turmeric does all of that and more besides.

The ancient Greeks used turmeric to create orange and yellow dyes and traditional Chinese physicians used it 3 000 years ago to treat arthritis, and liver and chest conditions. Around 1870, scientists created 'turmeric paper' – thin strips of paper brushed with a mixture of water and the brilliant yellow root powder and then dried. They found if this paper were to be exposed to alkaline substances it turned red-brown. This turmeric paper was used for several decades as a test for alkalinity until it was replaced in the early 20th century by litmus paper which is still used today!

CULTIVATION Turmeric prefers light shade, and humid conditions in a tropical environment. Spray the leaves with water frequently.

PROPAGATION The sole means of propagation is by small pieces with a bud or eye of the ginger-like rhizome. Plant 1 metre apart in richly composted well-dug soil.

HARVESTING AND PROCESSING Harvest the rhizomes at the end of autumn before the coldest time of the year. Dry the pieces of root in the sun, turning daily. Then grind these down to a fine powder.

COMPANION PLANTING The mints enjoy being close to turmeric as they thrive in its shade and moisture. Melissa and violets also do well next to turmeric.

USES OF TURMERIC

Culinary In Indian pharmacopoeias turmeric is listed as an important digestive herb and is added to sauces, rice dishes, curries, vegetable dishes, like brinjals and green peppers, and it turns curried eggs into a gourmet dish. In several cultures turmeric is added to savoury dishes because it is effective against the salmonella bacterium, which causes food poisoning.

Medicinal Research on turmeric has found the yellow pigment curcumin to be an effective immune system stimulant with excellent anti-inflammatory action and strong anti-microbial properties. Ongoing research now finds it is a valuable protective remedy for those at risk of developing cancer, but more research is still needed. For circulatory ailments turmeric is proving to be important, and for acidity, bloating and gastritis, a cup of tumeric tea is beautifully soothing, and it eases nausea, sour belching and heartburn, and helps to lower cholesterol. To make turmeric tea add 1 teaspoon turmeric powder to 1 cup of boiling water, mix well and sip slowly. Take one cup a day for 10 days, then give it a break for 2-4 days.

Turmeric has anticoagulant actions, which lessen the pain in arthritic swellings, soothe skin ailments like psoriasis, eczema and fungal infections, and improve the liver's action. Made into a paste with a little warm water, it is an excellent poultice for psoriasis outbreaks, wounds and grazes and for athlete's foot. Turmeric is now also being prescribed by some doctors to lower the risk of strokes – taken as 1 cup of turmeric tea on alternate days. Asthma sufferers find relief from turmeric tea to which 1 teaspoon of aniseed has been added. An Indian grandmother told me ½ teaspoon turmeric powder in a little hot water eases anxiety, travel sickness and sore feet! Quite a herb, isn't it? And we thought it was only good in curries!

Vetiver Grass

Khus-khus grass

Family **Gramineae**

Species *Vetiveria zizanioides*

Origin **India**

Plant **perennial**

Height **1,5 m; space 1,5 m apart**

Soil **any soil**

Exposure **full sun**

Propagation **division of the grass clump**

Uses **culinary, medicinal, cosmetic**

Indigenous to India originally, some argue that it is also so widespread in Java, Brazil and Réunion Island that it is indigenous to those countries as well. On a botanical tour of Réunion Island, I was excited to see tracts of land under vetiver cultivation, with lots of handcrafts on exhibition and on sale in the markets and bundles of fragrant roots offered for sale everywhere. Hats and baskets are woven out of the tough grass and it is also used for thatching, and the roots are so exquisitely fragrant for scenting cupboards, I am astonished it is so rarely grown.

Foolproof and undemanding, with its mass of fragrant roots offering probably the most important aid to soil and water retention, vetiver is used as living contours, embankments and retainer walls in arid countries throughout the world.

CULTIVATION A deep weekly watering is all that this easy-to-grow plant requires. The thick mass of fine hairy roots extends vigorously within a few weeks, forming a substantial clump within two seasons.

PROPAGATION Plant a small tuft cut from the mother clump, leaves cut off, in a compost-filled hole in full sun, spaced 1,5 metres apart. Keep it well watered until it is established.

HARVESTING AND PROCESSING After 2-3 years (and then every August) dig up the clump, chop off the fragrant roots, separate the tufts of grass and plant them out 1,5 m apart. You will literally have 50 or more plants from every clump.

COMPANION PLANTING Cucumbers, squash and pumpkin thrive planted next to it.

USES OF VETIVER GRASS

Culinary A tea made from the fresh roots can be mixed with fruit juice and served chilled with crushed ice.

Medicinal Vetiver tea is taken for all sorts of anxieties, upsets, burn-out, for emotional healing, fear, guilt, depression and pain. In India and Brazil it is given for digestive upsets and restlessnesss. To make the tea use ¼ cup fresh leaves and/or roots. Pour over this 1 cup boiling water. Stand 5 minutes. Strain and sip slowly. A poultice of the roots warmed in hot water is bound over a swollen aching joint, held in place with crêpe bandages, or used as a rub with a little oil to ease stiffness and spasm.

Cosmetic The strong mossy smell of vetiver root has made it extremely popular in cosmetics, bath preparations and men's colognes and aftershaves. Fresh roots added to the bath tied in a face cloth and rubbed with soap make an exceptional body cleanser and muscle relaxant, not only softening the skin but also taking away those tense lines and muscle spasms. Vetiver massage cream (see recipe section) is wonderful for aching neck and shoulders and tired sore feet!

Other uses As a potpourri ingredient, vetiver acts as a superb fixative, holding the fragrant oils indefinitely. The root acts as an insect repellent. Hats woven of vetiver grass and dipped into water will keep the wearer cool and flies and mosquitoes away. Bundles of grass tied in four places and then tied into blinds – hung over an open window and sprayed with water – act as a natural looking air-conditioner.

Violet

Family **Violaceae**
Species ***Viola odorata***
Origin **Europe and Asia**
Plant **perennial**
Height **10 cm; space 30 cm apart**
Soil **Well-dug, well-composted soil**
Exposure **semi-shade**
Propagation **runners and clump division**
Uses **culinary, medicinal, cosmetic**

The much-loved garden violet goes back in history to the first century AD, growing in Syria, Turkey, North Africa and also in Europe. Loved and grown in both cottage gardens and the great palace gardens across the world, this charming herb has always been known as the flower of Aphrodite, the Goddess of Love. It was Napoleon's favourite flower – Josephine wore violets on her wedding day and Napoleon gave her violets on every anniversary and finally planted them on her grave. The sweet violet was so loved by the Greeks that they made it the symbol of Athens. **Warning**: Never confuse the old-fashioned purple garden violet with the pot plant, African violet. It is only the garden violet or sweet violet (*Viola odorata*) that is used medicinally. The African violet is poisonous.

CULTIVATION Resilient, tough, and an easy-to-grow perennial, it requires little except a well-dug bed with lots of compost dug in and a twice-weekly deep watering. In late winter and spring the flowers are at their most prolific, but you will always have a few flowers throughout the year and the heart-shaped leaves are evergreen. It literally never has an off period.

PROPAGATION Propagation is by runners sharply dug off the mother clump in autumn.

HARVESTING AND PROCESSING Pick leaves at any time of the year and flowers when they appear.

COMPANION PLANTING Violets act as a trap for insects, luring them away from other plants – for example, edging a bed of lettuces and spinach – the insects prefer the violets and leave the others alone. Try violets alongside cabbages and kale to keep them aphid-free.

USES OF VIOLETS

Culinary Our grandmothers made crystallised violets – these crisp and dainty little flowers can be used to decorate cakes and desserts. The fresh flowers and leaves added to salads and fruit salads give a fresh mild taste and look beautiful. Violet jam is quite exceptional and made in spring for someone special, is an unforgettable gift.

Medicinal Rootstock, leaves and flowers have been used through the centuries as a tea for coughs and colds, bronchitis and 'flu. Violet tea is an excellent decongestant and a soothing expectorant and it is particularly helpful in treating whooping cough, sinus headaches and blocked sinuses. It also has a cooling nature and has been used since the earliest centuries for treating hangovers! To make the tea use $\frac{1}{4}$ cup fresh leaves and flowers. Pour over this 1 cup boiling water. Stand 5 minutes. Strain, sweeten with honey if liked and sip slowly. For a headache often just chewing 5 flowers, and another 3 or 4 an hour later, will ease it. It is also excellent for hay fever, both chewing the flowers as well as taking a cup of violet tea. Many a nursing mother has used violet leaves mashed to a pulp with warm water and a little almond oil as a soothing poultice for sore cracked nipples. Violets also have a long-time reputation for treating tumours, both benign and cancerous.

Cosmetic There was intense interest in the violet in the last half of the 19th century, and violet creams, lotions and perfumes were sold everywhere. There is no doubt that its soothing action, as a cream or lotion (see recipe section), is an excellent treatment for fragile thread veins on the face and for sensitive skins, rashes and spots.

Other uses In the compost heap violet leaves break down quickly, helping the compost to heat up.

Watercress & Landcress

Scurvy grass

Family **Cruciferae**

Species *Nasturtium officinale* ● *Lepidum sativum*

Origin Europe and temperate regions throughout the world

Plant annual or biennial (perennial in cool areas)

Height 15 cm

Soil water-logged soil, moving water

Exposure sun and partial shade

Propagation seed, rooted pieces

Uses culinary, medicinal

Watercress (*Nasturtium officinale*) is an ancient food and medicinal plant that in spring and early summer appears in gently flowing streams in temperate areas throughout the world. The ancient Greeks used it in salads and soups, it formed part of religious ceremonies and festivals, and the sick, the mentally disabled, and the aged were urged to include it in the diet to build both physical and mental health. The very similar landcress (*Lepidum sativum*) was grown in ancient Egypt, Italy and Greece as an energiser and strengthener for the soldiers and pyramid builders. Both are superb circulatory herbs, and it has since been scientifically established that both have a high vitamin C content and a remarkable supply of health building minerals. Both landcress and watercress were staple foods in spring and autumn and the seed was found in pharoah's tombs.

CULTIVATION Watercress likes partial shade and – as its name suggests – very damp conditions. It can be biennial in favourable conditions. The ideal situation is along the edges of furrows in running water, under a dripping tap or grown in a pot in a bowl of water which continually overflows. It runs to seed easily, so needs to be picked frequently. Landcress is sown from seed in compost-rich moist ground in sun or partial shade in autumn.

PROPAGATION Easily grown from seed, watercress needs cool conditions, so if you live in a hot part of the country it is advisable to sow in autumn for a winter salad crop. Landcress is propagated from seed only. It self seeds readily, appearing all over the garden in late autumn and winter and early spring, and it transplants easily.

HARVESTING AND PROCESSING Pick the outer lower leaves or the side-shoot rosettes. Sprouts of landcress grown indoors on trays of wet cotton wool should be snipped off with scissors. This is part of the wonderful mustard and cress ritual so loved by children all over the world. Lay a large piece of cotton wool in a flat dish or tray, soak with water and then sprinkle the cress and the mustard seeds over it – keep them in separate sections. Never let it dry out and once the little seeds sprout, let them grow to at least 4 cm in height before pulling them up to eat or cutting them off with kitchen scissors.

USES OF WATERCRESS

Culinary Best known as an ingredient in salads and stirfries, watercress is also delicious steamed and it makes a mouth-watering soup with onions and potatoes.

Medicinal Watercress is an excellent source of iodine, so will greatly help an under-active thyroid. It also is a superb diuretic, expectorant and a natural laxative. Excellent for gout, to flush uric acid from the system; it is also effective for respiratory tract infections, chronic catarrh, bronchitis and excessive mucous, TB, and to boost the whole immune system as a 'flu and cold preventative. Rich in vitamins A and C, watercress belongs to the powerful crucifer family – others are broccoli, cabbage, kale, cauliflower and horseradish – and should feature prominently in the diet of anyone with cancer or as a cancer preventative. It is thought to stimulate the appetite and to relieve indigestion and was once considered to be a spring tonic and blood-purifying herb.

Cosmetic Eaten three times a week, watercress helps to clear the skin. Apply the juice to skin blemishes frequently.

Other uses Watercress that has gone to seed is one of the best compost-makers I know of.

Watercress   *Landcress*

Winter Savory

Family	Labiatae
Species	*Satureja montana*
Origin	Mediterranean region
Plant	perennial
Height	12-15 cm; space 20 cm apart
Soil	Well-dug, well-composted soil
Exposure	full sun
Propagation	cuttings
Uses	culinary, medicinal, cosmetic

Winter savory is a much respected herb that has been used as a food flavouring and medicine for over 2 000 years. It was once considered an aphrodisiac and the ancient Egyptians and Romans used it in love potions. With its close cousin, summer savory (*S. hortensis*), it was an ingredient in a wide variety of wines and drinks sold as aphrodisiacs over the last several centuries! It was the Romans who did the most to popularise this easily grown herb – they used it in breads, vegetable dishes and with wines to treat a variety of ailments. From Italy it spread quickly into the rest of Europe, and to America by the 15th century – a valued antiseptic herb, as well as one of the much sought-after strewing herbs. Little sprays of tiny white flowers, prolific in summer, last well as garnishes and in tiny posies or tussie-mussies.

CULTIVATION Winter savory needs well-dug, rich, loamy soil with a good yearly dressing of compost in full sun for it to flourish unattended for many years. It never reaches much more than 12-15 cm in height.

PROPAGATION Propagation is by cuttings which root easily in moist sand-filled trays. Often bits of the actual plant can be cut away with a sharp spade and quickly planted into damp prepared soil where they will continue to grow as though nothing had ever happened.

HARVESTING AND PROCESSING Being a tough evergreen perennial, winter savory can be picked at any time of the year. It also dries well and can be combined with thyme, oregano and celery as an excellent flavouring for all savoury dishes.

COMPANION PLANTING Excellent as a companion plant to tomatoes, beans and onions; much loved by bees, both winter and summer savory are ideal for planting near hives.

USES OF WINTER SAVORY

Culinary Winter savory is one of the world's best digestives: a mere sprig in the cooking pot will break down all the dried bean, lentil and cabbage gases. A sprig steamed with fresh green beans or green pea soup makes the world of difference. The taste of winter (and summer) savory is pungent, peppery, and it has an almost thyme-and-mint combination, which makes it delicious with cheese and pasta dishes as well. Dried winter savory is used to flavour salami and other dried sausages and patés.

Medicinal The non-woody flowering tops contain resins, tannins and components like carvacol and cymene, which give winter savory astringent, antiseptic, antispasmodic, expectorant and tonic properties. Made into a tea it will give relief to sore throats, coughs and colds, digestive upsets, flatulence, thick mucus in the bronchii and menstrual pains. To make the tea use ¼ cup fresh sprigs and pour over this 1 cup boiling water. Stand 5 minutes and strain. Add a squeeze of lemon juice and sip slowly. A tea that is made with equal quantities fresh green lucerne acts as an immune system builder and an effective gargle.

Gardeners love to rub the soothing crushed leaves over insect bites and stings as it immediately cools the area. I keep winter savory sprigs in a bottle of grape vinegar for the staff at the Herbal Centre to rub onto wasp stings.

Cosmetic With its antiseptic, astringent qualities, it can be used in a facial steam (see recipe section) or lotion and can also be added to the bath – especially good after a long day's sport or when one is exhausted.

Wormwood

Family **Compositae**
Species *Artemesia absinthium*
Origin **Europe, Central Asia and eastern parts of the USA where it has naturalised**
Plant **perennial**
Height **30-70 cm; space 1 m apart**
Soil **well-drained, thrives in compost-enriched soil**
Exposure **sun**
Propagation **cuttings mainly, seed is fairly slow to germinate**
Uses **medicinal, insecticide**

Wormwood is one of the most truly bitter herbs known to mankind. An ancient and extraordinary herb with myth, magic and history woven about its revered past, it is probably best known as the bitter flavouring agent in absinthe – a strong addictive alcoholic drink made in France in the 19th century – and the old favourite vermouth.

A silky, feathery, beautiful grey plant, it gets its name from being used through the centuries as a vermifuge, and was hung at the door to protect the home from the evil spirits. Healers painted pictures of wormwood on their walls and doors as a protection and as a symbol of their profession. Wormwood extract and oil was mixed into the inks that were used on scrolls and parchment in the Middle Ages to protect from insect damage and to deter mice.

CULTIVATION Plant in well-dug, well-composted soil, in full sun about 1 metre apart. Keep moist until well established. It gets untidy if not trimmed. Staking may be necessary. Water twice weekly.

PROPAGATION Cuttings taken in spring and early summer root easily. Sow fresh seed in trays and prick out seedlings when big enough to handle and plant in bags to harden off before planting out in full sun.

HARVESTING AND PROCESSING Pick sprays of leaves and use fresh any time of the year in insect-repelling sprays.

COMPANION PLANTING Grow wormwood near carrots and potatoes, but note that it has an inhibiting effect on fennel, sage, anise and caraway.

USES OF WORMWOOD

Medicinal Medical research finds that wormwood has astonishing anti-inflammatory abilities, as well as antidepressant and pain-relieving actions. This is possibly why medieval monks used a wormwood dressing of hot leaves bound over sprains, arthritic and rheumatic swellings, and bound over a swollen colic throbbing stomach to ease the burning pain. Today its medicinal values have been largely forgotten and wormwood is used mainly as a superb insecticide. **Warning**: There are many plants that fall under the *Artemesia* mantle, virtually all are pungently aromatic and potentially dangerous. Do not take wormwood internally, except under medical supervision. Habitual use of wormwood, and incidently of absinthe, could cause convulsions, fits, stomach cramps, intoxication, vomiting, delirium and vertigo.

Mugwort (*Artemesia vulgaris*) has similar properties and is not as dangerous as wormwood, taken internally as an anti-rheumatic, stimulating digestion tonic, a uterine stimulant and a menstrual regulator. Our own indigenous *Artemesia* or 'wildeals' (*Artemesia afra*) is another gentler alternative. Always let your doctor guide you on taking any *Artemesia* internally. Avoid any contact during pregnancy.

Insecticide A wormwood tea (see recipe section) was used centuries ago to disinfect cuts and grazes and that same tea acts as an excellent repellent for fleas – use it to wash the carpet, to spray around young seedlings for aphids, white fly and ants in the kitchen. Dogs washed in a bath containing very diluted wormwood tea will not have any fleas. Dried powdered wormwood is a good insecticide that deters ants and fruit flies from trees and act as a repellent for aphids, mite and weevils.

Yarrow

Millefoil ● Milfoil ● Nosebleed ● Soldier's Woundwort
● Carpenter's Weed

Family **Compositae**

Species *Achillea millefolium*

Origin **Europe and Western Asia**

Plant **perennial**

Height **60 cm flowering head; space 50 cm apart**

Soil **any soil**

Exposure **full sun**

Propagation **runners**

Uses **medicinal, cosmetic**

Ancient and revered, no cottage or cloister garden was without yarrow. Once known as 'Herba Militaris', yarrow was used to staunch war wounds. Achilles reputedly used yarrow leaves to heal the warriors during the Battle of Troy, hence its Latin name *Achillea*. So important was this lovely plant that robes were embroidered with yarrow sprigs and the leaves pressed into precious books to keep them insect free. For the snow-bound winters yarrow was preserved in vinegar to treat the soldiers and the sick. The ancient Chinese used yarrow as the herb of divination and yarrow sticks carefully stripped and measured were used when consulting their ancient oracle, the I Ching.

CULTIVATION Yarrow is an excellent plant for dry, hot conditions. It prefers light, sandy soil but I have grown excellent specimens in thick, clay soil that only had a few spadefuls of compost dug into it. Plant the feathery little 'crowns' 50 cm apart and they will spread with runners to form a thick mat of fine fern-like leaves from which the 30-60 cm stems of flat-headed 'million flowers' arise.

PROPAGATION Rooted runners dug off the mother clump and immediately planted 50 cm apart in compost-enriched moist soil. Water twice weekly for the first few weeks after planting out. Divide the clump every 2-3 years.

HARVESTING AND PROCESSING Pick the flowers as they start to open. The leaves can be picked at any time of the year. **Note**: It is only the old-fashioned pink and white yarrow that I write of here.

COMPANION PLANTING Beneficial to all vegetables, especially mealies and cucumbers. Edge the vegetable beds with yarrow as it is an excellent insecticide.

USES OF YARROW

Medicinal Yarrow actually stops bleeding. In Scotland a traditional wound ointment made with yarrow is still made today. It also increases sweating and is a mild diuretic and an anti-inflammatory herb of note. Yarrow is probably one of the best fever-breaking herbs, and modern research now approves! If you get a rose thorn scrape or a grazed knuckle or a deep leg scratch while gardening, just apply a crushed leaf and hold it for a minute over the area. I use a rolled-up fresh leaf placed in the nostril to stop a nosebleed, or warmed leaves held behind an ear that aches. Take a cup of yarrow tea daily to reduce high blood pressure, to regulate menstrual flow and for premenstrual tension. It will also help to clear the system of cold and 'flu germs and used as a mouthwash helps to heal gums and mouth infections. The tea is also an age-old treatment for chickenpox, measles and rheumatism, and even diabetes. To make the tea use ¼ cup fresh leaves and a few flowers. Pour over this 1 cup boiling water. Stand 5 minutes. Strain and sip slowly. Take a cup a day for 7 days, then give it a break for one week and continue. Yarrow's ability to soothe bruises is well known – use as a warm poultice over the area.

Cosmetic Yarrow lotion (see recipe section) is a superb treatment for problem skins and a remarkable cleanser and freshener that tightens pores and firm the skin.

Other uses A handful of fresh yarrow leaves dug into the compost heap will activate it and break it down and ferment even the toughest material in a matter of weeks.

Epilogue

My publisher's stipulation for this book: I was only allowed to select 100 of the most important herbs. And this has caused me much angst and indecision!

My many years of working with these precious plants has only sharpened my interest, augmented my passion, and overwhelmed me with the great diversity and the unending wonder of nature's miracle plants. To select my best 100 herbs has been pure agony! I could have found equal that number that I want to teach you about, but publishing space prohibits that.

Instead, I leave you with a short list of herbs that you will notice as they come to the fore in the century ahead. Little known at present, except in homeopathic and medical research circles, but, given the speed with which we search for cures for more and more increasingly worrying epidemics and illnesses, nature is going to be turned to by more and more scientists, as a last resort, perhaps.

I want to be there when they do, when we are again made aware, through scientific validation, of the wonders of these often well-known everyday plants that ancient civilisations and cultures knew and used; plants that do not just grow obscurely in distant jungles in faraway lands, but plants that are here and now, and part of our lives, growing in our gardens just as these 100 herbs do – there for our daily use, in our own country.

Here are only a few of what's coming:

- *Aspilia mossambicensis*: A leaf swallowed as the chimps do in Tanzania has a 'velcro' effect, attaching to worms in the intestine and expelling them.
- *Astragalus membranaceus*: Encourages the bone marrow to produce phagocytes – cells that destroy viruses and bacteria.
- *Camptotheca acuminata* (Cancer Tree or Tree of Joy): From Tibet, its primary constituent is camptothecin, which inhibits the enzyme linked with cell division and so stunts tumour growth.

- *Cinchona pubescens*: A tropical tree from Peru that cures malaria.
- *Coleus forskohlii*: An Indian treatment for high blood pressure, bronchial asthma and glaucoma.
- *Dioscorea species*; *Dioscorea villosa* (Yam): For oral contraception and for menopause.
- *Ephedra sinica* (Ma Huang): The Chinese asthmatic herb.
- *Eupatorium species* (Gravel Root): Clears urinary stones.
- *Guaiacum officinale*: A South American tree that clears venereal disease and herpes, and is a local anaesthetic.
- *Hydrastis canadensis* (Golden Seal): Activates white blood cells, destroys viruses and shrinks tumours.
- *Physostigma venenosum* (Calabar Bean): Treats eye ailments and optic nerve damage and is presently being researched for Alzheimer's disease.
- *Rauwolfia serpentina*: From India, it treats hypertension and acts as a tranquilliser to a racing heart.
- *Schisandra chinensis*: This herb stimulates the nervous system, improves mental clarity and reflex nervous responses and is an adaptogenic herb, helping the body adapt to stress.
- *Withania somnifera* (Ashwaganda): Recovery from long-term illness like lupus or rheumatoid arthritis, as a cancer preventative.
- *Zanthoxylum americanum* (Prickly Ash): The toothache tree.

These are just a handful of the medicines of the future. I want to be there to share these new medicines, to grow them and to use them with you. I look forward to the next book ... perhaps the next 100 best herbs. As my old herbalist friend from Mexico said so long ago, 'Via con Dios'. Go with God – we will find these herbs.

Herbal Centre

De Wildt

North West Province

South Africa

End of Summer 2002

Recipes

CULINARY

The culinary uses of herbs are legendary, but since this is not intended as a recipe book and space is limited, I share here only a handful of my favourite recipes mentioned in the main text.

BASIL PESTO
Serve this classic sauce with pasta, baked potatoes, grills, etc.

4 cups fresh sweet basil leaves • 2-3 cloves garlic, peeled • sea salt to taste • 4 tablespoons pine nuts or walnuts or pecan nuts • 5-6 tablespoons olive oil • 4 tablespoons parmesan cheese

In a large pestle and mortar pound the leaves with the garlic. Add the nuts, salt and a little oil, pounding all the time. Add the parmesan alternatively with the rest of the oil until a smooth paste is formed. Serves 6

CALIFORNIAN POPPY HEALTH BOOSTER SALAD
This golden winter salad is not only a feast for the eye, it is an extraordinary health booster.

1 pineapple cut into small chunks • 1 small pawpaw or papino cut into chunks • 1 cup celery thinly sliced • 1 cup finely shredded green outer leaves of cabbage • 1 cup Californian poppy petals • 1 cup finely grated raw carrots • 1 cup finely grated raw butternut • juice of 1 lemon • 2 tablespoons finely chopped parsley • 2 tablespoons finely chopped mint

Mix everything together and serve with crusty brown bread and cheese. Serves 6-8

CORIANDER PICKLING SPICE
Marinade fish or meat or chicken in this spicy flavouring or use it hot to pour over onions or slices of cucumber.

3 tablespoons coriander seeds • 1 tablespoon cumin seeds • 1 tablespoon mustard seed • ½ tablespoon caraway seed • ½ cup caramel brown sugar • 2 cups good quality grape vinegar

With a pestle and mortar crush the seeds into the sugar. When well mixed, add the grape vinegar and mix well. Store in a screw-top bottle. It keeps well.

DILL PICKLES
As a young bride I was taught to make dill pickles by a neighbouring farmer's wife who spoke no English, read no books and yet used the recipe that was handed down the centuries and was taught to her by her grandmother. It remains one of the best recipes I know.

30 small, unpeeled cucumbers • 2 litres good white grape vinegar • 4 tablespoons dill seeds • 2 tablespoons mustard seeds • 2 tablespoons coriander seeds • 2 cups dark honey

Cut the cucumbers lengthways into finger-sized pieces and pack into small screw-top bottles. Gently simmer the grape vinegar, dill, mustard and coriander seeds and honey in a saucepan for 15 minutes. Stir carefully and ladle the hot spicy vinegar into the bottles, seal and store at least 2 weeks before you eat the pickles either on bread and butter or served with cold meats and beetroot salad. This amount is enough to fill about 4-6 small to medium-sized screw-top jars.

DILL WATER
This delicious iced dill tea improves both the appetite and the digestion.

2 teaspoons dill seeds, crushed lightly or ¼ cup fresh dill leaves and flowers • 3 cloves • honey to taste

Pour 1 cup of boiling water over the dill seeds. Add the cloves and leave to stand 5 minutes. Stir well and strain. Sweeten with honey and refrigerate. Serve with the meal, taking one sip at a time. Serves 1

LAVENDER AND GRANADILLA DRINK
Wonderfully thirst quenching on a hot day, this has become one of the favourite drinks at the Herbal Centre.

½ cup fresh lavender flowers (use Lavandula intermedia 'Margaret Roberts') • 1 stick cinnamon • 4 sprigs of melissa • 6 allspice berries • 1 litre granadilla juice • honey to taste

Pour 1 litre of boiling water over the lavender flowers, add the cinnamon stick, melissa and allspice berries. Leave to cool and strain. Add the granadilla juice and sweeten with a touch of honey. Serve chilled. Serves 6

CLASSIC MINT SAUCE
Serve over roast mutton or mutton sausages or baked potatoes.

1 cup garden mint sprigs finely chopped • ½ cup grape vinegar • ½ cup brown sugar • ½ cup warm water

Mix everything well until the sugar has dissolved. Stand for at least 1 hour before serving. Serves 4-6

MINT COOL DRINK
Use corn mint or spearmint – they combine beautifully with all fruits. We love using mango, granadilla or pineapple juice.

1 cup corn mint or spearmint sprigs • 1 litre of your favourite fruit juice • honey to taste

Place the mint sprigs in a jug and pour over this 1 litre of boiling water. Stand aside and cool. Strain, add the fruit juice and sweeten with a little honey. Serve chilled with ice and mint leaves. Serves 6

MOCK CAPERS
Pickled in vinegar fresh green nasturtium seeds are delicious in cheese sandwiches, served with cold meats, mixed into cream cheese and chopped into mayonnaise.

fresh green nasturtium seeds • a fresh bay leaf • 1 cup brown grape vinegar • 1 tablespoon coriander seeds • 6 cardamom pods • ½ cup honey

Pack as many fresh green nasturtium seeds into a small pickling jar as it will hold. Tuck in the bay leaf down the side. Heat the grape vinegar with the coriander seeds, cardamom pods and honey. Bring to the boil and simmer 1 minute. Pour the hot vinegar mixture over the nasturtium seeds and seal. Leave to infuse at least 10 days before eating.

Oats Health Breakfast

The perfect start to a chilly winter's day!

1 cup large oats flakes (not the instant kind) ● 2 cups boiling water ● ½ cup raisins ● ⅓ cup linseed ● ½ cup sunflower seeds

The night before, combine all the ingredients in a wide-mouthed thermos flask and mix well. The next morning it will still be hot. Spoon out and serve with plain yoghurt, honey and a sliced banana. Serves 1-2

Pickled Paprika

We use this old Hungarian recipe to pickle paprika in late summer for the winter months.

about 15-20 ripe paprikas ● 1 tablespoon coriander ● 1 tablespoon cumin seeds ● 10 cardamom pods ● bay leaves ● 1 litre brown grape vinegar ● 1 cup brown sugar ● 2 teaspoons coarse sea salt

Cut the succulent, ripe fruit into strips. Discard the seeds and pack into two large glass jars. Sprinkle in the coriander seeds, cumin seeds, cardamom and bay leaves. Boil the vinegar with the sugar and salt. Pour the hot vinegar over the paprika slices to the top. Seal well. Leave for at least 2 weeks before opening. Serve with cheese and cold meats, on cream cheese sandwiches or chop into stirfries.

Paprika Powder

Slice fully ripe paprikas and discard the seeds. Dry in the shade. (I thread nylon fishing line through each piece and hang the bright garland to dry over the stove.) When brittle, crush with a little coarse salt in a pestle and mortar or powder in a food processor. Store the paprika powder in a screw-top jar. Sprinkle over roasts and salads, stirfries and potatoes the way the Hungarians do.

Chicken and Nettle Broth

Our grandmothers made this nourishing soup all through winter to treat all sorts of ailments and build up resistance to the cold. You can grate or chop the vegetables or cook them whole and chop later.

a whole chicken ● a little sea salt ● 2 large onions, roughly chopped ● 4 large carrots, grated or thinly sliced ●

4 celery stalks and leaves, chopped ● ½ cup parsley, chopped ● 1 cup nettles, roughly chopped

Boil the chicken in 2 litres water with a little sea salt and the onions, carrots, celery, parsley and nettles until the meat falls off the bone. Then chop up the chicken and the vegetables and serve it for supper in big steaming bowls. This is pure, comforting health food that we need to recreate in our modern kitchens. It should simmer gently all day on the stove so that every little bit of goodness goes into the water, which you keep topped up. Don't even think of making this in a microwave.

Raspberry Vinegar

This makes a superb salad dressing. Into a bottle of good white grape vinegar, push in about 1 cup of fresh ripe raspberries and 1 raspberry leaf. Cork it and keep it out of the sun. Give it a daily shake. Leave to stand and mature for 3 weeks before using. The fruit will be perfectly preserved in the vinegar and will impart its glorious deep red colour to the vinegar. There is no need to strain out the fruit. Store in a dark cupboard to maintain the colour and flavour. Use in stirfries, sauces and with salads.

Classic Rocket Salad

This is one of the best known of all rocket dishes, much loved by Italian chefs.

500 g lean bacon, chopped into small pieces ● a little olive oil ● freshly ground black pepper ● 2 teaspoons crushed coriander seeds ● 4 cups of rocket leaves ● 1 cup green pepper, thinly sliced ● 1 cup dandelion leaves ● 1 cup mozarella cheese, cut into cubes ● juice of 1 lemon

Fry the bacon in the olive oil. Add the coriander seeds and black pepper. When the bacon is crisp, remove from the pan with a slotted spoon and drain on kitchen paper. In a salad bowl, tear the rocket leaves into smaller pieces. Add the green pepper and dandelion leaves. Lastly add the bacon pieces and the mozarella cubes. Squeeze over it all the juice of the lemon. Serve immediately. Serves 4-6

Rose Geranium Butter

This is a special culinary treat, perfect for a Sunday morning breakfast served with warm toast, scones or flapjacks.

3-4 tablespoons of rose geranium leaves, finely minced ● 1 cup soft butter ● 1 teaspoon cinnamon

Mix all the ingredients well. Spread onto scones, toast, pancakes, gingerbread, etc. and top with a little apple jelly or apricot jam.

HEALTH AND BEAUTY

This is a small collection of natural, easily applied remedies and beauty aids, all of which have stood the test of time. These are the remedies our great grandparents relied on – comforting, healing aids that ease the condition and soothe the pain. Caution: Never use these remedies to replace standard medical treatment. Always consult with your medical practitioner before you embark on any course of self-treatment.

BASIC LOTION

One of the best ways to use herbs is in the form of a versatile **lotion** that can be dabbed onto the skin with cotton wool pads, sprayed on as a **spritz** or used as a refreshing **splash**. It can be used for cuts, grazes and rashes; as a cleansing or astringent lotion, a facial tonic or aftershave lotion; added to the bath; or used as a final rinse for the hair. Most herbs can be made into a lotion – see the list below and refer back to the main entry on each herb for information on how to use the particular lotion. Use only fresh herbs. Make a fresh batch each day and apply frequently to the affected area. The recipe below makes 1 litre.

1 litre water ● Leaves, flowers, sprigs or roots of the herb of your choice (refer to the list below)

Simmer the recommended quantity of the herb in 1 litre water for 15 to 20 minutes. Stand to cool. Strain and use as recommended.

VARIATION

Use only the parts of the plant mentioned and do not combine herbs unless specified so below. Refer to the main herb entry for guidance on how to use the lotion. Use only fresh leaves and flowers.

Amaranth – 1 cup leaves
Bay – ½ cup leaves
Buckwheat – 1 cup leaves, flowers and seeds plus a cinnamon stick and 10 cloves
Burdock – ¾ cup leaves and stems and ½ cup chopped root
Calendula – 1 cup flowers
Catmint – 1 cup flowers (use *Nepeta mussini*) plus 5 cloves
Celery – 1 cup leaves
Chervil – 1 cup leaves
Comfrey – 1 cup leaves, roughly chopped
Costmary – 1 cup leaves plus ½ comfrey leaf
Elder – 1 cup flowers
Evening Primrose – 1 cup flowers plus 5 cloves
Feverfew – 1 cup leaves and a few flowers
Ground Ivy – 1 cup leaves
Hawthorn – 1 cup fresh berries or ½ cup dried berries (soaked overnight)
Lemon Grass – 1 cup leaves, roughly chopped
Lemon Verbena – 1 cup leaves
Lovage – use ½ cup leaves and boil for 10 minutes only
Lucerne – 1 cup sprigs and flowers
Melissa – 1 cup sprigs
Oregano – 1 cup sprigs
Parsley – 1 cup leaves and sprigs plus 5 cloves
Red Clover – 1 cup flowers and a few leaves
Rose – 1 cup rose petals
Roselle – ½ cup petals, calyxes and leaves
Soapwort – 2 cups leaves, flowers and stems
Strawberry – 1 cup leaves plus 1 cinnamon stick plus 10 cloves
Tansy – 1 cup leaves
Tea tree – use 1 cup sprigs; add 10 drops of tea tree essential oil to the cooled lotion
Thyme – 1 cup lemon thyme plus the rind of 1 lemon; add ½ cup apple cider vinegar to the cooled lotion
Violet – 1 cup leaves and flowers
Winter Savory – 1 cup sprigs
Yarrow – 1½ cups leaves and flowers

CARNATION MILK FOR SUNBURN

This gentle, easy-to-make treatment is very soothing for sunburnt skin. Simmer 1 cup carnation petals in 2 cups milk in a double boiler for 10 minutes. Strain. Add 2 teaspoons almond oil. Mix well. Dab onto the area when pleasantly warm or put it into a spritz bottle and spray the area frequently.

HORSERADISH FRECKLE LOTION

Simmer ½ cup grated horseradish leaves and flowers in 500 ml water for 10 minutes. Cool and strain. Dab on with soaked cotton wool pads.

POPPY PETAL ACNE LOTION

Use this as a wash or lotion for teenage acne or for oily, spotty skin.

1 cup field poppy petals ● *3 slices of lemon* ●
a dash of apple cider vinegar

Boil the petals with the lemon slices in 1 litre water for 10 minutes. Cool and strain. Add a dash of apple cider vinegar and dab on with soaked cotton wool pads.

QUEEN OF HUNGARY'S WATER

This is a modern version of the famous refining lotion used by Queen Isabella, still a beauty at age 78. Simmer 2 cups rosemary flower heads, 1 cup lemon verbena leaves, rind of 1 lemon, thinly pared, 6 cloves and ½ cup sage leaves together in 2 litres of collected rain water. Simmer gently for 20 minutes, cool, strain and keep in a sterilised bottle. Wring out pads of cotton wool in this and use as a toner after you have washed your face. Keep excess in the fridge.

ROSEWATER

Rosewater dates back to AD 980-1037, when the Arab physician Avicenna used it to treat skin ailments and mixed it with honey for use as a cough syrup. Boil 6 cups rose petals, a small twist of lemon rind and 4 cloves gently in 2 litres water for 15 minutes, with the lid on. Remove from the heat, strain and pour into pretty glass bottles with screw tops. Keep refrigerated. Use as a splash or spray over the face and neck and as a freshener in a spritz bottle on a long hot journey.

ROSEWATER AND GLYCERINE BODY LOTION

Take 4 tablespoons rosewater and add it to 2 tablespoons of glycerine bought from your chemist and 10 drops of rose essential oil and whisk gently. Pour into a screw-top bottle. For extra moisture, whisk in 1-3 tablespoons of good quality aqueous cream and 1 tablespoon almond oil. Use as a massage oil for dry skin, after the bath.

SILVER BIRCH LOTION FOR PROBLEM SKIN

Boil 1 cup silver birch leaves and catkins in 1 litre of water with 1 stick cinnamon for 20 minutes. Cool and strain. Add ½ cup witch hazel. Store in a screw-top bottle. Use on a pad of cotton wool to cleanse oily skin or to dab onto skin spots.

SAGE CLEANSING LOTION

Heat ½ cup sage leaves in 2 cups apple cider vinegar for 20 minute in a double boiler. Let it cool and pour into a screw-top bottle. Use as a cleansing lotion for oily skin and blackheads.

FACIAL STEAMER

A deep cleansing facial steam is a wonderful way of getting the skin really clean and refine the pores. Afterwards, strain the steamer and add to the bath for a whole body treat! Simmer 2 cups leaves and sprigs of the herb of your choice (see below) in 2 litres water for 15 to 20 minutes. Remove from the stove, and making a towel tent over the head, steam the face gently over the fragrant brew.

VARIATION: **Basil** ● **Fennel** ● **Mint** ● **Winter Savory**

FACIAL SCRUB

This scrub is good for dry, rough winter skin. Mix 1 cup flower petals of your choice (see below) with 1 cup large oat flakes (not the instant kind) and mix with enough apple cider vinegar to form a paste. Use on the face, hands, elbows and knees.

VARIATION: **Buckwheat** flowers ● **Californian Poppy** ● **Calendula** ● **Field Poppy** ● **Linseed** flowers ● **Lucerne** flowers ● **Rose**

STRAWBERRY SCRUB

This old-fashioned skin cleanser is a fabulous toner and rejuvenator for tired grey skin.

1 cup mashed strawberries ● *½ cup wheat germ* ●
1 tablespoon whole oats flakes (not the instant kind)
or bran ● *juice of ½ lemon*

Mix well and use as a mask and a scrub, gently working it into the skin. Leave to penetrate 15 minutes, then rinse off with tepid water into which a dash of apple cider vinegar has been added, then spray with strawberry leaf lotion.

LINSEED FACE PACK

This is a soothing face pack for pimples and acne. Soak 1 cup of linseeds in 1½ cups boiling water. Leave to stand for 1 hour before using as a face pack. Spread over the face in small circular movements. Relax for 15 minutes and rinse off with lukewarm water to which a dash of apple cider vinegar has been added.

HAIR AND SCALP TREATMENTS

CHAMOMILE HAIR RINSE

Pour 2 litres of boiling water over 2-3 tablespoons of dried chamomile flowers, or 4 tablespoons of fresh flowers and a few of the feathery leaves. Let it stand until pleasantly warm. Strain through muslin and once you have shampooed your hair, use this fragrant brew as your final hair rinse. Massage it well into the scalp and really soak the hair in it. Now, and this is the great secret our grandmother's knew, go and dry your hair in the sun! Brush it well in the sun as it dries and you'll be astonished at the soft manageability of your hair!

Nettle Hair Treatment

Boil 3 cups nettle sprigs and leaves in 2 litres of water for 10 minutes. Cool and strain. Use to comb into the hair, massage into the scalp and drink a cup of nettle tea 4 times a week. The condition of the hair immediately starts to improve.

Rosemary Hair Rinse

This rinse is particularly helpful after chemotherapy – but do have a cup of rosemary tea daily as well. Simmer 2 cups of rosemary sprigs in 2 litres of water for 20 minutes. Cool to lukewarm and strain. Use this after the final hair rinse after shampooing the hair. Massage well into the scalp. Keep excess in the fridge to comb into the hair and to massage into the scalp daily.

Soapwort Shampoo

This is wonderful for scalp ailments like eczema and psoriasis and for animals. Boil ½ bucket of leaves, flowers, stems and roots in ½ bucket of water. Simmer gently for 20 minutes. Cool and strain. Discard the soapwort and use the soapy water as a natural shampoo.

BATH VINEGARS

Many herbs can be preserved in vinegar and used to soothe sprains and bruises or aching legs and cramps. The vinegar can be added to the bath for problem skin or to relax sore muscles, used as a freshening tonic on the face, or added to the final rinse water for an itchy scalp and shiny hair. Refer back to the main entry on each herb for information on how to use the particular vinegar. Use only fresh herbs.

As a general guide, pack into a clear glass bottle leaves and flowers of herbs that will impart their fragrance and healing properties (see the box below). Fill the bottle with good quality grape vinegar or apple cider vinegar and place it in the sun for 1 week, giving it a daily shake. After a week, strain out the spent leaves and flowers and replace with fresh ones. Repeat the process. Do this 3 times, then finally strain out the vinegar and pour into a pretty bottle and add a fresh sprig, leaf or flower for identification. Cork well and use as recommended.

VARIATION

Use only the parts of the plant mentioned and do not combine herbs. Refer to the main herb entry for guidance on how to use the vinegar.

Bay leaves ● **Borage** leaves and flowers ● **Calendula** leaves and flowers ● **Chamomile** flowers ● **Echinacea** flowers, leaves, stems and root (use apple cider vinegar) ● **Elder flowers** ● **Lavender** sprigs and flowers ● **Mint** leaves and flowers (use any variety) ● **Myrtle** sprigs and a few berries ● **Rose-scented geranium** leaves and sprigs ● **Rose** petals ● **Rosemary** sprigs ● **Sorrel** leaves ● **Southernwood** sprigs (also called Lad's Love Vinegar) ● **Tarragon** sprigs (use apple cider vinegar)

BASIC SKIN CREAM

This superb, rich cream can be used as a facial cleanser to remove make-up and the grime of city pollution that hammers our skin constantly; as a nourishing moisturiser for the face, hands, feet, elbows and knees; as a gentle massage cream; or as a soothing cream for wind- and sunburn, bites, stings and rashes. Use only fresh herbs and a good quality aqueous cream. Refer back to the main entry on each herb for information on how to use the particular cream.

Leaves or flowers of the herb of your choice (refer to the list below) ● 1 cup aqueous cream ● 2 teaspoons Vitamin E oil ● 2 tablespoons almond oil (bought from the chemist)

Gently simmer the recommended quantity of herb and the aqueous cream in a double boiler for 15-20 minutes. Strain and add the Vitamin E and almond oil. Mix well and pour in a sterilised jar.

VARIATION

Use only the parts of the plant mentioned and do not combine herbs unless specified below. Refer to the main herb entry for guidance on how to use the cream.

Bergamot – ¾ cup leaves and flowers
Borage – 1 cup fresh leaves and flowers
Buckwheat – 1 cup leaves, flowers and stems
Calendula – 1 cup petals
Chamomile – 2-3 tablespoons chamomile flowers and a few leaves
Chervil – 1 cup leaves plus the juice of a lemon and 3 tablespoons lemon rind
Comfrey – 1 cup chopped leaves
Elder – 1 cup berries and ½ cup flowers
Evening Primrose – 1 cup leaves, flowers and seed capsules
Field Poppy – 1 cup petals
Mullein – 1 cup flowers and leaves
Myrtle – 1 cup leaves, flowers and berries
Red Clover – 1 cup flowers
Rose – 1 cup petals
Rose-scented Geranium –1 cup leaves; add 10 drops of rose geranium essential oil
Silver Birch – 1 cup leaves and catkins; add 1 tablespoon sesame oil
St John's Wort – 1 cup fresh flowering tops; add 1 teaspoon clove oil
Vetiver – 1 cup fresh chopped roots
Violet – 1 cup leaves and flowers

OTHER TREATMENTS

Lavender Bath

Try this bath for aching muscles, sore feet, aching back and shoulders – to soothe away tension, anxiety and stress, and to clear problem skin. Gently simmer 3 cups of lavender leaves and flowering sprigs (Grandmother's Lavender is best) in 3 litres of water for 20 minutes. Cool to lukewarm. Strain. Add to your bath, relax and soak for 30 minutes.

ROSELLE SOAP

Grate finely your favourite bar of soap – a fine baby soap is excellent. Boil 1 cup of finely chopped roselle calyxes in 1 litre of water for 20 minutes. Add a little at a time to the grated soap, stirring all the time, to make a soft dough, calyxes included. Pour into a suitable cling-wrap lined mould and allow to dry. Unwrap and keep uncovered in a cupboard for 1 month before using. This is excellent for problem skin.

SOAPWORT FOOT BATH

Boil 4 cups soapwort leaves, flowers and stems in 2 litres of water for about 10 minutes. Cool until pleasantly warm. Pour the entire mixture – leaves and all – into a large basin. Immerse the feet in the warm brew and rub all over with the leaves and stems, especially around the heels. Soak feet for 10 minutes in the warm brew then briskly dry and put on cotton socks.

VARIATION: Use 1½ cups of **Lemon Grass** leaves. Massage feet with lemon grass cream before putting on socks.

SEA SALT CELLULITE TREATMENT

Tie a handful or two of **fennel**, **fenugreek** or **honeysuckle** flowers in a face cloth with a cup of coarse sea salt. Soak it well and use as a rub all over the cellulite areas in circular movements. Then toss it all into the bath and relax in the fragrant salty water.

MASSAGE CREAMS, OILS AND OINTMENTS

CARAWAY MASSAGE OIL

Use this oil in a clockwise direction over the stomach for severe bloating, windy colicky pains and flatulence. Start low down on the right, up over the waistline and down the left side.

½ cup almond oil or medicinal olive oil (bought from the chemist) ● 2 teaspoons lightly crushed caraway seeds

Heat the almond or olive oil and the caraway seeds in a double boiler for 10 minutes. Strain through a fine strainer and bottle the oil. Use warm as a massage oil (warm the whole little bottle by standing it in hot water every time you use it). It keeps well.

VARIATION: Use 1½ cups of **Lemon Verbena** leaves.

CAYENNE OINTMENT FOR ACHING FEET

Mix 2 teaspoons of cayenne pepper and 2 tablespoons almond oil into 1 cup good quality aqueous cream and gently simmer in a double boiler for 15 minutes. Cool and pour into a sterilised jar. **Caution**: Do not use on broken skin and avoid touching the eye area.

ECHINACEA HEALING CREAM

This is my most useful cream for rashes, bites and itches and it soothes cracked lips and dry fingernails as well.

1 cup echinacea petals, leaves and chopped stem and root ● 1 cup aqueous cream ● 2 teaspoons Vitamin E oil ● 10 drops lavender essential oil ● 10 drops lemon essential oil ● 10 drops tea tree oil

Gently simmer the petals, leaves, stem and root and the aqueous cream in a double boiler for 20 minutes. Strain and add the Vitamin E oil. Add 10 drops each of lavender, lemon and tea tree essential oil. Mix well and pour in a sterilised jar.

EUCALYPTUS RUB FOR ACHING JOINTS

Combine ½ cup almond oil, 1 teaspoon eucalyptus oil (bought from the chemist) and 10 cloves in a bottle and shake well. Use as a massage oil or rub into painful joints, aching feet or shoulders, add a few drops to the bath or rub onto the chest to relieve congestion.

GINGER CIRCULATION CREAM

Use this cream for aching legs and feet or to soften dry skin and hands and feet.

1 cup minced fresh ginger ● 1 cup aqueous cream ● 2 teaspoons powdered cloves ● ½ teaspoon cayenne pepper ● peppermint essential oil

Gently simmer the ginger, cloves, cayenne pepper and the aqueous cream in a double boiler for 15 minutes. Strain and add 6 drops peppermint essential oil. Mix well and spoon into a sterilised jar. Seal well.

HORSERADISH OINTMENT FOR CHILBLAINS

This ointment is also excellent for chilled feet and as a massage cream for aching muscles and sore, stiff joints. Simmer 3 teaspoons grated horseradish in 1 cup aqueous cream in a double boiler for 20 minutes. Strain and add 2 teaspoons of Vitamin E oil. Store in a sterilised jar. Apply frequently.

LAVENDER MASSAGE CREAM FOR ACHES AND PAINS

Use this nourishing cream lavishly!

1 cup lavender flowers (use Lavandula intermedia) ● 1 cup aqueous cream ● pure lavender essential oil ● 2 tablespoons almond oil ● 2 teaspoons Vitamin E oil

Simmer the lavender flowers and the aqueous cream for 20 minutes in a double boiler. Strain, add 10 drops pure lavender essential oil and stir well. Add the almond and Vitamin E oil. Mix well. Pour into a sterilised screw-top jar and seal.

LEMON GRASS MASSAGE CREAM

Use this massage cream for aching feet and calves and a stiff neck and shoulders.

1 cup chopped lemon grass leaves ● 1 cup aqueous cream ● pure lemon grass or lemon essential oil ● 2 teaspoons Vitamin E oil

Simmer the lemon grass leaves and the aqueous cream for 20 minutes in a double boiler. Cool and strain. Add the Vitamin E oil and 10 drops pure lemon grass or lemon essential oil and stir well. Seal in a sterilised jar.

MARJORAM MASSAGE CREAM

Use this massage cream for stiff muscles and bruises.

1 cup flowering sprigs, chopped ● 1 cup aqueous cream ● clove oil ● 2 teaspoons Vitamin E oil

Simmer the marjoram sprigs and the aqueous cream for 20 minutes in a double boiler. Cool and strain. Add the Vitamin E oil and 10 drops clove oil and mix well. Seal in a sterilised jar.

MULLEIN MASSAGE OIL

Use as a massage oil, dry skin treatment or for haemorrhoids, inflamed eyelids or chilblains.

½ cup almond oil ● 2 tablespoons wheat germ oil ● 1 tablespoon avocado oil or sweet oil ● 1 cup mullein flowers and leaves, roughly chopped

Simmer everything together in a double boiler for 20 minutes. Strain and pour into a sterilised bottle.

ST JOHN'S WORT OIL

Also known as Turkey Red Oil, this is an excellent antiseptic used for everything from wounds, grazes, burns and cramps to swellings and nerve pain. The red colour of the oil is due to the presence of hypericin, a strong antiviral that it is being researched for the treatment of HIV and Aids.

1 cup almond oil ● 1 cup fresh flowering heads (use only Hypericum perforatum) ● 2 teaspoons Vitamin E oil

Gently heat the almond oil and the flowering heads in a double boiler for 20 minutes. Cool and strain. The next day repeat this procedure using the same oil but with fresh flowering heads. Repeat for a third time until the oil becomes richly red. Add the Vitamin E oil and mix well. Bottle in a dark glass bottle.

OTHER REMEDIES AND TONICS

BARLEY WATER

Boil 1 cup pearl barley bought from the supermarket, or 1 cup of your own organically grown barley, 1½ litres of water. Simmer for approximately 40 minutes with the lid partially on (check that it does not boil over). Top up the water every now and then. Set aside to cool. Strain. Pour off the water into a jug and refrigerate. Eat the grains as a rice served with a little salt and lemon juice. Take a glass of barley water flavoured with fresh lemon juice daily to detoxify and for high blood cholesterol. Barley water is one of the most important health drinks all of us should consider as a daily cleanser and detoxifier.

CARAWAY COUGH REMEDY

Finely crush 2 tablespoons caraway seeds, pour over this ½ cup boiling water. Stand 10 minutes. Add 3 tablespoons honey and 3 tablespoons lemon juice and mix well. Take 2 teaspoons at a time, frequently, to ease congestion and cough.

CARNATION TONIC WINE

In a bottle of red wine steep ½-1 cup carnation petals, 10 cloves, a cinnamon stick and ½ cup of honey for 2 weeks. Shake daily. Strain. Sip a small glass slowly.

GOLDENROD DOUCHE

Use this douche 3 nights running to clear vaginal thrush. Simmer 2 cups of goldenrod flowering heads (or 1½ cups dried flowers) in 2 litres of water for 15 minutes. Cool for 10 minutes, then strain, add ½ cup apple cider vinegar and use as a douche – use it all up. Repeat the next night and again for the third. Use this brew also as a wash and as a lotion frequently.

HORSERADISH COUGH SYRUP

Simmer ½ cup honey with 1 tablespoon finely grated horseradish and 1 tablespoon lemon juice in a double boiler for 10 minutes. Cool and strain. Take for chest ailments, coughs, colds and urinary tract infections.

MUSTARD HEALTH BOOSTING DRINK

Make a tea with ¼ cup fresh mustard leaves and 1 cup boiling water. Stand 5 minutes and strain. Add ½ cup fresh carrot juice and ½ cup fresh apple juice to the cooled tea. Sip slowly.

ROSE BRANDY HOT TODDY

Take this at the first sign of a cold.

1 bottle of brandy ● 2 cups brown sugar ● 1 cinnamon stick ● 12 cloves ● a sprig of rosemary ● 1 cup rose petals ● ½ cup thinly sliced ripe rose hips

Warm 1 cup of brandy and the brown sugar, cinnamon stick, cloves and sprig of rosemary in the top of a double boiler. Add the rose petals and rose hips. Simmer for 10 minutes, covered. Add this mixture to the rest of the brandy, pushing in the cinnamon stick and rosemary sprig. Shake up well. Cork and store. For a hot toddy add 1-2 tablespoons to a cup of boiling water with a squeeze of lemon juice and a little honey. Sip slowly.

ROSEMARY WONDER WATER

My grandmother used dried rosemary, although through the years I have come to like fresh rosemary more. Crush 2 sprigs rosemary, about 15 cm long, 1-2 teaspoons powdered nutmeg, 1 thumb-length piece ginger root, finely grated, and 1 cinnamon stick together in a mortar and pound them well. Steep in 1 bottle claret (or red wine if preferred) – keep it well corked for a fortnight. Strain through muslin, recork well, and resist tasting it as long as possible. It really needs a month to mature. Drink a sherry glass at the end of a stress-filled day.

SAGE COUGH MIXTURE

Mix together ½ cup each of finely chopped sage leaves, honey and lemon juice. Take 2 teaspoons at a time.

> ***VARIATION***: Add 1 teaspoon crushed **Rocket** seeds to the above mixture.

Natural insecticides

Home-brewed sprays are infinitely preferable to the powerful commercial chemical sprays on the market which are so harmful to all living things.

Basic Insect-repelling Spray

Use this spray to combat aphids, scale, mealie bug, fungus, mildew, white fly and ants. Use ½ bucket of roughly chopped leaves, flowers and stalks (see box below) and ½ bucket of khakibos or marigold leaves. Pour over this 1 bucket of boiling water and leave to draw overnight. Next morning strain and add ½ cup of washing powder (I usually use Sunlight soap washing powder). (You can also add 2 tablespoons of Jeyes Fluid and/or 3 roughly chopped whole garlic bulbs to the mixture.) Mix well and splash or spray onto plants, water around plants or pour down ant holes once a week to clear the infestation. Repeat after rain. If you use the spray over vegetables and fruit, rinse them well before eating.

VARIATION

The following herbs can be used alone or in combination with rue, southernwood or tansy to increase the potency of the spray.

Basil ● **Bergamot** ● **Catmint** ● **Cayenne Pepper** (use 4 cups of seeds and roughly chopped skins) ● **Chamomile** ● **Chives** ● **Coriander** ● **Elder** leaves ● **Feverfew** ● **Lemon Grass** ● **Marjoram** ● **Melissa** ● **Mint** ● **Nasturtium** ● **Nettle** ● **Oregano** ● **Pyrethrum** flowers ● **Rosemary** ● **Rue** ● **Soapwort** ● **Southernwood** ● **Tansy** ● **Thyme** ● **Winter Savory** ● **Wormwood**

Wormwood Tea

Use this tea as a shampoo for dogs, or use undiluted to wash down carpets. Add wormwood sprigs to dogs bedding, tucked underneath, also under carpets. Pour ½ bucket of boiling water over 3 cups wormwood sprigs. Stand until cold. Then strain. Add ½ bucket of warm water, then pour over the dogs after shampooing them.

Liquid Fertiliser

In a large drum pour 6 buckets of water. Stir in 2 buckets of roughly chopped amaranth or comfrey leaves and stems and flowers. Add 1 bucket of manure. Stir with a spade every day for a minute or two and keep covered. It soon smells, so keep the lid on. After 2 weeks draw off the liquid and use it to water pot plants and special plantings. Add the remainder to the compost heap.

Basic Foliar Feed

Take ½ bucket fresh green leaves, stems and flowers (choose from the box below) and pour over this 1 bucket of boiling water. Add ¼ bucket of comfrey or yarrow leaves lightly chopped for extra nourishment if you have them available. Stir with a spade, cover and leave 3 days. Strain off the liquid and splash or spray onto plants and water in a little around them. Do this once a week for 3 weeks and watch them grow!

> **VARIATION**: Use any of the following for the above foliar feed: **Buckwheat** ● **Pennywort** ● **Echinacea**, **Lucerne** ● **Scented Geranium** (any variety).

Bergamot Herbal Incense

This incense will keep mosquitoes away from the patio or braai area.

1 cup bergamot ● 1 cup khakibos ● 1 cup rue ● ¾ cup flour ● water

Dry the herbs on newspaper in the shade. When dry, mix the herbs into the flour with just enough water to make a thick paste. Mould into small 50c-sized patties, flatten and dry well. Burn in a saucer or tin in a safe place.

Carnation Deodoriser

Because of its clove-like scent, carnations can be combined with cloves and clove oils to keep insects out of cupboards. This ancient recipe was used by our grandmothers to keep toilets and bathrooms deodorised.

2 cups dried carnation petals ● 1 cup cloves ● 3-4 teaspoons clove oil

Soak the cloves in the clove oil (bought from your chemist) overnight. Add the carnation petals and store in an airtight bottle for 1 week. Give it a daily shake and add more clove oil as it matures. Sew into sachets, or fill small bowls with the heady mixture and place in drawers and cupboards or in the bathroom. This mixture will sweeten the dankest, mustiest cupboard even at the coast and chase every fishmoth away. Revive from time to time with clove oil.

> **VARIATION**: **Lavender** ● **Lemon Verbena** ● **Myrtle** ● **Lemon Thyme** ● or use dried **Lemon rind**

Thyme Potpourri with Lemon Verbena

You can also add dried lavender or rosemary sprigs to this superb deodorising potpourri.

4 cups thyme sprigs (any variety except Thymus vulgaris) ● 3 cups lemon verbena leaves ● 2 cups minced lemon peel ● 1 cup cinnamon pieces ● ½ cup cloves ● 2 teaspoons lemon or citrus (not citronella) or lavender oil ● 1 teaspoon clove oil

Dry the thyme sprigs, lemon verbena leaves and minced lemon peel on newspaper in the shade. Turn daily. Combine the lemon peel, cinnamon pieces, cloves and lemon and clove oil in a sealed jar and leave overnight. Then add the thyme and lemon verbena leaves. Mix everything together and add more lemon oil. Fill bowls and sachets and tuck into cupboards or use as a bathroom freshener.

Therapeutic Index

The following is a list of ailments and properties mentioned in this book. Refer to the individual herb entry for more information about the method of application and possible side-effects of a herb. Always consult your medical practitioner before treating yourself or your family with home remedies.

abscess – burdock, comfrey, echinacea, fenugreek, feverfew, honeysuckle, rue

aches and pains – basil, bay, cayenne pepper, chervil, eucalyptus, horseradish, lavender, lemon grass, loofah, mustard, rose, silver birch, thyme

aching joints – Californian poppy, goldenrod, honeysuckle, horseradish, linseed, loofah, marjoram, oregano, vetiver grass

acne – anise, black seed, burdock, calendula, dandelion, echinacea, field poppy, garlic, oats, parsley, pennywort, roselle, sage, silver birch, sorrel, tea tree

allergic rhinitis – thyme

Alzheimer's disease – ginkgo

amnesia – pennywort, rosemary, sage

anaemia – amaranth, elderflower, linseed, nettle, roselle

anal fissures – calendula, pennywort

analgesic – anise, Californian poppy, cumin, feverfew, lavender, lovage, mint, rosemary, tarragon, vetiver grass, wormwood

anger – rose, rose-scented geranium

anorexia – fenugreek, sesame

anti-ageing – buckwheat, dandelion, evening primrose, pennywort, thyme

anti-allergenic – aloe vera, bulbinella, ginkgo, nettle

antibacterial – basil, cayenne pepper, chives, eucalyptus, garlic, green tea, lavender, lemon grass, myrtle, nasturtium, olive, stevia, strawberry, tea tree, thyme

antibiotic – burdock, cayenne pepper, chives, echinacea, horseradish, St John's wort, tea tree, thyme

anti-cancer – buckwheat, burdock, fenugreek, garlic, green tea, paprika, red clover, soya beans, strawberry, tarragon, turmeric, violet, watercress

anticoagulant – turmeric

anticonvulsant – celery, anticonvulsant – lovage

antidepressant – melissa, pennywort, wormwood

antifungal – aloe vera, garlic, goldenrod, lemon grass, neem, sage, tea tree, thyme, turmeric

anti-inflammatory – chamomile, feverfew, ginkgo, goldenrod, turmeric, honeysuckle, linseed, neem, pennywort, rosemary, silver birch, St John's wort, tea tree, wormwood, yarrow

anti-microbial – echinacea, lemon grass, lovage, turmeric

antioxidant – cayenne pepper, goldenrod, green tea, hawthorn, paprika, roselle

anti-rheumatic – celery, comfrey, dandelion, pennywort

antiseptic – bay, bergamot, burdock, celery, chamomile, garlic, horseradish, lavender, lemon grass, linseed, mint, myrtle, neem, pennywort, rosemary, sage, silver birch, sorrel, tea tree, thyme, winter savory

antispasmodic – Californian poppy, caraway, celery, cumin, dill, ginkgo, honeysuckle, lavender, melissa, mint, mustard, rose-scented geranium, thyme, winter savory

anti-thrombotic – oats, pennywort

antiviral – echinacea, neem, olive, St John's wort, strawberry

anxiety – bergamot, Californian poppy, catmint, chamomile, cornflower, elderflower, lavender, marjoram, melissa, oats, oregano, rosemary, rue, St John's wort, vetiver grass

arteriosclerosis – ginkgo, pennywort, red clover

appetite, poor – dill, lovage

arthritis – aloe vera, barley, black seed, burdock, cayenne pepper, celery, comfrey, cumin, eucalyptus, evening primrose, feverfew, goldenrod, horseradish, lavender, linseed, lovage, marjoram, mustard, nettle, oregano, parsley, pennywort, red clover, rosemary, rue, silver birch, St John's wort, turmeric

asthma – anise, black seed, evening primrose, ginkgo, honeysuckle, maidenhair fern, nettle, rue, sesame, thyme

astringent – bay, goldenrod, green tea, lemon grass, raspberry, rosemary, strawberry, winter savory

athlete's foot – garlic, lavender, lemon grass, tea tree, thyme, turmeric

backache – bergamot, evening primrose, goldenrod, lavender, thyme

bedsores – pennywort

bedwetting – Californian poppy, catmint

belching – anise, coriander, cumin, melissa, mint, turmeric

Bell's palsy – pennywort, rue

bile flow, stimulate – aloe vera, dandelion, mint

biliousness – anise, green tea, melissa, milk thistle, peppermint

bites and stings – basil, bulbinella, catmint, cumin, dandelion, echinacea, fenugreek, feverfew, field poppy, green tea, lavender, melissa, mullein, nettle, parsley, red clover, rocket, roselle, salad burnet, soapwort, tarragon, tea tree

bladder ailments – barley, borage, celery, echinacea, fennel, ginkgo, goldenrod, hawthorn, linseed, mullein, neem, paprika, parsley, rose, silver birch

bleeding – comfrey, yarrow

blisters – aloe vera, bulbinella, fenugreek

bloating – anise, caraway, chervil, coriander, cumin, dill, melissa, mint, parsley, turmeric

blocked nose – costmary, cumin, eucalyptus, honeysuckle, mullein, tea tree

blocked sinuses – eucalyptus, mint, violet

blood builder – amaranth, dandelion, pennywort

blood clotting, promotes – amaranth

blood clotting, retards – chives

blood pressure, high – aloe vera, buckwheat, cayenne pepper, celery, chervil, dandelion, evening primrose, garlic, ginkgo, green tea, hawthorn, honeysuckle, melissa, olive, parsley, rue, sesame, stevia, strawberry, yarrow

blood pressure, leveller – moringa, rosemary

blood purifier – celery, fennel, moringa, nettle, parsley

blood sugar, high – burdock, neem, olive

blood sugar regulator – chives, fenugreek, stevia

boils – black seed, burdock, fenugreek, feverfew, honeysuckle, linseed, neem, rue, tea tree

bone-builder – comfrey, dandelion, moringa, oats

breast milk production, promotes – anise, caraway, fenugreek, moringa, nettle, sesame

breasts, tender – evening primrose, loofah, red clover

breath sweetener – anise, caraway, coriander, cumin, dill, fenugreek, marjoram, oregano, parsley, stevia

bronchitis – anise, bergamot, black seed, comfrey, garlic, honeysuckle, lemon verbena, loofah, lovage, mullein, mustard, red clover, rocket, southernwood, tea tree, thyme, violet, watercress

bruises – borage, caraway, cayenne pepper, chamomile, cornflower, feverfew, lavender, marjoram, myrtle, neem, rocket, tansy

burns – bulbinella, elderflower, fenugreek, field poppy, olive, St John's wort

calluses – fenugreek, mustard, rocket, rose, soapwort

catarrh – barley, black seed, goldenrod, ground ivy, honeysuckle, lovage, mullein, nasturtium, nettle, southernwood, watercress

cellulite – honeysuckle, pennywort

chapped lips – bulbinella, calendula, echinacea, evening primrose, mullein

chest ailments – celery, comfrey, eucalyptus, ground ivy, horseradish, linseed, maidenhair fern, moringa, rocket, roselle, thyme, turmeric, watercress

chickenpox – maidenhair fern, melissa, tea tree, yarrow

chilblains – buckwheat, calendula, chervil, hawthorn, horseradish, lovage, mullein, pennywort

childbirth, eases – raspberry

childbirth, induces – fenugreek

chills – black seed, maidenhair fern, peppermint, sage

cholesterol, high – barley, basil, cayenne pepper, chives, evening primrose, fenugreek, garlic, ginger, green tea, oats, olive, soya beans, stevia, turmeric

chronic fatigue syndrome – amaranth, green tea, olive, pennywort

circulation, poor – aloe vera, buckwheat, cayenne pepper, celery, chervil, cumin, evening primrose, garlic, ginger, hawthorn, horseradish, lemon grass, lovage, , mustard, myrtle, olive, pennywort, rosemary, silver birch, soya beans, thyme, turmeric, watercress

cleanser – celery, chervil, fennel, nettle, parsley, strawberry

colds – bergamot, black seed, borage, burdock, catmint, cayenne pepper, chamomile, costmary, cumin, dill, echinacea, elderflower, eucalyptus, garlic, green tea, honeysuckle, horseradish, lemon verbena, lucerne, maidenhair fern, marjoram, mustard, oats, oregano, pennywort, raspberry, red clover, rose, roselle, sage, tea tree, thyme, violet, winter savory, yarrow

colic – anise, bergamot, black seed, caraway, catmint, chervil, coriander, cumin, dill, fennel, fenugreek, ginger, ground ivy, lavender, lemon verbena, lovage, melissa, mint, wormwood,

colitis – basil, lemon grass, melissa

concentration, poor – Californian poppy, ginkgo, pennywort, sage

congestion – bergamot, chives, comfrey, eucalyptus, ginkgo, lemon verbena, loofah, mint, nasturtium, sage, southernwood

constipation – aloe vera, barley, chervil, fennel, melissa, mustard, oats, pennywort, sesame, soya beans (see also **laxative**)

convalescence – barley, buckwheat, lucerne, red clover, rose, strawberry

coughs – amaranth, anise, basil, bergamot, black seed, caraway, costmary, dill, elderflower, garlic, green tea, ground ivy, horseradish, linseed, loofah, lovage, lucerne, maidenhair fern, mullein, mustard, nasturtium, paprika, raspberry, red clover, rocket, rose, roselle, sage, sesame, southernwood, tea tree, thyme, violet, winter savory

cramps – barley, basil, caraway, costmary, fenugreek, lemon verbena, myrtle, rose-scented geranium, St John's wort

cuts and grazes – bulbinella, catmint, chamomile, cornflower, elderflower, feverfew, field poppy, lavender, lovage, melissa, mullein, olive, paprika, parsley, salad burnet, soapwort, tansy, tarragon, turmeric, wormwood, yarrow

cystitis – celery, fennel, garlic, ginkgo, goldenrod, olive, parsley, tea tree

cysts – sesame, violet

deodoriser – lavender, lemon grass, lemon verbena, lovage, marjoram, mint, oregano, rosemary

depression – bergamot, lavender, lemon verbena, melissa, milk thistle, oats, olive, rose, rosemary, rose-scented geranium, St John's wort

despair – lavender, melissa, rose

detoxifying – basil, burdock, celery, cumin, dandelion, fennel, lovage, mint, nettle, parsley, sesame, silver birch, sorrel, soya beans, strawberry

diabetes – aloe vera, barley, olive, rosemary, soya beans, strawberry, yarrow

diarrhoea – aloe vera, amaranth, barley, black seed, catmint, fenugreek, ginger, goldenrod, ground ivy, hawthorn, honeysuckle, moringa, raspberry, salad burnet, strawberry

digestion, aid to – anise, bay, cayenne pepper, chervil, coriander, cumin, green tea, lovage, marjoram, melissa, mint, mustard, oregano, pennywort, sorrel, strawberry

digestive ailments – anise, cumin, evening primrose, feverfew, lemon grass, lemon verbena, lovage, melissa, thyme, vetiver grass, winter savory

disinfectant – lavender, nasturtium, rosemary, sage

disorientation – ginkgo, olive, pennywort

diuretic – caraway, celery, chervil, cornflower, dill, fennel, goldenrod, green tea, ground ivy, honeysuckle, horseradish, lovage, moringa, mustard, nettle, olive, parsley, pennywort, raspberry, silver birch, sorrel, strawberry, watercress, yarrow

diverticulitis – melissa

dizziness – olive, sesame

dysentery – amaranth, honeysuckle, moringa, nettle

ear infection – echinacea, ground ivy, mullein, yarrow

eczema – basil, borage, burdock, chamomile, dandelion, elderflower, evening primrose, myrtle, neem, nettle, pennywort, red clover, salad burnet, sesame, soapwort, turmeric

emphysema – comfrey, eucalyptus, horseradish, nasturtium, sage

energising – ginger, lucerne, oats, pennywort, rosemary

epilepsy – anise, elderflower, pennywort, rose, rosemary, rue

erysipelas sores – elderflower, pennywort, soapwort

exhaustion – maidenhair fern, marjoram, oregano, rose, rosemary, vetiver grass

expectorant – caraway, ginger, honeysuckle, horseradish, mullein, nasturtium, rocket, tea tree, thyme, violet, watercress, winter savory

eye ailments – calendula, caraway, chamomile, cornflower, elderflower, green tea, mullein, raspberry

fatigue – lucerne, mint, pennywort, rosemary

fear – lavender, melissa, rose-scented geranium, vetiver grass

feet, aching – bay, horseradish, lemon verbena, myrtle, rosemary

fever – barley, black seed, burdock, cumin, fenugreek, feverfew, ground ivy, horseradish, lemon grass, loofah, mint, nasturtium, neem, olive, parsley, pennywort, pyrethrum, yarrow

fever blisters – bulbinella, melissa, soapwort, stevia, tea tree

fibrocytic breasts – basil, pennywort

fissures – pennywort, sesame

flatulence – anise, bergamot, black seed, caraway, chervil, coriander, cumin, dill, fennel, ginger, melissa, mint, parsley, tarragon, winter savory

'flu – black seed, borage, burdock, catmint, cayenne pepper, dill, echinacea, elderflower, garlic, horseradish, lucerne, marjoram, melissa, mustard, oats, oregano, tea tree, violet, yarrow

fluid retention – celery, dill, fennel, green tea, nettle, parsley, silver birch

fractures – comfrey, pennywort

frigidity – anise, lavender, melissa, rose-scented geranium

gallstones – buckwheat, dandelion

gastric ulcer – fenugreek, melissa, mint

gastritis – fenugreek, ground ivy, melissa, mint, strawberry, turmeric

gastroenteritis – goldenrod, melissa

glands, swollen – neem, pennywort

glandular fever – pennywort, rosemary, tea tree

gout – aloe vera, barley, burdock, cayenne pepper, celery, goldenrod, honeysuckle, moringa, nettle, parsley, silver birch, strawberry, watercress

grief – cornflower, oats, pennywort, rose-scented geranium

griping – anise, coriander, lavender, melissa, peppermint
guilt – Californian poppy, carnation, vetiver grass
gum problems see **mouth ailments**

haemorrhage – nettle, pennywort, silver birch
haemorrhoids – calendula, cayenne pepper, chamomile, comfrey, ginkgo, green tea, mullein, myrtle, neem, pennywort, salad burnet
hangover – thyme, violet
hay fever – barley, nettle, thyme, violet
headache – black seed, dill, feverfew, honeysuckle, lavender, lemon grass, lemon verbena, melissa, mint, moringa, rosemary, rose-scented geranium, violet
heart ailments – buckwheat, chives, garlic, ginkgo, green tea, hawthorn, moringa, rue
heartache – honeysuckle, lemon verbena
heartburn – anise, caraway, cayenne pepper, coriander, cumin, fennel, ground ivy, melissa, mint, turmeric
heels, cracked – buckwheat, elderflower, lavender, rose, rose-scented geranium
heat prostration – anise, borage, marjoram
helplessness – olive, rose-scented geranium
hepatitis – barley, celery, fennel, milk thistle, parsley, pennywort
hiccups – anise, dill
HIV/AIDS – echinacea, St John's wort
homesickness – honeysuckle, pennywort
hyperactivity – Californian poppy, catmint, evening primrose, ginkgo, melissa, sage
hypertension – basil, black seed
hysteria – lavender, melissa

immune system booster – bergamot, black seed, cayenne pepper, chives, echinacea, garlic, green tea, lemon grass, mustard, olive, paprika , tea tree, turmeric, watercress, winter savory
impotence – anise, ginkgo, pennywort
incontinence – ginkgo, lineseed, milk thistle, mullein
indigestion – aloe vera, basil, bergamot, calendula, Californian poppy, caraway, cayenne pepper, chamomile, cumin, dill, fennel, ground ivy, lovage, melissa, mint, raspberry, rose, sage, salad burnet, tarragon, watercress
infertility – evening primrose, nettle
insomnia – bergamot, black seed, Californian poppy, cumin, dill, elderflower, lavender, melissa, rose, rose-scented geranium, St John's wort, thyme
intestinal parasites – black seed, feverfew, nasturtium, neem, rue, southernwood
irritability – green tea, lavender, melissa, mint, tea tree

kidney ailments – aloe vera, barley, bergamot, borage, burdock, celery, elderflower, goldenrod, ground ivy, hawthorn, honeysuckle, lineseed, lovage, mullein, neem, nettle, paprika, raspberry, sesame, silver birch, soya beans, strawberry

laryngitis – cayenne pepper, echinacea, sage
laxative – dandelion, horseradish, lineseed, sorrel, watercress (see also **constipation**)
leg cramps – evening primrose, lavender
leg ulcers – comfrey, ginkgo, pennywort
leprosy – neem, pennywort
lice – lavender, rosemary, thyme
liver ailments – bergamot, calendula, chervil, cornflower, dandelion, honeysuckle, milk thistle, neem, pennywort, sesame, soya beans, St John's wort, strawberry, turmeric
'liverishness' – milk thistle, parsley
lupus – pennywort, silver birch
lymphatic ailments – elderflower

malaria – neem

measles – burdock, maidenhair fern, pennywort, yarrow
melancholia – melissa, milk thistle
memory loss – ginkgo, hawthorn, rosemary, sage
menopausal problems – borage, evening primrose, lucerne, melissa, oats, pennywort, red clover, sage, sorrel, soya beans
menstrual problems – amaranth, anise, basil, bergamot, black seed, caraway, catmint, dill, fenugreek, feverfew, hawthorn, lovage, lucerne, marjoram, oregano, parsley, rose, rue, sage, southernwood, winter savory, yarrow (see also **premenstrual tension**)
mental deterioration – ginkgo
migraine – basil, cayenne pepper, feverfew, mint
milk production, promotes – cumin, dill, milk thistle
miscarriage – black seed
mood swings – coriander, ginkgo, melissa
mouth ailments – amaranth, basil, bulbinella, calendula, echinacea, elderflower, honeysuckle, marjoram, oregano, pennywort, raspberry, sage, sorrel, thyme, yarrow
multiple sclerosis – ginkgo, oats, olive, rue
mumps – burdock, echinacea
muscular pain see **aches and pains**

nausea – anise, bergamot, black seed, ginger, turmeric, lemon verbena, lovage, marjoram, melissa, mint, oregano, parsley
nervous problems – Californian poppy, carnation, coriander, ginger, green tea, lavender, lemon verbena, melissa, oats, pennywort, St John's wort
neuralgia – elderflower, St John's wort
nightmares – Californian poppy, lavender, melissa, rose-scented geranium
nipples, sore – calendula, pennywort, violet
nosebleed – yarrow

oestrogenic – evening primrose, lucerne, oats, red clover, sage, soya beans
osteoporosis – barley, oats
over-excitement – Californian poppy, lavender, melissa, rose-scented geranium
over-indulgence – lovage, melissa, mint
pain-killing see **analgesic**
palpitations – basil, lemon verbena
panic attacks – lavender, melissa, milk thistle, oats, rose-scented geranium
Parkinson's disease – evening primrose, melissa, oats, rose, rose-scented geranium
peptic ulcers – basil, melissa, mint, pennywort
perspiration, excessive – black seed, lavender
perspiration, promotes – catmint
phlebitis – pennywort
pleurisy – comfrey, echinacea, loofah, mustard, pennywort
pneumonia – anise, comfrey, lucerne, mullein
premenstrual tension – borage, evening primrose, rose, rose-scented geranium, yarrow
problem skin – aloe vera, amaranth, anise, basil, bay , bergamot, borage, bulbinella, carnation, catmint, chamomile, chervil, echinacea, fennel, feverfew, field poppy, ground ivy, honeysuckle, lavender, lemon verbena, lovage, marjoram, mint, mustard, myrtle, oats, oregano, parsley, red clover, roselle, tea tree, yarrow
prostate problems – neem, nettle, oats, parsley
psoriasis – basil, borage, burdock, elderflower, evening primrose, pennywort, red clover, silver birch, soapwort, turmeric

rashes – black seed, bulbinella, catmint, chamomile, cornflower, dandelion, echinacea, elderflower, fenugreek, field poppy, ground ivy, melissa, mullein, neem, olive, parsley, pennywort, red clover, rocket, roselle, sage, salad burnet, silver birch, soapwort, tarragon, tea tree
relaxing – lavender, melissa, mint, rose-scented geranium

respiratory ailments – anise, bergamot, comfrey, echinacea, eucalyptus, fennel, ginger, linseed, loofah, lovage, mullein, rue, sesame, watercress

restlessness – catmint, melissa, vetiver grass

rheumatic fever – echinacea, honeysuckle

rheumatism – aloe vera, bay, black seed, burdock, cayenne pepper, celery, eucalyptus, evening primrose, honeysuckle, horseradish, lavender, lovage, marjoram, moringa, mustard, oregano, parsley, pennywort, raspberry, rose, rosemary, rue, silver birch, strawberry, tansy, yarrow

ringworm – garlic, rue, strawberry, tea tree, thyme

runny nose – maidenhair fern, sage

scabies – rosemary, thyme

scalp infections – basil, lavender, rosemary, soapwort

scar tissue – comfrey, evening primrose, pennywort, sesame

schizophrenia – evening primrose, pennywort

sciatica – Californian poppy, nettle, oats

scratches see **cuts and grazes**

scrofula – nasturtium, pennywort

scurvy – ground ivy, lemon grass, sorrel, tarragon

sedative – aloe vera, Californian poppy, celery, chamomile, cornflower, lavender, lovage, melissa, rose-scented geranium

senile dementia – ginkgo, pennywort

shingles – cayenne pepper, melissa

sinusitus – bergamot, cayenne pepper, eucalyptus, garlic, myrtle, tea tree

skin, ageing – borage, buckwheat, evening primrose, goldenrod, pennywort

skin ailments – aloe vera, borage, calendula, comfrey, elderflower, lavender, lemon grass, moringa, myrtle, nasturtium, oats, pennywort, rose, rose-scented geranium, sesame, silver birch, strawberry, violet

skin cancer – silver birch, strawberry, violet

skin, dry – borage, bulbinella, evening primrose, pennywort, sage

skin growths – comfrey, elderflower, sesame

skin, itchy – amaranth, borage, bulbinella, calendula, evening primrose, salad burnet, soapwort

skin lesions – comfrey, pennywort, silver birch

skin, oily see **problem skin**

sleep walking – Californian poppy

sleeplessness see **insomnia**

slimming – celery, dill, fennel, parsley, silver birch

smelly feet – cumin, ginger, lavender

sore throat – barley, burdock, cumin, elderflower, goldenrod, honeysuckle, lavender, lovage, maidenhair fern, mint, mustard, nasturtium, paprika, pennywort, raspberry, red clover, roselle, sage, stevia, tea tree, thyme, winter savory

sores – echinacea, feverfew, pennywort, soapwort

spasms – black seed, dill, melissa, mint, rose-scented geranium, vetiver grass

spastic colon – melissa, mint

sprains – aloe vera, cayenne pepper, cornflower, feverfew, marjoram, myrtle, neem, oregano, rocket, St John's wort, wormwood

stiffness – aloe vera, basil, Californian poppy, horseradish, lavender, marjoram, oregano, rose-scented geranium, silver birch, vetiver grass

stimulant – cayenne pepper, green tea, lemon grass, lemon thyme, lemon verbena, rosemary

stomach ailments – aloe vera, barley, black seed, burdock, chamomile, comfrey, costmary, fenugreek, goldenrod, melissa, mint, moringa, neem, silver birch

strains – comfrey, horseradish, St John's wort

stress – catmint, cornflower, lavender, lemon grass, melissa, oats, pennywort, rose, rosemary, rose-scented geranium

sunburn – basil, bulbinella, calendula, carnation, chamomile, cornflower, dandelion, elderflower, evening primrose, fenugreek, green tea, honeysuckle, mullein, oats, pennywort, red clover, roselle, salad burnet, soapwort, strawberry

swellings – amaranth, barley, elderflower, feverfew, green tea, moringa, pennywort, sesame, silver birch, soapwort, turmeric, wormwood

tearfulness – melissa, rose-scented geranium

temper tantrums – coriander, lavender, melissa

tension – catmint, dill, lavender, lemon grass, pennywort, rose, St John's wort

throat infections – comfrey, echinacea, mullein, nasturtium, raspberry, sage

thyroid problems – melissa, oats, watercress

tinnitus – ginkgo, ground ivy, sesame

tonic – aloe vera, buckwheat, caraway, carnation, celery, chervil, cornflower, elderflower, green tea, ground ivy, lemon grass, lucerne, milk thistle, mustard, oats, pennywort, rose, silver birch, sorrel, southernwood, soya beans, strawberry, tarragon, watercress, winter savory

tonsillitis – basil, cayenne pepper, echinacea, pennywort, sage

tooth decay – green tea, neem, stevia

toothache – anise, black seed, Californian poppy, elderflower, marjoram, mullein, oregano, rue, tarragon

travel sickness – ginger, melissa, mint

tuberculosis – chives, echinacea, honeysuckle, nasturtium, pennywort, watercress

tumours – pennywort, sesame, violet

ulcers – amaranth, calendula, chamomile, comfrey, echinacea, fenugreek, neem, raspberry

urinary tract infections – basil, celery, fennel, goldenrod, lovage, parsley, pennywort

vaginal discharge – amaranth, ginkgo, tea tree

vaginal thrush – goldenrod, thyme

varicose veins – borage, buckwheat, calendula, cayenne pepper, chervil, ginkgo, myrtle, pennywort

venereal disease – comfrey, echinacea, pennywort

vertigo – ginkgo, rosemary

vomiting – bergamot, black seed, lovage, melissa, mint

warts – dandelion, tea tree

wheezing – eucalyptus, ginkgo, tea tree

whooping cough – anise, comfrey, dill, echinacea, maidenhair fern, red clover, violet

womb strengthener – feverfew, raspberry

worms see **intestinal parasites**

wounds – aloe vera, amaranth, bulbinella, comfrey, echinacea, feverfew, goldenrod, honeysuckle, lovage, mullein, myrtle, nasturtium, neem, paprika, raspberry, salad burnet, southernwood, St John's wort, turmeric

Plant Index